Martin Street · Nick Barton · Thomas Terberger (eds.)

Humans, environment and chronology of the late glacial of the North European Plain

RGZM – TAGUNGEN
Band 6

Römisch-Germanisches
Zentralmuseum
Forschungsinstitut für
Vor- und Frühgeschichte

R **G** **Z** **M**

Römisch-Germanisches Zentralmuseum
Forschungsinstitut für Vor- und Frühgeschichte

Martin Street · Nick Barton · Thomas Terberger (eds.)

HUMANS, ENVIRONMENT AND CHRONOLOGY OF THE LATE GLACIAL OF THE NORTH EUROPEAN PLAIN

Proceedings of Workshop 14
(Commission XXXII »The Final Palaeolithic of the Great European Plain / Le Paléolithique Final de la Grande Plaine Européenne«)
of the 15th U.I.S.P.P. Congress, Lisbon, September 2006

Verlag des Römisch-Germanischen Zentralmuseums   Mainz 2009

Redaktion und Satz:
Martin Street, Martina Sensburg, Hans G. Frenz.

Umschlagbild: Gestaltung Reinhard Köster, RGZM. – Bildvorlage
frei nach: Enooesweetok 1915, Drawings by Enooesweetok of
the Sikosilingmint tribe of Eskimo, Fox Land, Baffin Land.
Portfolio privately published by Robert Flaherty (Toronto 1915).

Bibliografische Information
der Deutschen Nationalbibliothek
Die Deutsche Nationalbibliothek verzeichnet diese Publikation in
der Deutschen Nationalbibliografie; detaillierte bibliografische
Daten sind im Internet über **http://dnb.d-nb.de** abrufbar.

ISBN 978-3-88467-143-6
ISNN 1862-4812

© 2009 Verlag des Römisch-Germanischen Zentralmuseums
Mainz

Herstellung: betz-druck GmbH, Darmstadt
Printed in Germany

CONTENTS

AUTHORS

Nick Barton
  Institute of Archaeology
  36 Beaumont Street
  Oxford OX1 2PG, UK
  nick.barton@arch.ox.ac.uk

Olivier Bignon
  Archéozoologie, histoire des sociétés
  humaines et des peuplements animaux
  UMR 5197 CNRS
  and
  Membre associé de l'équipe Ethnologie
  préhistorique
  UMR 7041 CNRS Muséum national
  d'Histoire naturelle, Bâtiment d'Ana-
  tomie comparée
  55 rue Buffon
  F-75005 Paris
  bignon@mnhn.fr

Przemysław Bobrowski
  Institute Archaeology and Ethnology
  Polish Academy of Sciences
  Branch Poznań
  Ul. Rubież 46
  PL-61-612 Poznań
  bobrowski@iaepan.poznan.pl

Erik Brinch Petersen
  School of Archaeology
  Saxo Institute
  University of Copenhagen
  Njalsgade 80
  DK-2300 Copenhagen S
  ebp@hum.ku.dk

Eva David
  CNRS-UMR 7055 Préhistoire et
  Technologie
  Maison Archéologie et Ethnologie
  21, Allée de l'Université
  F-92023 NANTERRE cedex
  eva.david@mae.u-paris10.fr

Marc De Bie
  Vlaams Instituut voor het Onroerend
  Erfgoed
  and
  Vrije Universiteit Brussel
  Prehistoric Archaeology Unit
  Celestijnenlaan 200E
  B-3001 Heverlee
  marc.debie@rwo.vlaanderen.be

Koen Deforce
  Vlaams Instituut voor het Onroerend
  Erfgoed
  Koning Albert II-Laan 19 bus 5
  B-1210 Brussels
  koen.deforce@rwo.vlaan-deren.be

Tom F. G Higham
  Oxford Radiocarbon Accelerator Unit,
  RLAHA
  Dyson Perrins Building
  University of Oxford
  Oxford OX1 3QY
  UK

Roger M. Jacobi
  Department of Prehistory and Europe
  Franks House
  The British Museum
  London N1 5QJ
  UK
  and
  Department of Palaeontology
  Natural History Museum
  London SW7 5BD
  UK

Jacek Kabaciński
  Institute of Archaeology end Ethnology
  Polish Academy of Sciences
  ul. Rubież 46
  PL-61-612 Poznań
  jacek.kabacinski@iaepan.poznan.pl

Michał Kobusiewicz
  Institute of Archaeology & Ethnology
  Polish Academy of Sciences
  ul. Rubież 46
  PL-61-612 Poznań
  kobusiewicz@iaepan.poznan.pl

Krzysztof Kowalski
  National Museum in Szczecin
  Staromłyńska Str. 27
  PL-70-561 Szczecin

Lars Larsson
  Department of Archaeology and
  Ancient History
  Lund University
  Fack 117
  S-221 00 LUND
  Lars.Larsson@ark.lu.se

Tom C. Lord
  Lower Winskill
  Langcliffe, Nr. Settle,
  North Yorks, BD24 9PZ
  UK

Rebecca Miller
  University of Liège
  Service of Prehistory
  7, place du XX août, bât. A1
  B-4000 Liège
  miller@ulg.ac.be

Pierre Noiret
  University of Liège
  Service of Prehistory
  7, place du XX août, bât. A1
  B-4000 Liège
  pnoiret@ulg.ac.be

Jacques Pelegrin
  CNRS-UMR 7055 Préhistoire et
  Technologie
  Maison Archéologie et Ethnologie
  21, Allée de l'Université
  F-92023 NANTERRE cedex
  jacques.pelegrin@mae.u-paris10.fr

Marta Połtowicz-Bobak
  Instytut Archeologii UR
  Ul. Hoffmanowej 8
  PL-35 016 Rzeszów
  martap@univ.rzeszow.pl

Tomasz Płonka
  Instytut Archeologii Uniwersytetu
  Wrocławskiego
  Szewska Str. 48
  PL-50-139 Wrocław

Iwona Sobkowiak-Tabaka
  Institute of Archaeology and Ethnology
  Polish Academy of Sciences
  ul. Rubież 46
  PL-61-612 Poznań
  iwona.sobkowiak@iaepan.poznan.pl

Martin Street
  Römisch-Germanisches Zentralmuseum
  Mainz
  Forschungsbereich Altsteinzeit
  Schloss Monrepos
  D-56567 Neuwied
  street@rgzm.de

Thomas Terberger
  Lehrstuhl für Ur- und Frühgeschichte
  Universität Greifswald
  Hans-Fallada-Straße 1
  D - 17489 Greifswald
  terberge@uni-greifswald.de

Marijn Van Gils
  Vlaams Instituut voor het Onroerend
  Erfgoed
  Prehistoric Archaeology Unit
  Celestijnenlaan 200E
  B-3001 Heverlee
  marijn.vangils@rwo.vlaanderen.be

MARTIN STREET · THOMAS TERBERGER · NICK BARTON

FOREWORD

The present volume »Humans, environment and chronology of the Late Glacial of the North European Plain« arose from a workshop (WS 14) organised by the editors under the remit of U.I.S.P.P. Commission XXXII as part of the 15th Congress of the Union International des Sciences Préhistoriques et Protohistoriques held in Lisbon in September 2006. Commission XXXII focuses specifically on »The Final Palaeolithic of the Great European Plain« and was formed in 1998 following a meeting organized in that year at Kraków (Poland) by U.I.S.P.P. Commission 8 (Upper Palaeolithic) in honour of B. Ginter. The themes of the Kraków meeting provided a blueprint for later conferences and workshops of Commission XXXII and underlined the geographical spread and international appeal of the presented research, with contributions from the British Isles to the Russian Plain and from southern Scandinavia to the Balkans (Kobusiewicz / Kozłowski 1999).

The first meeting of the newly constituted Commission XXXII followed in 1999 at Stockholm (Eriksen / Bratlund 2002). Once again, the presented papers represented the wide range of European countries relevant to the theme and, as at Kraków, their subject matter included not only archaeological but also palaeo-ecological topics. A specialist Commission XXXII workshop, »Drifted apart. Stone Age sites in bioturbated sediments and their value for intra-site spatial analysis«, was organized by M. de Bie and J.-P. Caspar at the 2001 quinquennial U.I.S.P.P. Congress in Liège. It is hoped that it may still be possible to publish a number of the presented papers (pers. comm. M. de Bie, May 2008).

From 2002 onwards, Commission XXXII meetings have taken place annually in the form of conferences and workshops held at changing venues. The proceedings of meetings held at Greifswald (Germany) in 2002 and Poznań (Poland) in 2003 were published as comprehensive volumes (Terberger / Eriksen 2004; Kobusiewicz / Kabaciński 2007). In both volumes a trend seems to be visible; papers from the Greifswald meeting were predominantly of German origin (with Polish and Scandinavian contributions) while the Poznań volume is clearly weighted towards Poland and Eastern Europe, with a German and a Swedish contribution forming the exception to this rule. Possibly this tendency reflects the difficulty of regular (annual) attendance at the Commission meetings in the face of problems of logistics and funding. Seen more positively it does offer the potential for assembling regionally/thematically arranged research groupings. Moreover, the inclusion in the Greifswald publication of papers from Italy and Japan demonstrates the continuing interest in the northern European Late Glacial by workers in other regions and presents contrasting case studies of contemporary archaeological developments in more distant regions.

Further meetings took place at Vilnius (Lithuania) in 2004 and at Rzeszów (Poland) in 2005. Several papers from the former conference have been published together in an issue of Archaeologia Baltica (Volume 7, 2006), the majority of them from Poland, the Baltic States and other eastern European countries. Work on publication of papers from the Rzeszów meeting is in progress (pers. comm. M. Połtowicz-Bobak).

It was against this background that the Commission XXXII meeting was held at the 2006 quinquennial U.I.S.P.P. Congress in Lisbon. In view of the southern European location, far from the customary venues, it was decided to deliberately invite and accept papers covering a broader time-frame, beginning with the first Upper Palaeolithic recolonisation of regions deserted by humans during the Last Glacial Maximum (LGM) and extending to the earliest postglacial adoption of Mesolithic modes of settlement and subsistence. In chronostratigraphic terms this extends from the late Pleniglacial/early Late Glacial to the Preboreal. Equally, it was decided that the process of recolonisation of the North European Plain should be seen to be a logical development proceeding from the Late Glacial recolonisation of Europe from LGM refugia as a whole, thus including the preliminary phase of resettlement of the upland zone landscapes (Mittelgebirge) by Upper Magdalenian humans.

In consequence, papers from the Lisbon workshop present information on a range of themes which include not only research on the late Palaeolithic of the North European Plain itself (here including southern Scandinavia and the eastern Baltic), but also on aspects of the Magdalenian at the edge of the North European Plain in northern France, Belgium and southern Poland and the following phase of northward population movement represented by the Creswellian and Hamburgian. Within this geographical and chronological framework the individual studies treat matters as diverse as lithic procurement, technology and typology, subsistence practises and the use of the landscape, the timing and mechanisms of recolonisation and questions of identity and symbolism.

The publication of the conference proceedings fulfils the essential need of bringing much of this information into the wider public and academic domain. We hope some of the flavour of this research and the new directions in which it is developing will emerge from this volume.

References and exhaustive bibliography of previous meetings of U.I.S.P.P. Commission XXXII

Åkerlund 2002: A. Åkerlund, Life without close neighbours. Some reflections on the first peopling of east Central Sweden. In: B. V. Eriksen / B. Bratlund (eds.), Recent studies in the Final Palaeolithic of the European plain. Proceedings of a U.I.S.P.P. Symposium, Stockholm 1999. Jutland Archaeological Society Publications 39 (Århus 2002) 43-47.

Alexandrowicz 1999: W. P. Alexandrowicz, Evolution of the malacological assemblages in Northern Poland during the Late Glacial and Early Holocene. In: M. Kobusiewicz / J. K. Kozłowski (eds.), Post-Pleniglacial re-colonisation of the Great European Lowland. Folia Quaternaria 70 (Kraków 1999) 39-69.

Barton 1999: R. N. E. Barton, Colonisation and resettlement of Europe in the Late Glacial: a view from the western periphery. In: M. Kobusiewicz / J. K. Kozłowski (eds.), Post-Pleniglacial re-colonisation of the Great European Lowland. Folia Quaternaria 70 (Kraków 1999) 71-86.

Benecke 2004: N. Benecke, Faunal succession in the lowlands of northern Central Europe at the Pleistocene-Holocene transition. In: Th. Terberger / B. V. Eriksen (eds.), Hunters in a changing world. Environment and Archaeology of the Pleistocene-Holocene Transition (ca. 11000-9000 B.C.) in Northern Central Europe. Workshop of the U.I.S.P.P.-Commission XXXII at Greifswald 2002. Internationale Archäologie, Arbeitsgemeinschaft, Symposium, Tagung, Kongress 5 (Rahden/Westfalen 2004) 43-51.

Bobrowski / Sobkowiak-Tabaka 2006: P. Bobrowski / I. Sobkowiak-Tabaka, How far east did Hamburgian Culture Reach? Archaeologia Baltica 7, 11-20.

Bratlund 1999: B. Bratlund, Review of the faunal evidence from the Late Glacial in Northern Europe. In: M. Kobusiewicz / J. K. Kozłowski (eds.), Post-Pleniglacial re-colonisation of the Great European Lowland. Folia Quaternaria 70 (Kraków 1999) 31-37.

2002: B. Bratlund, The faunal remains from Wilczyce. In: B. V. Eriksen / B. Bratlund (eds.), Recent studies in the Final Palaeolithic of the European plain. Proceedings of a U.I.S.P.P. Symposium, Stockholm 1999. Jutland Archaeological Society Publications 39 (Århus 2002) 101-107.

Bratlund / Eriksen 2002: B. Bratlund / B. V. Eriksen, Recent studies in the Final Palaeolithic of the European plain – an introduction. Recent studies in the Final Palaeolithic of the European plain. Proceedings of a U.I.S.P.P. Symposium, Stockholm 1999. Jutland Archaeological Society Publications 39 (Århus 2002) 9-10.

Burdukiewicz 1999: J. M. Burdukiewicz, Concerning chronology of the Hamburgian Culture. In: M. Kobusiewicz / J. K. Kozłowski (eds.), Post-Pleniglacial re-colonisation of the Great European Lowland. Folia Quaternaria 70 (Kraków 1999) 127-146.

Burdukiewicz / Szynkiewicz / Malkiewicz 2007: J. M. Burdukiewicz / A. Szynkiewicz / M. Malkiewicz, Paleoenvironmental setting of the Late Paleolithic sites in the Kopanica Valley. In: M. Kobusiewicz / J. Kabaciński (eds.), Studies in the Final Palaeolithic settlement of the Great European Plain (Poznań 2007) 67-85.

Casati / Sørensen / Vennersdorf 2004: C. Casati / L. Sørensen / M. Vennersdorf, Current research of the early Mesolithic on Bornholm, Denmark. In: Th. Terberger / B. V. Eriksen (eds.), Hunters in a changing world. Environment and Archaeology of the Pleistocene-Holocene Transition (ca. 11000-9000 B.C.) in Northern Central Europe. Workshop of the U.I.S.P.P.-Commission XXXII at Greifswald 2002. Internationale Archäologie, Arbeitsgemeinschaft, Symposium, Tagung, Kongress 5 (Rahden/Westfalen 2004) 113-132.

Clausen 2004: I. Clausen, The Reindeer antler axe of the Allerød period from Klappholz LA 63, Kreis Schleswig-Flensburg / Germany. Is it a relict of the Federmesser, Bromme or Ahrensburg culture? In: Th. Terberger / B. V. Eriksen (eds.), Hunters in a changing world. Environment and Archaeology of the Pleistocene-Holocene Transition (ca. 11000-9000 B.C.) in Northern Central Europe. Workshop of the U.I.S.P.P.-Commission XXXII at Greifswald 2002. Internationale Archäologie, Arbeitsgemeinschaft, Symposium, Tagung, Kongress 5 (Rahden/Westfalen 2004) 141-164.

Cohen 1999: V. Cohen, The population of South Russian Plain after the maximum of the second Pleniglacial. In: M. Kobusiewicz / J. K. Kozłowski (eds.), Post-Pleniglacial re-colonisation of the Great European Lowland. Folia Quaternaria 70 (Kraków 1999) 363-384.

Crombé / Verbruggen 2002: P. Crombé / C. Verbruggen, The Lateglacial and early Postglacial occupation of northern Belgium: the evidence from Sandy Flanders. In: B. V. Eriksen / B. Bratlund (eds.), Recent studies in the Final Palaeolithic of the European plain. Proceedings of a U.I.S.P.P. Symposium, Stockholm 1999. Jutland Archaeological Society Publications 39 (Århus 2002) 165-180.

Cyrek 1999: K. Cyrek, Menschliche Penetration der Höhlen im mittleren Teil der Krakówsko-Czestochowska-Hochebene zwischen dem 18. und dem 11. Jahrtausend (vom Interstadial Lascaux bis zum Interstadial Alleröd). In: M. Kobusiewicz / J. K. Kozłowski (eds.), Post-Pleniglacial re-colonisation of the Great European Lowland. Folia Quaternaria 70 (Kraków 1999) 269-288.

2006: K. Cyrek, Spätpaläolithikum und Mesolithikum im Wisłatal zwischen Toruń und Grudziàdz. Archaeologia Baltica 7, 43-57.

Cziesla 2004: E. Cziesla, Late Upper Palaeolithic and Mesolithic cultural continuity – or: bone and antler objects from the Havelland. In: Th. Terberger / B. V. Eriksen (eds.), Hunters in a changing world. Environment and Archaeology of the Pleistocene-Holocene Transition (ca. 11000-9000 B.C.) in Northern Central Europe. Workshop of the U.I.S.P.P.-Commission XXXII at Greifswald 2002. Internationale Archäologie, Arbeitsgemeinschaft, Symposium, Tagung, Kongress 5 (Rahden/Westfalen 2004) 165-182.

Dalmeri / Ferrari / Peresani 2004: G. Dalmeri / S. Ferrari / M. Peresani, Rise and fall in the utilization of trapezoidal microliths during the late Upper Palaeolithic in Europe – an overview from the Italian record. In: Th. Terberger / B. V. Eriksen (eds.), Hunters in a changing world. Environment and Archaeology of the Pleistocene-Holocene Transition (ca. 11000-9000 B.C.) in Northern Central Europe. Workshop of the U.I.S.P.P.-Commission XXXII at Greifswald 2002. Internationale Archäologie, Arbeitsgemeinschaft, Symposium, Tagung, Kongress 5 (Rahden/Westfalen 2004) 243-251.

De Bie / Schurmans / Caspar 2002: M. De Bie / U. A. Schurmans / J.-P. Caspar, On knapping spots and living areas: intra-site differentiation at Late Palaeolithic Rekem. In: B. V. Eriksen / B. Bratlund (eds.), Recent studies in the Final Palaeolithic of the European plain. Proceedings of a U.I.S.P.P. Symposium, Stockholm 1999. Jutland Archaeological Society Publications 39 (Århus 2002) 139-164.

de Klerk 2004: P. de Klerk, Changes in vegetation and environment at the Lateglacial-Holocene transition in Vorpommern (Northeast Germany). In: Th. Terberger / B. V. Eriksen (eds.), Hunters in a changing world. Environment and Archaeology of the Pleistocene-Holocene Transition (ca. 11000-9000 B.C.) in Northern Central Europe. Workshop of the U.I.S.P.P.-Commission XXXII at Greifswald 2002. Internationale Archäologie, Arbeitsgemeinschaft, Symposium, Tagung, Kongress 5 (Rahden/Westfalen 2004) 27-42.

Dobosi 1999: V. T. Dobosi, Postpleniglacial repeopling of the Hungarian Plain. In: M. Kobusiewicz / J. K. Kozłowski (eds.), Post-Pleniglacial re-colonisation of the Great European Lowland. Folia Quaternaria 70 (Kraków 1999) 297-315.

2007: V. T. Dobosi, On the edges of the plains. In: M. Kobusiewicz / J. Kabaciński (eds.), Studies in the Final Palaeolithic settlement of the Great European Plain (Poznań 2007) 151-155.

Eberhards / Zagorska 2002: G. Eberhards / I. Zagorska, The environment and the earliest settlement of Latvia, East Baltic. In: B. V. Eriksen / B. Bratlund (eds.), Recent studies in the Final Palaeolithic of the European plain. Proceedings of a U.I.S.P.P. Symposium, Stockholm 1999. Jutland Archaeological Society Publications 39 (Århus 2002) 85-90.

Eriksen 1999: B. V. Eriksen, Late Palaeolithic settlement in Denmark - how do we read the record? In: M. Kobusiewicz / J. K. Kozłowski (eds.), Post-Pleniglacial re-colonisation of the Great European Lowland. Folia Quaternaria 70 (Kraków 1999) 157-173.

2002: B. V. Eriksen, Reconsidering the geochronological framework of Lateglacial hunter-gatherer colonization of southern Scandinavia. In: B. V. Eriksen / B. Bratlund (eds.), Recent studies in the Final Palaeolithic of the European plain. Proceedings of a U.I.S.P.P. Symposium, Stockholm 1999. Jutland Archaeological Society Publications 39 (Århus 2002) 25-41.

Eriksen / Bratlund 2002: B. V. Eriksen / B. Bratlund (eds.), Recent studies in the Final Palaeolithic of the European plain. Proceedings of a U.I.S.P.P. Symposium, Stockholm 1999. Jutland Archaeological Society Publications 39 (Århus 2002).

Fiedorczuk / Schild 2002: J. Fiedorczuk / R. Schild, Wilczyce – a new late Magdalenian site in Poland. In: B. V. Eriksen / B. Bratlund (eds.), Recent studies in the Final Palaeolithic of the European plain. Proceedings of a U.I.S.P.P. Symposium, Stockholm 1999. Jutland Archaeological Society Publications 39 (Århus 2002) 91-100.

Galimova 2006: M. Galimova, Final Palaeolithic-Early Mesolithic Cultures with Trapezia in the Volga and Dnieper Basins: The Question of Origin. Archaeologia Baltica 7, 136-148.

Galiński 2007: T. Galiński, My own excavations and discoveries of Final Paleolithic assemblages on the European Plain. In: M. Kobusiewicz / J. Kabaciński (eds.), Studies in the Final Palaeolithic settlement of the Great European Plain (Poznań 2007) 129-137.

Ginter / Połtowicz 2007: B. Ginter / M. Połtowicz, Magdalenian settlement in Poland before the Bølling oscillation. In: M. Kobusiewicz / J. Kabaciński (eds.), Studies in the Final Palaeolithic settlement of the Great European Plain (Poznań 2007) 7-19.

Gramsch 2004: B. Gramsch, From the Late Palaeolithic to the early Mesolithic in northeastern Germany. In: Th. Terberger / B. V. Eriksen (eds.), Hunters in a changing world. Environment and Archaeology of the Pleistocene-Holocene Transition (ca. 11 000-9 000 B.C.) in Northern Central Europe. Workshop of the U.I.S.P.P.-Commission XXXII at Greifswald 2002. Internationale Archäologie, Arbeitsgemeinschaft, Symposium, Tagung, Kongress 5 (Rahden/Westfalen 2004) 183-201.

Hansen / Brinch Petersen / Sørensen 2004: K. M. Hansen / E. Brinch Petersen / K. A. Sørensen, Filling the gap: Early Preboreal Maglemose elk deposits at Lundby, Sjaelland, Denmark. In: Th. Terberger / B. V. Eriksen (eds.), Hunters in a changing world. Environment and Archaeology of the Pleistocene-Holocene Transition (ca. 11 000-9 000 B.C.) in Northern Central Europe. Workshop of the U.I.S.P.P.-Commission XXXII at Greifswald 2002. Internationale Archäologie, Arbeitsgemeinschaft, Symposium, Tagung, Kongress 5 (Rahden/Westfalen 2004) 75-84.

Johansson 2002: A. D. Johansson, Late Palaeolithic settlement in South Zealand, eastern Denmark. In: B. V. Eriksen / B. Bratlund (eds.), Recent studies in the Final Palaeolithic of the European plain. Proceedings of a U.I.S.P.P. Symposium, Stockholm 1999. Jutland Archaeological Society Publications 39 (Århus 2002) 75-83.

Jungner et al. 2007: H. Jungner / L. Lukševica / E. Lukševics / I. Zagorska, Ancient reindeer (*Rangifer tarandus*) in Latvia. In: M. Kobusiewicz / J. Kabaciński (eds.), Studies in the Final Palaeolithic settlement of the Great European Plain (Poznań 2007) 201-208.

Kabaciński / Kobusiewicz 2007: J. Kabaciński / M. Kobusiewicz, Kragola near Koło (Central Poland) – the easternmost settlement of Hamburgian Culture. In: M. Kobusiewicz / J. Kabaciński (eds.), Studies in the Final Palaeolithic settlement of the Great European Plain (Poznań 2007) 21-51.

Kabaciński et al. 1999: J. Kabaciński / B. Bratlund / L. Kubiak / D. Makowiecki / R. Schild / K. Tobolski, The Hamburgian settlement at Mirkowice: recent results and research perspectives. In: M. Kobusiewicz / J. K. Kozłowski (eds.), Post-Pleniglacial re-colonisation of the Great European Lowland. Folia Quaternaria 70 (Kraków 1999) 211-238.

2002: J. Kabaciński / R. Schild / B. Bratlund / L. Kubiak-Martens / K. Tobolski / K. van der Borg / A. Pazdur, The Lateglacial sequence at the Hamburgian site at Mirkowice: stratigraphy and geochronology. In: B. V. Eriksen / B. Bratlund (eds.), Recent studies in the Final Palaeolithic of the European plain. Proceedings of a U.I.S.P.P. Symposium, Stockholm 1999. Jutland Archaeological Society Publications 39 (Århus 2002) 109-116.

Kaiser 2004: K. Kaiser, Geomorphic characterization of the Pleistocene – Holocene transition in Northeast Germany. In: Th. Terberger / B. V. Eriksen (eds.), Hunters in a changing world. Environment and Archaeology of the Pleistocene-Holocene Transition (ca. 11 000-9 000 B.C.) in Northern Central Europe. Workshop of the U.I.S.P.P.-Commission XXXII at Greifswald 2002. Internationale Archäologie, Arbeitsgemeinschaft, Symposium, Tagung, Kongress 5 (Rahden/Westfalen 2004) 53-73.

Kaminská 2007: L. Kaminská, The Final Paleolithic in Slovakia. In: M. Kobusiewicz / J. Kabaciński (eds.), Studies in the Final Palaeolithic settlement of the Great European Plain (Poznań 2007) 111-127.

Kindgren 2002: H. Kindgren, Tosskärr. Stenkyrka 94 revisited. In: B. V. Eriksen / B. Bratlund (eds.), Recent studies in the Final Palaeolithic of the European plain. Proceedings of a U.I.S.P.P. Symposium, Stockholm 1999. Jutland Archaeological Society Publications 39 (Århus 2002) 49-60.

Kobusiewicz 1999: M. Kobusiewicz, The final Pleistocene recolonisation of the northwestern Polish Plain. In: M. Kobusiewicz / J. K. Kozłowski (eds.), Post-Pleniglacial re-colonisation of the Great European Lowland. Folia Quaternaria 70 (Kraków 1999) 197-210.

2002: M. Kobusiewicz, Ahrensburgian and Sviderian: two different modes of adaptation? In: B. V. Eriksen / B. Bratlund (eds.), Recent studies in the Final Palaeolithic of the European plain. Proceedings of a U.I.S.P.P. Symposium, Stockholm 1999. Jutland Archaeological Society Publications 39 (Århus 2002) 117-122.

2004: M. Kobusiewicz, The problem of the Palaeolithic - Mesolithic transition on the Polish Plain: state of research. In: Th. Terberger / B. V. Eriksen (eds.), Hunters in a changing world. Environment and Archaeology of the Pleistocene-Holocene Transition (ca. 11 000-9 000 B.C.) in Northern Central Europe. Workshop of the U.I.S.P.P.-Commission XXXII at Greifswald 2002. Internationale Archäologie, Arbeitsgemeinschaft, Symposium, Tagung, Kongress 5 (Rahden/Westfalen 2004) 133-139.

Kobusiewicz / Kabaciński 2007: M. Kobusiewicz / J. Kabaciński (eds.), Studies in the Final Palaeolithic of the Great European Plain (Poznań 2007).

Kobusiewicz / Kozłowski 1999: M. Kobusiewicz / J. K. Kozłowski (eds.), Post-Pleniglacial re-colonisation of the Great European Lowland. Papers presented at the Conference organised by the Intenational Union of Prehistoric and Protohistoric Sciences, Commission 8, held at the Jagellonian University Kraków in June 1998. Folia Quaternaria 70 (Kraków 1999).

Kolstrup 2002: E. Kolstrup, Some classical methods used for reconstruction of Lateglacial environments in the European plain: potentials and limitations. In: B. V. Eriksen / B. Bratlund (eds.), Recent studies in the Final Palaeolithic of the European plain.Proceedings of a U.I.S.P.P. Symposium, Stockholm 1999. Jutland Archaeological Society Publications 39 (Århus 2002) 11-23.

Kozłowski 1999: J. K. Kozłowski, Les origines de la récolonisation de la partie septentrionale de l'Europe centrale après le Pleniglaciaire. In: M. Kobusiewicz / J. K. Kozłowski (eds.), Post-Pleniglacial re-colonisation of the Great European Lowland. Folia Quaternaria 70 (Kraków 1999) 317-331.

2006: S. K. Kozłowski, Mapping the Central / East European Terminal Palaeolithic/Earliest Mesolithic. Archaeologia Baltica 7, 29-35.

Kudo 2004: Y. Kudo, Reconsidering the geochronological and archaeological framework of the late Pleistocene – early Holocene transition on the Japanese islands. In: Th. Terberger / B. V. Eriksen (eds.), Hunters in a changing world. Environment and Archaeology of the Pleistocene-Holocene Transition (ca. 11 000-9 000 B.C.) in Northern Central Europe. Workshop of the U.I.S.P.P.-Commission XXXII at Greifswald 2002. Internationale Archäologie, Arbeitsgemeinschaft, Symposium, Tagung, Kongress 5 (Rahden/Westfalen 2004) 253-268.

Larsson 1999: L. Larsson, Perspectives on the colonisation of the Scandinavian peninsula. In: M. Kobusiewicz / J. K. Kozłowski (eds.), Post-Pleniglacial re-colonisation of the Great European Lowland. Folia Quaternaria 70 (Kraków 1999) 175-196.

Larsson et al. 2002: L. Larsson / R. Liljegren / O. Magnell / J. Ekström, Archaeo-faunal aspects of bog finds from Hässleberga, southern Scania, Sweden. In: B. V. Eriksen / B. Bratlund (eds.), Recent studies in the Final Palaeolithic of the European plain. Proceedings of a U.I.S.P.P. Symposium, Stockholm 1999. Jutland Archaeological Society Publications 39 (Århus 2002) 61-74.

Libera / Szeliga 2006: J. Libera / M. Szeliga, Late Palaeolithic Workshops in the Lublin Region, Based on the Local Cretaceous Flint Resources, through the Prism of New Discoveries. An Overview of the Issue. Archaeologia Baltica 7, 160-177.

Madeyska 1999: T. Madeyska, Palaeogeography of European Lowland during the Late Vistulian. In: M. Kobusiewicz / J. K. Kozłowski (eds.), Post-Pleniglacial re-colonisation of the Great European Lowland. Folia Quaternaria 70 (Kraków 1999) 7-30.

Migal 2007: W. Migal, On preferential points of the Final Paleolithic in the Central European Lowland. In: M. Kobusiewicz / J. Kabaciński (eds.), Studies in the Final Palaeolithic settlement of the Great European Plain (Poznań 2007) 185-200.

Mihajlovic 1999: D. Mihajlovic, Intensification of settlement in the Late Glacial of south-western Balkans. In: M. Kobusiewicz / J. K. Kozłowski (eds.), Post-Pleniglacial re-colonisation of the Great European Lowland. Folia Quaternaria 70 (Kraków 1999) 385-392.

Mikhailova 2006: N. Mikhailova, The Cult of the Deer and »Shamans« in Deer Hunting Society. Archaeologia Baltica 7, 187-198.

Nielsen 2002: E. H. Nielsen, The Lateglacial settlement of the Central Swiss Plateau. In: B. V. Eriksen / B. Bratlund (eds.), Recent studies in the Final Palaeolithic of the European plain. Proceedings of a U.I.S.P.P. Symposium, Stockholm 1999. Jutland Archaeological Society Publications 39 (Århus 2002) 189-201.

Nuzhnyi 2006: D. Nuzhnyi, The Latest Epigravettian Assemblages of the Middle Dnieper Basin (Northern Ukraine). Archaeologia Baltica 7, 58-93.

Otte 1999: M. Otte, Civilisations du tardiglaciaire en Europe du Nord-Ouest. In: M. Kobusiewicz / J. K. Kozłowski (eds.), Post-Pleniglacial re-colonisation of the Great European Lowland. Folia Quaternaria 70 (Kraków 1999) 115-125.

Pasda 2002: C. Pasda, A short note on man in the Allerød / Younger Dryas environment of Lower Lusatia (Brandenburg, Germany). In: B. V. Eriksen / B. Bratlund (eds.), Recent studies in the Final Palaeolithic of the European plain. Proceedings of a

U.I.S.P.P. Symposium, Stockholm 1999. Jutland Archaeological Society Publications 39 (Århus 2002) 123-128.

Płonka 2007: T. Płonka, Late Paleolithic settlement in the western reaches of the Gorzów Dale. In: M. Kobusiewicz / J. Kabaciński (eds.), Studies in the Final Palaeolithic settlement of the Great European Plain (Poznań 2007) 99-109.

Połtowicz 2006: M. Połtowicz, The Magdalenian Period in Poland and Neighbouring Areas. Archaeologia Baltica 7, 21-28.

Rensink 1999: E. Rensink, The Magdalenian site of Eyserheide and the Late Glacial human colonisation of the Southern Netherlands. In: M. Kobusiewicz / J. K. Kozłowski (eds.), Post-Pleniglacial re-colonisation of the Great European Lowland. Folia Quaternaria 70 (Kraków 1999) 87-100.

2002: E. Rensink, Late Palaeolithic sites in the Maas valley of the southern Netherlands: prospects, surveys and results. In: B. V. Eriksen / B. Bratlund (eds.), Recent studies in the Final Palaeolithic of the European plain. Proceedings of a U.I.S.P.P. Symposium, Stockholm 1999. Jutland Archaeological Society Publications 39 (Århus 2002) 181-188.

Schild et al. 1999: R. Schild / K. Tobolski / L. Kubiak-Martens / M. F. Pazdur / A. Pazdur / J. C. Vogel / T. W. Stafford jr., Stratigraphy, palaeoecology and radiochronology of the site of Calowanie. In: M. Kobusiewicz / J. K. Kozłowski (eds.), Post-Pleniglacial re-colonisation of the Great European Lowland. Folia Quaternaria 70 (Kraków 1999) 239-268.

2007: R. Schild / H. Królik / A. J. Tomaszewski / E. Ciepielewska, Sociotopographic patterning of Rydno as seen after nearly a centennial of exploration. In: M. Kobusiewicz / J. Kabaciński (eds.), Studies in the Final Palaeolithic settlement of the Great European Plain (Poznań 2007) 87-97.

Schmitt 2007: L. Schmitt, The West Swedish Hensbacka from an anthropological point of view, and recent developments concerning the final drainage of the Baltic Ice Lake. In: M. Kobusiewicz / J. Kabaciński (eds.), Studies in the Final Palaeolithic settlement of the Great European Plain (Poznań 2007) 139-150.

Sørensen / Sternke 2004: M. Sørensen / F. Sternke, Norregard VI – Lateglacial hunters in transition. In: Th. Terberger / B. V. Eriksen (eds.), Hunters in a changing world. Environment and Archaeology of the Pleistocene-Holocene Transition (ca. 11000-9000 B.C.) in Northern Central Europe. Workshop of the U.I.S.P.P.-Commission XXXII at Greifswald 2002. Internationale Archäologie, Arbeitsgemeinschaft, Symposium, Tagung, Kongress 5 (Rahden/Westfalen 2004) 85-111.

Sorokin 2007: A. N. Sorokin, The Final Paleolithic of central Russia: Problem and Solution. In: M. Kobusiewicz / J. Kabaciński (eds.), Studies in the Final Palaeolithic settlement of the Great European Plain (Poznań 2007) 157-173.

Stanāikaitò 2006: M. Stanāikaitò, Late Glacial Environmental History in Lithuania. Archaeologia Baltica 7, 199-208.

Stapert 2004: D. Stapert, Maglemose huts and Duvensee: Spatial anaysis with »ANALITHIC«. In: Th. Terberger / B. V. Eriksen (eds.), Hunters in a changing world. Environment and Archaeology of the Pleistocene-Holocene Transition (ca. 11 000-9 000

B.C.) in Northern Central Europe. Workshop of the U.I.S.P.P.-Commission XXXII at Greifswald 2002. Internationale Archäologie, Arbeitsgemeinschaft, Symposium, Tagung, Kongress 5 (Rahden/Westfalen 2004) 223-241.

Straus / Otte 1999: L. G. Straus / M. Otte, La grotte du Bois Laiterie (Profondeville, Belgique): halte de chasse magdalénienne. In: M. Kobusiewicz / J. K. Kozłowski (eds.), Post-Pleniglacial re-colonisation of the Great European Lowland. Folia Quaternaria 70 (Kraków 1999) 101-113.

Stupak 2006: D. Stupak, Chipped Flint Technologies in Swiderian Complexes of the Ukrainian Polissya Region. Archaeologia Baltica 7, 109-119.

Sulgostowska 2006: Z. Sulgostowska, Final Palaeolithic Societies' Mobility in Poland as Seen from the Distribution of Flints. Archaeologia Baltica 7, 36-42.

2007: Z. Sulgostowska, Ochre among the Mazovian societies. In: M. Kobusiewicz / J. Kabaciński (eds.), Studies in the Final Palaeolithic settlement of the Great European Plain (Poznań 2007) 175-183.

Terberger 2004: Th. Terberger, The Younger Dryas-Preboreal transition in northern Germany – facts and concepts in discussion. In: Th. Terberger / B. V. Eriksen (eds.), Hunters in a changing world. Environment and Archaeology of the Pleistocene-Holocene Transition (ca. 11000-9000 B.C.) in Northern Central Europe. Workshop of the U.I.S.P.P.-Commission XXXII at Greifswald 2002. Internationale Archäologie, Arbeitsgemeinschaft, Symposium, Tagung, Kongress 5 (Rahden/Westfalen 2004) 203-222.

Terberger / Eriksen 2004: Th. Terberger / B. V. Eriksen (eds.), Hunters in a changing world. Environment and Archaeology of the Pleistocene-Holocene Transition (ca. 11000-9000 B.C.) in Northern Central Europe. Workshop of the U.I.S.P.P.-Commission XXXII at Greifswald 2002. Internationale Archäologie, Arbeitsgemeinschaft, Symposium, Tagung, Kongress 5 (Rahden/Westfalen 2004).

Terberger / Lübke 2007: Th. Terberger /, H. Lübke, Between East and West – Hamburgian in Northeast Germany? In: M. Kobusiewicz / J. Kabaciński (eds.), Studies in the Final Palaeolithic settlement of the Great European Plain (Poznań 2007) 53-65.

Tromnau 1999: G. Tromnau, Some remarks concerning the excavations at Meiendorf and Stellmoor in the tunnel valley of Ahrensburg by Alfred Rust. In: M. Kobusiewicz / J. K. Kozłowski (eds.), Post-Pleniglacial re-colonisation of the Great European Lowland. Folia Quaternaria 70 (Kraków 1999) 147-155.

2006: G. Tromnau, Comments Concerning the Gaps between Schleswig-Holstein and the Middle Oder in the Expansion Area of Hamburgian Culture. Archaeologia Baltica 7, 7-10.

Usinger 2004: H. Usinger, Vegetation and climate of the lowlands of northern Central Europe and adjacent areas around the Younger Dryas-Preboreal transition – with special emphasis on the Preboreal oscillation. In: Th. Terberger / B. V. Eriksen (eds.), Hunters in a changing world. Environment and Archaeology of the Pleistocene-Holocene Transition (ca. 11000-9000 B.C.) in Northern Central Europe. Workshop of the U.I.S.P.P.-Commission XXXII at Greifswald 2002. Internationale Archäologie, Arbeitsgemeinschaft, Symposium, Tagung, Kongress 5 (Rahden/Westfalen 2004) 1-26.

Veil / Breest 2002: S. Veil / K. Breest, The archaeological context of the art objects from the Federmesser site of Weitsche, Ldkr. Lüchow-Dannenberg, Lower Saxony (Germany) – a preliminary report. In: B. V. Eriksen / B. Bratlund (eds.), Recent studies in the Final Palaeolithic of the European plain. Jutland Archaeological Society Publications 39 (Århus 2002), 129-138.

Vencl 1999: S. Vencl, Late Upper and Late Palaeolithic in the Czech Republic. In: M. Kobusiewicz / J. K. Kozłowski (eds.), Post-Pleniglacial re-colonisation of the Great European Lowland. Folia Quaternaria 70 (Kraków 1999) 289-296.

Zagorska 2006: I. Zagorska, The Earliest Antler and Bone Harpoons from the East Baltic. Archaeologia Baltica 7, 178-186.

Zaliznyak 1999: L. Zaliznyak, Terminal Palaeolithic of Ukraine, Belarus and Lithuania (survey of cultural differentiation). In: M. Kobusiewicz / J. K. Kozłowski (eds.), Post-Pleniglacial re-colonisation of the Great European Lowland. Folia Quaternaria 70 (Kraków 1999) 333-361.

2006: L. Zaliznyak, The Archaeology of the Occupation of the East European Taiga Zone at the turn of the Palaeolithic-Mesolithic. Archaeologia Baltica 7, 94-108.

ROGER M. JACOBI · THOMAS F. G. HIGHAM · TOM C. LORD

IMPROVING THE CHRONOLOGY OF THE HUMAN OCCUPATION OF BRITAIN DURING THE LATE GLACIAL

Three variables hamper the effectiveness and reliability of radiocarbon dating during the Late Glacial period. The first is calibration, the second, measurement precision and the third, dating accuracy. The past 20 years have seen significant developments leading towards the resolution of some of the problems associated with these factors. INTCAL04 (Reimer et al. 2004), for instance, extends calibration back to 26 000 calBP, well beyond the period of the Late Glacial, although the plateaux within the Late Glacial blunt the effectiveness of radiocarbon as seen through the prism of its calibration. Simple increases in measurement precision alone, of which there are some recent examples in the field of AMS dating (see eg. Bronk Ramsey et al. 2004; Bronk Ramsey / Higham / Leach 2004), are not sufficient to solve wholly the problems associated with the calibration of single dates through plateaux. The application of Bayesian methods, which offer the Quaternary scientist the attraction of incorporating radiocarbon dates within models that integrate sediment stratigraphy, tephra markers and other independent chronological data, is a step forward (Blackwell / Buck 2003; Blockley et al. 2004).

Dating accuracy is the principal focus of this paper. As in most examples of archaeological chronology building in European archaeology, a vast number of the radiocarbon measurements obtained over the last few decades can be considered problematic. The challenge is in how to deal with this historical information effectively without being criticised for too subjective application of the data. Various ways of coping with this situation have been proposed. Some scholars have recommended »auditing« or applying »discard protocols« to the European Palaeolithic radiocarbon database, with various tools designed to assess the reliability of dates based on both archaeological and analytical criteria (eg. Pettitt et al. 2003; Gamble et al. 2004; 2005). Gamble and colleagues (2005) report that around 40 % of the radiocarbon dates obtained from sites in western Europe fail this auditing process. These approaches follow in the footsteps of previous work in other archaeological contexts (Spriggs 1989; Anderson 1991; Spriggs / Anderson, 1993; Higham / Hogg 1997; Kuzmin / Tankersley 1996; see also Fitzpatrick 2006).

Whilst these attempts to deal with the data are laudable, there are significant problems associated with them insofar as the dated evidence of human activities from the Late Glacial is concerned. In the case of bone determinations, it is very difficult to identify whether a date is reliable or unreliable based on the analysis of published radiocarbon dating information alone. This is because the published information on the vast majority of bone determinations contains no associated useful analytical information that would enable an assessment to be made of the potential for problems. It is only comparatively recently that even some of the main measuring facilities have begun routinely to collect data such as C:N atomic ratios, % C, % N, % weight collagen, and the like. Our experience suggests that without these data it is virtually impossible to ascertain reliability and even with it, questions sometimes remain, because the sensitivity of these individual methods for detecting contamination is poor. A number of analytical datapoints, however, allows one to determine likely problem measurements. At the Oxford Radiocarbon Accelerator Unit (ORAU), we fail bone samples that are outside key analytical thresholds, thereby removing potentially problematic samples before they are dated.

Such are the difficulties in assessing past dating reliability, in terms of bone, that our approach to the problem has been to redate key sites and specimens, particularly where there exist determinations obtained

Fig. 1 Localities in England from which radiocarbon determinations are reported in this paper: Sun Hole, Cheddar Gorge, Somerset; Kent's Cavern, Torquay, Devon; Victoria Cave, Settle, North Yorkshire; Poulton-le-Fylde, Blackpool, Lancashire; Sproughton, Suffolk.

previously that appear to be aberrant or at odds with archaeological observations (Jacobi / Higham / Bronk Ramsey 2006; Higham / Jacobi / Bronk Ramsey 2006). Rather than analyse the frequency distributions of large amounts of radiocarbon data and obtain »coarse« results, our work is based around the selection of key sites containing reliable archaeological samples of human or humanly-modified material, to attempt to derive high-quality AMS radiocarbon dates which can be utilised at a future time within a robust Bayesian modelling approach. In this paper, we consider the chronologies of five frequently-mentioned sites from the British Late Glacial (**Fig. 1**). Further work planned will take the analysis of these, and other, results further, and seek to consider the data derived in their entirety to look for patterns. This work is ongoing, but is a slow process.

Methods: Radiocarbon dating

Radiocarbon dating of material from the British Late Glacial has been undertaken at ORAU since the inception of the laboratory. Several different methods of chemical pre-treatment have been applied to the bones dated. Briefly, these include the isolation of amino acids, the ion exchange treatment of gela-

R. M. Jacobi · Th. F. G Higham · T. C. Lord - Improving the chronology of the human occupation

tin, and the extraction of filtered gelatin[1] (for details see Higham / Jacobi / Bronk Ramsey 2006; Gillespie / Hedges / Wand 1984; Gillespie / Hedges 1983; Law / Hedges 1989; Hedges et al. 1989b). The ion-exchanged gelatin method of dating, which was abandoned in 2000 due to problems associated with column resin bleed and the difficulty in excluding this as a potential contaminant (see also Burky et al. 1998), may have been responsible for certain aberrant results dating to this period. Our redating suggests that this is likely to be most significant when the samples are very small (<3-5 mgs extractable gelatin).

Since 2001, ORAU has applied an ultrafiltration protocol to the dating of bone gelatin (Bronk Ramsey et al. 2004), and this is the method used to date bone described in this paper. Significant advances in routine dating have accrued, particularly for the dating of samples of bone from the British Middle Palaeolithic and early Upper Palaeolithic periods (Higham / Jacobi / Bronk Ramsey 2006; Jacobi / Higham / Bronk Ramsey 2006). In addition to improved pre-treatment chemistry, reduced backgrounds and improved measurement precision have resulted in an extension of the dateable range.

Sun Hole

The first site we want to describe is Sun Hole, which is a small fissure cave half-way up the cliffs on the northern (right-hand) side of Cheddar Gorge, Somerset. It is almost opposite Gough's Cave. An initially wide entrance passage contracts and rises to a boulder choke at its inner end. The entrance faces towards the south and is, therefore, sunlit, making it the warmest of the Cheddar caves. It is also protected from the north and east winds. The cave contains a deep sequence of Pleistocene sediments (Collcutt / Currant / Hawkes 1981) of which the deepest part excavated appears to be Middle Pleistocene (S. Parfitt pers. comm.).

Later Upper Palaeolithic flint artefacts were found in the upper part of the Pleistocene deposits during excavations by the University of Bristol Spelaeological Society which began in 1926. Only a few of the artefacts found prior to World War II survived the bombing of the Society's museum in November, 1940 and do so in a much damaged state (Jacobi 2004, fig. 36). Lost in 1940 were the records relating to the exploration of the Pleistocene sediments, with publication of work at the cave dealing only with the finds of more recent date (Tratman / Henderson 1928).

However, full documentation does survive for a group of nineteen pieces of flint excavated from 1951-1953. These were collected from the centre of the cave and on its western side towards the mouth. This is an important group, the more so since there are now four radiocarbon determinations which directly date human activity in the cave, of which three are on fauna excavated with the flints. Artefacts and fauna are preserved in the museum of the University of Bristol Spelaeological Society.

The artefacts are all patinated, but appear to have been made from a translucent or semi-translucent flint resembling that from Gough's Cave. If it is from the same source, this may have been Salisbury Plain, a distance, as the crow flies, of up to 70 km (Clayton n.d. cited in Jacobi 2004, 12). There are no refits within this group or with other artefacts provenanced to the cave. Pieces have been illustrated by Tratman (1955, fig. 10), Campbell (1977, fig. 128, 1. 4. 7-9) and Jacobi (2000, fig. 8, 3; 2004, fig. 35).

The group includes a single symmetrical bitruncated trapezoidal backed blade or »Cheddar« point (**Fig. 2, 1**). This is the most significant artefact within the small collection as these trapezoidal backed blades have, probably correctly, been taken as markers of the initial Final Magdalenian (»Creswellian«) re-settlement of the British Isles during the earliest part of the Late Glacial Interstadial (Jacobi 1991; 1997; 2004; Barton et al. 2003).

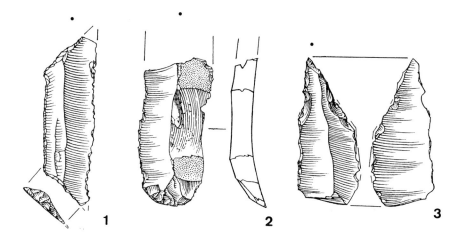

Fig. 2 Sun Hole, 1951-1953. – **1** Symmetrical bitruncated trapezoidal backed blade (»Cheddar« point), – **2** End-scraper, – **3** Piercer, – **4** Burin overlaid by rounding, – **5** Blade with rounded end (Museum of the University of Bristol Spelaeological Society).

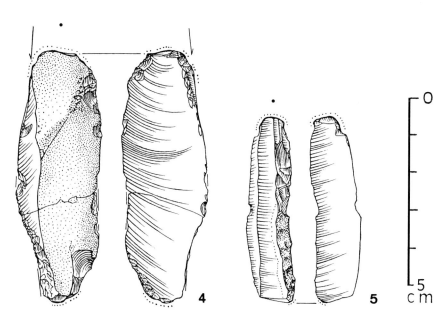

Other artefacts include an end-scraper at the distal end of a broken blade (**Fig. 2, 2**), a piercer (**Fig. 2, 3**) and a burin (**Fig. 2, 4**). The burin is interesting in that it is overlaid by rounding of a type which, it has been suggested, might have been produced by use of the flint with iron pyrites to produce fire (Stapert / Johansen 1999). Two other pieces have rounded ends (**Fig. 2, 5**).

Three broken blades possess the specific butt type known as a »talon en éperon« (Barton 1991). Their significance is similar to that of the bitruncated trapezoidal backed blades in that this form of platform preparation seems to have been associated with the earlier Later Upper Palaeolithic technologies in the British Isles and to be absent from more recent, Final Palaeolithic flint industries.

There are now four radiocarbon determinations from Sun Hole of direct relevance to Late Glacial human presence (**Table 1**). The first of these (OxA-535) was obtained in 1984, very early in the history of ORAU. The dated bone is a human left ulna (Sun Hole 2: Oakley / Campbell / Molleson 1971, 39) which, apparently, was found between 1926 and 1928 (for comments see Stringer 1986a, 60; 1986b, 46-47).

The three new determinations are for a humanly modified bone and teeth of wild horse (*Equus ferus*) which were recovered at the same time as the Later Upper Palaeolithic artefacts found in 1951-1953. OxA-14438 is on a fragment of left tibia which has been broken open to access the marrow, breakage having taken place »on anvil« resulting in the removal of opposing bone-flakes whose negative scars remain clearly visible.

Lab. Ref.	Material	Radiocarbon age BP	$\delta^{13}C$ (‰)	CN	Pret.yld (mgs)	%wt.coll.	%C
OxA-535	Human, left ulna	12210±160	-	-	-	-	-
OxA-14438	*Equus ferus*, left tibia	12545±55	-20.4	3.2	18.1	2.6	49.2
OxA-14476	*Equus ferus*, right P$_4$	12610±90	-20.7	3.4	3.3	0.5	41.4
OxA-14477	*Equus ferus*, right M$_1$	12540±75	-20.7	3.5	4.4	0.7	44.3
OxA-14827	*R. tarandus*, phalange	10145±55	-18.3	3.3	8.0	1.5	63.4

Table 1 Radiocarbon determinations from Sun Hole (OxA-535 is after Gowlett et al. 1986a, 118). ‰^{15}N values were obtained as part of the AMS combustion process, but are not reported here. It is worth pointing out that there is a significant difference between those deriving from the samples dating to 12.2-12.6 ka BP and the sample dating to 10.1 ka BP, as Stevens and Hedges (2004) data indicate. This provides clear support for the reliability of these new AMS measurements. Stable isotope ratios are expressed in ‰ relative to vPDB. Mass spectrometric precision is ± 0.2‰ for carbon. Pret. yield represents the weight of gelatin or ultrafiltered gelatin in milligrams. %yield is the wt. %collagen, which ideally should not be <1wt. % at ORAU. This represents the amount of collagen extracted as a percentage of the starting weight. %C is the carbon present in the combusted gelatin. For ultrafiltered gelatin this averages 41.0 ±1 %. CN is the atomic ratio of carbon to nitrogen, at ORAU this is acceptable if it ranges between 2.9-3.5.

OxA-14476 and 14477 are for two adjacent teeth from a right dentary. The lower border of the bone has clearly been broken away, again to expose the marrow, and the blows from this have coincidentally fractured several of the teeth transversely. Similar evidence for this process comes from other British Later Upper Palaeolithic sites including Gough's Cave, where information from deliberate breakage is supplemented by abundant cut-marks.

These three determinations are, we believe, the first reliable age estimates for when the cave was used for horse hunting and are thought to date the small collection of Final Magdalenian flint artefacts from this site. They are to be preferred to the determination previously obtained for the human ulna (OxA-535). This determination was obtained using the AC method described above, early in the history of ORAU, and there are reasons for viewing it with caution, especially in the light of these more recently obtained measurements. Despite the fact that this specimen has been used both for dating and as a source of stable isotopes (Richards et al. 2000), we were recently able to resample it for a new ultrafiltered determination.

As already noted, many of the radiocarbon determinations previously obtained from Late Glacial find-spots in the British Isles have had to be discarded. A result of this process is that the three determinations from Sun Hole now form the oldest group of dates from Britain documenting human activity in the Late Glacial. That the re-colonization of Britain would now seem to have taken place more recently than that of the Paris Basin (Bodu 2004) and the Ardennes (Charles 1996) is a conclusion supported by the more evolved typology of the earliest Later Upper Palaeolithic flint industries in the British Isles.

However, what remains uncertain is whether this re-colonization preceded, was contemporary with, or came after, the warming which initiated the Late Glacial Interstadial, since local proxy climatic data in the form of fossil beetles suggest that in north-west Europe this warming may have begun earlier than the time when it is first registered in the Greenland deep ice-cores (Walker / Coope / Lowe 1993; Walker et al. 2003; Blockley et al. 2006). It is unclear how this ambiguity can best be resolved.

A fourth new result from Sun Hole is for a proximal phalange of reindeer (*Rangifer tarandus*: **Table 1**). Its age is considerably more recent than that of the humanly-modified horse remains. None of the reindeer bones from Sun Hole shows evidence for human modification and some have clearly been gnawed, suggesting that their presence in the cave is due to the activities of a different predator – perhaps wolf (*Canis lupus*), whose bones have also been found at the site. We have now sampled for dating a dentary of wolf to determine when carnivores were using the cave. Currant (1986; 1991) has argued that reindeer remains

Lab. Ref.	Species/element	Radiocarbon age BP	δ13C (‰)	CN	Pret.yld (mgs)	%wt.coll.	%C
OxA-13683	*Cervus elaphus*, cut right metacarpal	12270±45	-20.6	3.3	35.6	7.3	45.6

Table 2   Radiocarbon date from Kent's Cavern. See caption for Table 1 for details of the analytical data shown.

from Gough's Cave are more recent than human occupation of that cave and date from the Younger Dryas Stadial. This conclusion would appear to be supported by the result from Sun Hole and by fresh radiocarbon determinations from the nearby site of Chelm's Combe.

Kent's Cavern

Here we report a new determination for a bone of red deer (*Cervus elaphus*) from Kent's Cavern. This cave system is in the Devonian limestone of Lincombe Hill in Wellswood, 2 km east of the centre of Torquay on the south Devon coast. The bone was found during the extensive investigations of the cave directed by William Pengelly from 1865-1880 (Pengelly 1884). Its find-spot was the »Vestibule«, the first chamber of the cave, immediately inside the »North Entrance«. It is a distal right metacarpal with clear cut-marks on the external face of the articulation (**Fig. 3**). The age obtained for this bone is shown in **Table 2**.
The result places the bone clearly within the first half of the Late Glacial Interstadial (the Bølling chronozone: Mangerud et al. 1974). Hunting of red deer at this time may also be documented at Gough's Cave

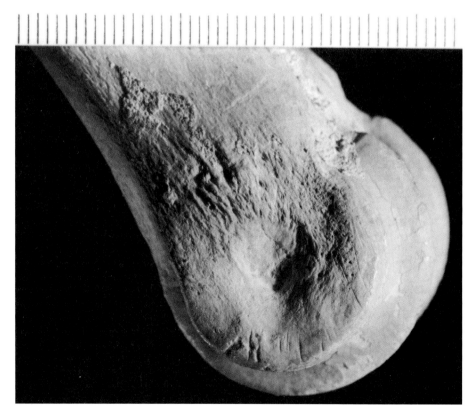

Fig. 3 Kent's Cavern, 1866. Detail of distal right metacarpal of red deer (*Cervus elaphus*) showing cut-marks on the external face of the articulation (Torquay Museum).

(Jacobi 2004, table 29), Aveline's Hole in Burrington Combe on the north side of Mendip (Somerset: Gowlett et al. 1986b, 209-210; Hedges et al. 1987, 290) and at King Arthur's Cave in the Wye Valley (Hereford and Worcester: Hedges et al. 1989a, 212; Bronk Ramsey et al. 2002, 20) although in each case we are re-examining some of the existing radiocarbon determinations.

The metacarpal from Kent's Cavern was found on 6 December, 1866 when a Holocene flowstone, the »Granular Stalagmite« was being lifted from above the Pleistocene deposits. In the Vestibule, Final Magdalenian (»Creswellian«) artefacts were found by Pengelly in a cave-earth immediately below this flowstone. Part of this cave-earth had become discoloured by occupation residues and where this discoloration was most apparent the cave-earth was termed the »black-band« (Pengelly 1868). It is unclear whether the red deer metacarpal was within the flowstone, and so above the sediments with Final Magdalenian artefacts, or at its base and had been dislodged from the surface of the underlying cave-earth as the flowstone was removed. Therefore, it is unknown whether its age should be extrapolated to the rich collection of artefacts found at the summit of the cave-earth in this part of the cave, which includes »Cheddar« and »Creswell« points, end-scrapers, burins and debitage (amongst which are pieces with »talons en éperon«), as well as a bone needle and barbed points made from reindeer antler (Jacobi 2004, figs 37-39). The real significance of this determination is that it adds Kent's Cavern to the small number of sites where there is evidence for the hunting of red deer during the first part of the Late Glacial Interstadial.

Victoria Cave

Victoria Cave is at an altitude of 440 m O.D. in the Langcliffe Scar escarpment, north-east of Settle in North Yorkshire. Initial exploration in the 1830s was followed by more systematic excavation from 1870-1878, first directed by William Boyd Dawkins and then by Richard Tiddeman (Murphy / Lord 2003; Lord et al. 2007). The more perceptive of these excavators was clearly Tiddeman who, in the interior of the cave, distinguished two bone-bearing deposits separated by sterile, finely-laminated clays. The bone-bearing deposits were described as the Lower Cave-Earth and the Upper Cave-Earth. The fauna from the Lower Cave-Earth is fully temperate and of Last Interglacial (Ipswichian) age (Gascoyne / Currant / Lord 1981; Gilmour et al. 2007). By contrast, radiocarbon determinations suggest that the oldest components of the fauna from the Upper Cave-Earth are Late Glacial (Lord et al. 2007).

Prior to excavation, Victoria Cave consisted of three interconnected chambers with a small entrance leading into the central chamber – Chamber A. In Late Glacial times this entry would have been from a broad, shallow rock-shelter which fronted the cave and whose floor was a deep scree apron. Chamber A was excavated by Dawkins from March to December, 1870. He removed the Upper Cave-Earth down to the surface of the Laminated Clay. Tiddeman later excavated the Lower Cave-Earth. The bone whose age we report here was found in the Upper Cave-Earth which, in this part of the cave, contained bones of Late Glacial, Romano-British and more recent ages (Lord et al. 2007).

Lab. Ref.	Species/element	Radiocarbon age BP	$\delta^{13}C$ (‰)	CN	Pret.yld. (mgs)	%wt.coll.	%C
OxA-15078	*Equus ferus*, cut atlas	12 325±50	-20.3	3.2	44.1	7.1	49.8

Table 3 Radiocarbon determination from Victoria Cave. See caption for Table 1 for details of the analytical data shown.

The bone we have dated is an atlas vertebra of wild horse with a group of very clear transverse cut-marks on the ventral surface of one of the anterior wings which resulted from removing the head. The result is shown in **Table 3**. The vertebra has been interpreted as having been scavenged by wolves from a human processing site somewhere near the cave and carried into it (Lord et al. 2007). In this, it resembles the single cut-marked phalange of horse from Gough's Old Cave which was suggested to have been scavenged carrion from the human habitation site in the entrance to Gough's Cave (Jacobi 2004, 81).

Locality	Lab. Ref.	Material	Radiocarbon age BP	δ^{13}C (‰)	CN	Pret.yld (mgs)	%wt.coll.	%C
Victoria Cave	OxA-2607[*]	Bilaterally barbed harpoon of *Rangifer tarandus* antler	10810±100	-21.3	-	-	-	-
	OxA-14888[+]	Bilaterally barbed harpoon of antler	10930±45	-20.0	3.3	13.4	9.5	43.4
Conistone Dib	OxA-2847[*]	Bone point	11210±90	-20.5	-	-	-	-
Kinsey Cave	OxA-2456[*]	Fragment of artefact made from *Rangifer tarandus* antler	11270±110	-21.9	-	-	-	-
Victoria Cave	OxA-2455[*]	Fragments of double-bevelled artefact made from *Rangifer tarandus* antler	11750±120	-20.6	-	-	-	-
	OxA-15078[+]	Atlas vertebra of *Equus ferus* with cut marks	12325±50	-20.3	3.2	44.1	7.1	49.8

Table 4 Radiocarbon determinations for Late Glacial human presence in north-west Yorkshire. − * Results from Hedges et al. (1992, 141-142); − + Results from Lord et al. (2007, table 1). See caption for Table 1 for details of the analytical data shown.

This is the oldest direct evidence for a human presence in the Yorkshire Dales. Whilst there are other age estimates which tell us that humans were present during the Late Glacial Interstadial these all belong within its second half (Allerød: **Table 4**). This is also the first time in the Dales that we can identify the prey of Late Glacial hunters, although reindeer antler and either elk (*Alces alces*) or giant deer (*Megaloceros giganteus*) bone were used for artefacts, the latter at Conistone Dib.

Victoria Cave is probably not the most northerly find-spot in the British Isles with evidence for human activity during the earlier part of the Interstadial. An artefact from Fairnington, near Kelso in the Scottish Borders appears to be a bitruncated trapezoidal backed blade (»Cheddar« point), not unlike those from Sun Hole and Kent's Cavern (Saville 2004, fig. 10.23). Further, the size and form of backed blades from Nab End (Ivy Scar) on Carperby Moor in Wensleydale (Laurie 2003, fig. 60.1) and from Lindale Low Cave, near Grange-over-Sands in Cumbria (Salisbury 1988, fig. 3.1) suggest that these too may date from the earlier rather than the latter part of the Late Glacial Interstadial.

Poulton-le-Fylde

In July, 1970 Mr and Mrs A. Scholey and Mr J. Audus found the bones of a male elk at a building site in Blackpool Old Road, High Furlong, Poulton-le-Fylde, about 3.2 km to the north-east of the centre of Blackpool in Lancashire. The elk was named Horace by its finders. Amongst the ribs was found part of a barbed point made from bone or antler (**Fig. 4, 1**). Subsequent excavation revealed bones of both hind legs and a second barbed point (**Fig. 4, 2**) was found lying across the lateral condylar surface of the left metatarsal. Compaction of the enclosing sediments had broken this point into two. Dental wear suggested an age at death for the elk of between 3?-6 years and, since it was about to shed its antlers, death is believed to have occurred between November and March (Barnes et al. 1971; Edwards 1972; Hallam et al. 1973). The context of the discovery was freshwater deposits in a small basin on the surface of glacial till. The sediments in this basin showed clays sandwiching calcareous gyttja and coarse detritus muds. This sequence, together with a significant increase in tree and shrub pollen at the expense of dryland pollen in the detritus muds, suggested dating of the skeleton to the Allerød Interstadial

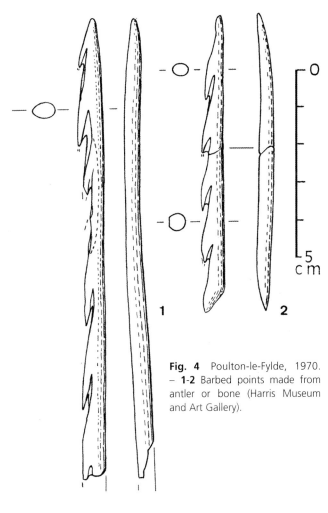

Fig. 4 Poulton-le-Fylde, 1970. – **1-2** Barbed points made from antler or bone (Harris Museum and Art Gallery).

of the European mainland. Twigs and leaves of birch (*Betula*) imply that trees existed locally, but the pollen of heliophytes also indicates that this was not closed woodland. Elk populations reach maximum numbers in areas which are in the early stages of forest succession (Peterson 1955).

Two samples of the coarse detritus mud were initially dated (**Table 5**). Whilst these determinations confirm the Late Glacial age of the sediments, subsequent discussion (Jacobi 1980, 60-61) has suggested that they could be overestimates of the true ages of the top and bottom of the detritus mud, because the material sampled might have included aquatic plants which had incorporated ^{14}C deficient carbon during photosynthesis. This is known as hardwater error (cf Shotton 1972).

Mary-Jane Mountain (in Megaw / Simpson 1979, 47) has further suggested that the elk was of more recent age than the Allerød and that the body had gradually sunk from a higher level because of its weight. However, the continuity of the overlying sediments, as shown in photographs of the hind leg bones, would argue against this.

	Lab. Ref.	Species/element	Radiocarbon age BP
Table 5 Radiocarbon dates from the site of Poulton-le-Fylde (after Welin / Engstrand / Vaczy 1974, 102-103).	IGS-C14/134 (St-3836)	Detritus mud	11665±140
	IGS-C14/135 (St-3832)	Detritus mud	12200±160

Lab. Ref.	Species/element	Radiocarbon age BP
OxA-150	*Alces alces*, metatarsal: amino-acids	12400±300
OxA-151	*Alces alces*, metatarsal: extracted humics/ preservatives	21500±250

Table 6 Radiocarbon date of bone from the Poulton-le-Fylde elk (after Gillespie et al. 1985, 238; Jacobi et al. 1986, 123).

In an attempt to resolve these doubts and to establish directly when humans had been hunting elk in northwest England a sample was taken from the right metatarsal in 1982. The result of an amino-acid extraction from this bone is shown in **Table 6**.

A »humic extraction« of the bone was also obtained, and while this is likely to have contained humic elements from the detritus mud, its age suggests that it can be regarded as consisting mainly of the preservatives with which the skeleton had been impregnated. Conservation in 1971 by the North West Museum Service had consisted of impregnation under vacuum with polyvinyl acetate emulsion (Premale) and soaking in a weak (1-2 %) solution of pentachlorophenol, an insecticide used to give added protection against mould (Brian Manning pers. comm.).

The age obtained for the amino-acids (**Table 6**) lacks the precision which we presently aim for in dating Late Glacial bone, but it demonstrated quite clearly that the elk had been wounded by Upper Palaeolithic hunters. Nevertheless, the age came as something of a surprise, since it suggested that the elk had lived during the early, pre-Allerød, part of the Late Glacial Interstadial. This fitted poorly with the data from other sites in western Britain with faunas of this age, for example Gough's Cave, where there is no confirmatory evidence for a presence of elk. This observation led to a suspicion that failure to remove petrochemical derivatives may have been an important influence on the age determined, and that inclusion of material with a depleted ^{14}C signal may have given a result which is too old.

For this reason, we sought to re-investigate the chronological aspects of this find by taking two further samples in September 2001. Both of the resulting determinations are for ultrafiltered gelatin. OxA-11151 differed slightly, in that it was pretreated without any solvent rinsing prior to the isolation of bone collagen for dating. OxA-13075, however, was pretreated with full solvent extraction using methanol, acetone and water. The resulting determinations are shown in **Table 7**.

Both dates are younger than the original determination and, in addition, they are statistically in agreement. The result for OxA-11151 suggests that the bulk of the contamination in the bone had been removed by ultrafiltration. Pentachlorophenol (PCP, $C_6C_{l5}OH$) has a molecular weight of 266.34 daltons and, therefore, would pass through the Oxford ultrafilters during pre-treatment if still present after gelatinisation. This suggests that, since OxA-11151 and -13075 are statistically identical, it was the ultrafiltration rather than the solvent extraction which

	OxA no.	Radiocarbon age BP	CN	$\delta^{13}C$ (‰)	$\delta^{15}N$ (‰)	Bone weight used (mgs)	Pret.yld. (mgs)	%C
Alces alces. left metacarpal								
NRC	11151	11660±60	3.4	-19.5	0.3	436	29.77	43.0
Alces alces. right metacarpal								
AF*	13075	11715±50	3.4	-20.1	0.6	644	19.6	41.0
NRC1	X-2066-43	16100±70	6.5	-31.8	1.0	644	95	46.5
NRC2								
NRC3	X-2100-6	24410±100	23.9	-41.7	-1.5	644	29.1	51.0

Table 7 New radiocarbon determinations for the Poulton-le-Fylde elk. See caption for Table 1 for details of the analytical data shown. Note: NRC means »non-routine chemistry«.

was responsible for the age shift since only one measurement was solvent extracted. These new results support the view that the original AMS date was slightly too old, and suggest that the elk and its hunters were in the area of Poulton-le-Fylde one winter during the early part of the Allerød. Further confirmation that elk were present in north-west England at this time comes from a new radiocarbon determination for one of a pair of upper cheek teeth found during excavations in July, 1991 at Bart's Shelter, near Scales in Cumbria (**Table 8**). As yet, there are no humanly-predated faunal assemblages from the British Isles with identifiable bone, which can be dated to the second half of the Late Glacial Interstadial (Allerød) and belong with the makers of so-called Federmessergruppen lithic industries. Instead, our knowledge of the prey potentially available to the Later Upper Palaeolithic hunters of this time comes from radiocarbon determinations on single pieces of identifiable fauna or on artefacts made from recognizable raw materials. The elk from Poulton-le-Fylde is a clear exception to this pattern, associating as it does a nearly complete skeleton with two barbed points. It also constitutes the only evidence from lowland Lancashire for human presence during the Late Glacial. Whether the camp from which these hunters operated can be located remains to be seen and, indeed, it may be beneath the Irish Sea.

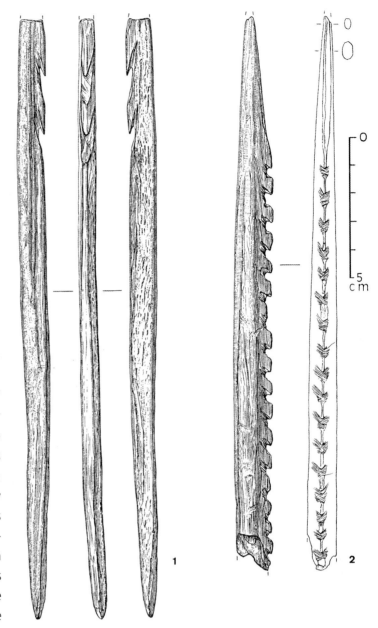

Fig. 5 Devil's Wood Pit, Sproughton, 1974. – **1** Barbed point made from antler. – **2** Barbed point made from bone and with closely spaced barbs separated by simple criss-cross cutting (Ipswich Museum).

Sproughton

In the early 1970s, investigations took place into the sediments and land forms revealed during commercial gravel extraction by Brush Aggregates Ltd at Devil's Wood Pit, Sproughton. The pit was dug into the floodplain of the River Gipping about 2 km above Ipswich, where the river becomes tidal and is known as the Orwell. Devil's Wood Pit was important for the opportunities it offered to observe the filling of the buried channel of the Gipping under dry conditions (Wymer / Rose 1976; Rose et al. 1980). Study has recently recommenced as part of doctoral research by Ruth Sowa.

Lab. Ref.	Species/element	Radiocarbon age BP	$\delta^{13}C$ (‰)	CN	Pret.yld (mgs)	%wt.coll.	%C
OxA-11646	*Alces alces*, right P³/P⁴	11600±70	-20.0	3.2	7.7	1.5	35.2

Table 8   Radiocarbon date from the site of Bart's Shelter, Cumbria. See caption for Table 1 for details of the analytical data shown.

The sections exposed showed a low energy fluvial series of Holocene age overlying a high energy fluvial series consisting of gravels and sands. A soil was recognized at the top of the gravels and sands. Just below this, and located on a sandy riffle-bar, was found a »long blade« flint industry (»bruised blade assemblage«: Barton 1998) of Terminal Palaeolithic age. This was excavated in December, 1972 (Wymer / Rose 1976; Barton 1986).

The gravels and sands were observed to fill a channel cut into older colluvial and lacustrine sediments. Within the gravels and sands are seams of willow (*Salix*) twigs and leaves and radiocarbon dating of these has demonstrated quite clearly that the gravels and sands were formed during the climatic deterioration at the end of the Late Glacial. Selection of willow twigs and leaves avoided the problems of hard water contamination suspected for Poulton-le-Fylde (Rose et al. 1980).

In 1974, Mr Russell Game, the driver of the mechanical excavator at the pit, retrieved two barbed points from the gravels and sands (Wymer 1975; Wymer / Jacobi / Rose 1975). New radiocarbon determinations for these are reported here.

One of these points has been made from antler (**Fig. 5, 1**) and the other from bone (**Fig. 5, 2**). The more interesting of the two is the bone point. It has been formed from a metapodial, perhaps of elk. The teeth are closely spaced and project very little from the stem. They have been separated by simple criss-cross cutting and this technique has been observed on other barbed points from the British Isles, all of which appear to have been made from bone. These come from Royston (Hertfordshire, or more probably from near Barrington in Cambridgeshire: Westerby 1931, 46; Clark 1932, 18; Jacobi 1986), Hornsea and Skipsea (Armstrong 1923; Clark / Godwin 1956), also Coneygarth Hill and Gildholme at Brandesburton (Clark / Godwin 1956) and Fosse Hill at Milldam Beck (Radley 1969) all in East Yorkshire, and from between the Leman and Ower Banks off the Norfolk coast and in the present North Sea (Burkitt 1932; Muir Evans 1933; Godwin / Godwin 1933).

The contexts of the two barbed points from Sproughton were considered to be of particular interest. As already noted, the gravels and sands were dated by radiocarbon determinations on willow twigs and leaves found at different depths within them. These ages were extrapolated to the barbed points and it was suggested that the bone point, found deep in the gravels and sands, was most likely to have become incorporated into them in Late Glacial times. Previously, British finds of bone points with close-set teeth separated by criss-cross cutting had been regarded as probably Mesolithic (Clark / Godwin 1956, 13), although none was satisfactorily dated. The find from Sproughton now suggested the likelihood of an Upper Palaeolithic age for this type. The antler point from Sproughton was considered to be of pre-Boreal or early Boreal age and

Lab. Ref.	Species/element	Radiocarbon age BP
OxA-517	bone barbed point	10910±150
OxA-518	antler barbed point	10700±160

Table 9   Initial radiocarbon dates for barbed points from Sproughton (after Gowlett et al. 1986a, 120; Cook / Barton 1986, 87-88).

Table 10	Radiocarbon date obtained for the bone point from the Leman and Ower Banks. (after Hedges et al. 1990, 104-105; Smith / Bonsall 1991).	Lab. Ref.	Species/element	Radiocarbon age BP
		OxA-1950	barbed point	11 740±150

so of Mesolithic date – possibly the contemporary of the large group of antler points from Star Carr in North Yorkshire (Clark 1954), although differing from any of these (Wymer / Jacobi / Rose 1975, 236-237).

In 1984 the two points were directly radiocarbon dated as part of a wider project to investigate the ages of Late Devensian and Early Holocene bone and antler artefacts from eastern Britain. The principal investigators were Jill Cook, Nick Barton and Clive Bonsall. The ages obtained are shown in **Table 9**.

There were two principal surprises. The first, that both points should clearly be Late Glacial (Later Upper Palaeolithic), and the second that, despite the fact that they should be so different from one another in terms of morphology and were separated vertically by a substantial thickness of the gravels and sands, they seemed to be of effectively the same age. The antler point was shown to be very much older than its context, since it was apparently extracted from gravels and sands more recent than willow twigs with an age of 9 880±120 BP (HAR-259: Wymer / Jacobi / Rose 1975, 236).

Further bone and antler artefacts from the British Isles have continued to be dated by the Oxford Radiocarbon Accelerator Unit including a number of barbed points. Amongst these is the point trawled from between the Leman and Ower Banks which, in the technique of its manufacture, resembles the bone point from Sproughton. The age obtained is shown in **Table 10**.

Despite their similarities, there was a surprising difference in age between the points from Leman and Ower and Sproughton. Whilst there is nothing inherently improbable in artefacts remaining similar in form and manufacturing technique over long periods, the observation of a wide age difference prompted us to consider whether the determinations for the points from Sproughton, obtained very early in the working life of ORAU, could be underestimates of their true ages. Some of the age shifts which have resulted from the redating of other bones, with ultrafiltration now included as part of the pre-treatment protocol, also made resampling of the points seem particularly desirable. Both of the points from Sproughton were resampled in 2005 and the new ages are shown in **Table 11**.

Both of the new determinations are older than those previously obtained, and that for the bone point clearly so. The two points are also no longer the same age and the age for the bone point is now closer to that of the point from between the Leman and Ower Banks. Whilst there is still a need for further radiocarbon determinations, we should at least consider the possibility that all British points with closely spaced barbs separated by simple criss-cross cutting could belong within the Allerød part of the Late Glacial Interstadial and possibly to only a part of it. We hope to investigate this proposition further.

A serious gap in our understanding of the Later Upper Palaeolithic (Late Glacial Interstadial) archaeology of Britain is an almost complete absence of sites in the floodplains of active river valleys. Why this gap should

Lab. Ref.	Species/element	Radiocarbon age BP	δ13C (‰)	CN	Pret.yld (mgs)	%wt.coll.	%C
OxA-14943	Bone barbed point	11 485±60	-21.8	3.3	7.8	3.0	43.4
OxA-15219	Antler barbed point	10 960±50	-20.2	3.2	9.1	4.1	42.2

Table 11 New AMS dates for the barbed points from Sproughton. See caption for Table 1 for details of the analytical data shown.

exist may partly be explained by the depositional history of the sediments exposed in the Devil's Wood Pit, if this is typical of other lowland river catchments. Here, Interstadial sediments were eroded and largely replaced by gravels and sands during the climatic deterioration at the end of the Late Glacial. Searches were made in the gravels and sands for flint artefacts, but these were almost wholly unsuccessful. Instead, only the more robust barbed points have survived in a recognizable state and the radiocarbon determinations for these tell us that Palaeolithic hunters were present in the Gipping Valley on at least two occasions during the Late Glacial Interstadial. The only other evidence for Later Upper Palaeolithic activity in the Ipswich area takes the form of tanged points and straight-backed bladelets found at Bolton and Laughlin's Brickfield west of Dale Hall Lane on its western outskirts. The brickfield was in a dry valley at right angles to the River Gipping (Moir 1932).

That bone and antler barbed points have survived to be found is due to their loss in watery environments and Cziesla and Pettitt (2003) have interpreted the finely barbed and notched points of the Later Upper Palaeolithic and Early Mesolithic as leister prongs. Alternatively, we might associate them with the hunting of elk which, particularly in summer, frequent swampy areas with rivers and streams, feeding on aquatic plants. Such a suggestion is supported both by the find from Poulton-le-Fylde and the fauna from Star Carr which includes elk, but is without fish (Wheeler 1978).

Conclusions

In this paper we have presented the first direct radiocarbon dates for human occupation of Sun Hole, evidence for the hunting of red deer at Kent's Cavern during the Late Glacial and a single determination from Victoria Cave which, currently, is the earliest evidence for a human presence in the Dales of north-west Yorkshire. We have also re-dated the elk from Poulton-le-Fylde and, by implication, the two bone or antler barbed points found with the skeleton. Finally, new determinations have been obtained for the two barbed points from Sproughton in east Suffolk.

These are the first results from a larger project to investigate the chronology of humans and animals in the British Late Glacial. As should already be apparent, this project is intended to be more than just an audit of the existing database. Instead, our aim is to continue to re-date those samples whose analytical data currently fail to meet the criteria outlined in the introduction to this paper. A further aim is to date additional samples where these seem likely to amplify our information for the period. We are encouraged that the time is right for such a project by the results already obtained from the redating of human bones, organic artefacts and animal bones from the Middle Devensian (Higham / Jacobi / Bronk Ramsey 2006; Jacobi / Higham / Bronk Ramsey 2006; Jacobi / Higham 2008) as well as by the results reported here. Reliability has been greatly improved by using the ultrafiltration pretreatment method and recent technical developments have resulted in much greater precision.

A number of questions come to mind which, it is hoped, can now be answered. These include:
– Did Late Glacial human re-colonization of the British Isles really take place as early as is implied by the oldest radiocarbon determinations from Gough's Cave (Jacobi 2004, table 29)?
– Was Gough's Cave really used over a period of as much as a thousand radiocarbon years (ibid.)?
– Gough's Cave and Kendrick's Cave on the Great Orme (Conwy, North Wales) have both produced human bones which, on present evidence, appear to partially overlap in age. At Gough's Cave it plausibly could be suggested from abundant cut-marks (documenting disarticulation and excarnation), patterns of breakage and discard in a midden that they are evidence for cannibalism (Andrews / Ferdández-Jalvo 2003). By contrast, the human remains from Kendrick's Cave consist of almost complete bones, with no cut-marks or evi-

dence for intentional breakage. Does this indicate two means of treating the dead at sites that were essentially contemporaneous with one another, or were the sites used at different times? If a chronological difference could be demonstrated, this might suggest that disposal of human remains changed within Britain over time, in the same way as has recently been documented for Germany between the Magdalenian and the period of the Federmessergruppen (Street / Terberger / Orschiedt 2006).

– At Creswell Crags there is evidence for the processing of Arctic (mountain) hares (*Lepus timidus*) from Pin Hole, Robin Hood Cave and Church Hole. At Mother Grundy's Parlour there are no humanly-modified hare bones and, instead, there are smashed teeth and bones of wild horse. At present, it is difficult to determine if hare-trapping and horse-hunting took place in the gorge at the same time, or if they are of slightly different ages. It is hoped that the greater precision now achievable will help resolve the question of whether the difference of cave-use at Mother Grundy's Parlour is explicable in chronological terms.

– Were humans present in the British Isles during the Younger Dryas Stadial?

– Did wild horse and reindeer genuinely survive into the early Post Glacial (Coard / Chamberlain 1999)?

The results presented in this paper give grounds for optimism that we should be able to answer some, if not all, of these questions.

Note

1 The ORAU laboratory codes for these pretreatments are AC, AI and AG, respectively. The ultrafiltration pre-treatment is coded AF.

References

Anderson 1991: A. J. Anderson, The chronology of colonisation in New Zealand. Antiquity 65, 767-795.

Andrews / Fernández-Jalvo 2003: P. Andrews / Y. Fernández-Jalvo, Cannibalism in Britain: taphonomy of the Creswellian (Pleistocene) faunal and human remains from Gough's Cave (Somerset, England). Bulletin of the Natural History Museum London 58 (supplement) 59-81.

Armstrong 1923: A. L. Armstrong, The Maglemose remains of Holderness and their Baltic counterparts. Proceedings of the Prehistoric Society of East Anglia 4, 1922-23 (1923) 57-70.

Barnes et al. 1971: B. Barnes / B. J. N. Edwards / J. S. Hallam / A. J. Stuart, Skeleton of a Late Glacial elk associated with barbed points from Poulton-le-Fylde, Lancashire. Nature 232, 488-489.

Barton 1986: R. N. E. Barton, Experiments with long blades from Sproughton, near Ipswich, Suffolk. In: D. A. Roe (ed.), Studies in the Upper Palaeolithic of Britain and Northwest Europe. British Archaeological Report (International Series) 296 (Oxford 1986) 129-141.

1991: R. N. E. Barton, The en éperon technique in the British Late Upper Palaeolithic. Lithics 11, 1990 (1991) 31-33.

1998: R. N. E. Barton, Long blade technology and the question of British Late Pleistocene/Early Holocene lithic assemblages. In: N. Ashton / F. Healy / P. Pettitt (eds.), Stone Age Archaeology. Essays in honour of John Wymer. Oxbow Monograph 102 (Lithic Studies Society Occasional Paper 6) (Oxford 1998) 158-164.

Barton et al. 2003: R. N. E. Barton / R. M. Jacobi / D. Stapert / M.

Street, The Lateglacial reoccupation of the British Isles and the Creswellian. Journal of Quaternary Science 18, 631-643.

Blackwell / Buck 2003: P. Blackwell / C. Buck, The Late Glacial human reoccupation of north-western Europe: new approaches to space-time modelling. Antiquity 77, 232-240.

Blockley et al.2004: S. Blockley / J. J. Lowe / M. J. C. Walker / A. Asioli / F. Trincardi / G. R. Coope / R. E. Donahue / A. M. Pollard, Bayesian analysis of radiocarbon chronologies: examples from the European Lateglacial. Journal of Quaternary Science 19, 159-176.

2006: S. P. E. Blockley / S. M. Blockley / R. E. Donahue / C. S. Lane / J. J. Lowe / A. M. Pollard, The chronology of abrupt climate change and Late Upper Palaeolithic human adaptation in Europe. Journal of Quaternary Science 21, 575-584.

Bodu 2004: P. Bodu, Datations absolues obtenues sur les séquences archéologiques tardiglaciaires du sud du Bassin parisien. In: B. Valentin / P. Bodu / M. Julien (eds.), Habitats et peuplements tardiglaciaires du Bassin parisien (Nanterre 2004) 175-177.

Bronk Ramsey et al. 2002: C. Bronk Ramsey / T. F. G. Higham / D. C. Owen / A. W. G. Pike / R. E. M. Hedges, Radiocarbon dates from the Oxford AMS system: Archaeometry datelist 31. Archaeometry 44, 1-149.

2004: C. Bronk Ramsey / T. F. G. Higham / A. Bowles / R. Hedges, Improvements to the pretreatment of bone at Oxford. Radiocarbon 46, 155-63.

Bronk Ramsey / Higham / Leach 2004: C. Bronk Ramsey / T. F. G Higham / P. Leach, Towards High Precision AMS: Progress and Limitations. Radiocarbon 46, 17-24.

Burkitt 1932: M. C. Burkitt, A Maglemose harpoon dredged up recently from the North Sea. Man 32, 118.

Burky et al. 1998: R. R. Burky / D. L. Kirner / R. E. Taylor / P. E. Hare / J. R. Southon, ^{14}C dating of bone using γ-carboxyglutamic acid and α-carboxyglycine (aminomalonate). Radiocarbon 40, 11-20.

Campbell 1977: J. B. Campbell, The Upper Palaeolithic of Britain: a study of man and nature in the Late Ice Age (Oxford 1977).

Charles 1996: R. Charles, Back into the North: the radiocarbon evidence for the human recolonisation of the north-west Ardennes after the Last Glacial Maximum. Proceedings of the Prehistoric Society 62, 1-19.

Clark 1932: J. G. D. Clark, The Mesolithic Age in Britain (Cambridge 1932).

1954: J. G. D. Clark, Excavations at Star Carr: an Early Mesolithic site at Seamer near Scarborough, Yorkshire (Cambridge 1954).

Clark / Godwin 1956: J. G. D. Clark / H. Godwin, A Maglemosian site at Brandesburton, Holderness, Yorkshire. Proceedings of the Prehistoric Society 22, 6-22.

Clayton n.d.: C. Clayton, Sources of Flint Raw Material to Gough's Cave, Cheddar. Unpublished manuscript.

Coard / Chamberlain 1999: R. Coard / A. T. Chamberlain, The nature and timing of faunal change in the British Isles across the Pleistocene/Holocene transition. The Holocene 9, 372-376.

Collcutt / Currant / Hawkes 1981: S. N. Collcutt / A. P. Currant / C. J. Hawkes, A further report on the excavations at Sun Hole, Cheddar. Proceedings of the University of Bristol Spelaeological Society 16, 21-38.

Cook / Barton 1986: J. Cook / R. N. E. Barton, Dating late Devensian – early Flandrian barbed points. In: J. A. J. Gowlett / R. E. M. Hedges (eds.), Archaeological Results from Accelerator Dating. Oxford University Committee for Archaeology Monograph 11 (Oxford 1986) 87-89.

Currant 1986: A. P. Currant, The Lateglacial mammal fauna of Gough's Cave, Cheddar, Somerset. Proceedings of the University of Bristol Spelaeological Society 17, 286-304.

1991: A. P. Currant, A Late Glacial Interstadial mammal fauna from Gough's Cave, Somerset, England. In: N. Barton / A. J. Roberts / D. A. Roe (eds.), The Late Glacial in north-west Europe: human adaptation and environmental change at the end of the Pleistocene. Council for British Archaeology Research Report 77 (Oxford 1991) 48-50.

Cziesla / Pettitt 2003: E. Cziesla / P. B. Pettitt, AMS-^{14}C-Datierungen von spätpaläolithischen und mesolithischen Funden aus dem Bützsee (Brandenburg). Archäologisches Korrespondenzblatt 33, 21-38.

Edwards 1972: B. J. N. Edwards, Two barbed bone points from a Late Glacial deposit at Poulton-le-Fylde, Lancs. Antiquaries Journal 52, 358.

Fitzpatrick 2006: S. M. Fitzpatrick, A critical approach to ^{14}C dating in the Caribbean: Using chronometric hygiene to evaluate chronological control and prehistoric settlement. Latin American Antiquity 17, 389-418.

Gamble et al. 2004: C. Gamble / S. W. G. Davies / P. B. Pettitt / M. R. Richards, Climate change and evolving human diversity in Europe during the last glacial. Philosophical Transactions of the Royal Society B359, 243-254.

2005: C. Gamble / S. W. G. Davies / P. B. Pettitt / L Hazelwood / M. Richards, The archaeological and genetic foundations of the European population during the Late Glacial: Implications for »agricultural thinking«. Cambridge Archaeological Journal 15/2, 193-223.

Gascoyne / Currant / Lord 1981: M. Gascoyne / A. P. Currant / T. C. Lord, Ipswichian fauna of Victoria Cave and the marine palaeoclimate record. Nature 294, 652-654.

Gillespie et al. 1985: R. Gillespie / J. A. J. Gowlett / E. T. Hall / R. E. M. Hedges / C. Perry, Radiocarbon dates from the Oxford AMS system: Archaeometry datelist 2. Archaeometry 27, 237-246.

Gillespie / Hedges 1983: R. Gillespie / R. E. M. Hedges, Sample chemistry for the Oxford high energy mass spectrometer. Radiocarbon 25, 771-774.

Gillespie / Hedges / Wand 1984: R. Gillespie / R. E. M. Hedges / J.

O. Wand, Radiocarbon dating of bone by accelerator mass spectrometry. Journal of Archaeological Science 11, 165-170.

Gilmour et al. 2007: M. Gilmour / A. P. Currant / R. M. Jacobi / C. B. Stringer, Recent TIMS dating results from British Late Pleistocene vertebrate faunal localities: context and interpretation. Journal of Quaternary Science 22, 793-800.

Godwin / Godwin 1933: H. Godwin / M. E. Godwin, British Maglemose harpoon sites. Antiquity 7, 36-48.

Gowlett et al. 1986a: J. A. J. Gowlett / E. T. Hall / R. E. M. Hedges / C. Perry, Radiocarbon dates from the Oxford AMS system: Archaeometry datelist 3. Archaeometry 28, 116-125.

1986b: J. A. J. Gowlett / R. E. M. Hedges / I. A. Law / C. Perry, Radiocarbon dates from the Oxford AMS system: Archaeometry datelist 4. Archaeometry 28, 206-221.

Hallam et al. 1973: J. S. Hallam / B. J. N. Edwards / B. Barnes / A. J. Stuart, The remains of a Late Glacial elk associated with barbed points from High Furlong, near Blackpool, Lancashire. Proceedings of the Prehistoric Society 39, 100-128.

Hedges et al. 1987: R. E. M. Hedges / R. A. Housley / I. A. Law / C. Perry / J. A. J. Gowlett, Radiocarbon dates from the Oxford AMS system: Archaeometry datelist 6. Archaeometry 29, 289-306.

1989a: R. E. M. Hedges / R. A. Housley / I. A. Law / C. Bronk Ramsey, Radiocarbon dates from the Oxford AMS system: Archaeometry datelist 9. Archaeometry 31, 207-234.

1989b: R. E. M. Hedges / I. A. Law / C. Bronk Ramsey / R. A. Housley, The Oxford accelerator mass spectrometry facility: technical developments in routine dating. Archaeometry datelist 8. Archaeometry 31, 99-113.

1990: R. E. M. Hedges / R. A. Housley / I. A. Law / C. Bronk Ramsey, Radiocarbon dates from the Oxford AMS system: Archaeometry datelist 10. Archaeometry 32, 101-108.

1992: R. E. M. Hedges / R. A. Housley / C. Bronk Ramsey / G. J. van Klinken, Radiocarbon dates from the Oxford AMS system: Archaeometry datelist 14. Archaeometry 34, 141-159.

Higham / Hogg 1997: T. F. G. Higham / A. G. Hogg, Evidence for late Polynesian colonisation of New Zealand: University of Waikato radiocarbon measurements. Radiocarbon 39, 149-192.

Higham / Jacobi / Bronk Ramsey 2006: T. F. G. Higham / R. M Jacobi / C. Bronk Ramsey, AMS radiocarbon dating of ancient bone using ultrafiltration. Radiocarbon 48, 179-195.

Jacobi 1980: R. M. Jacobi, The Upper Palaeolithic of Britain with special reference to Wales. In: J. A. Taylor (ed.), Culture and Environment in Prehistoric Wales. Selected Essays. British Archaeological Report 76 (Oxford 1980), 15-100.

1986: R. M. Jacobi, The barbed bone spearhead reputedly from Royston, Hertfordshire: a suggestion. Hertfordshire Archaeology 9, 1983-1986, 176-177.

1991: R. M. Jacobi, The Creswellian, Creswell and Cheddar. In:

N. Barton / A. J. Roberts / D.A. Roe (eds.), The Late Glacial in north-west Europe: human adaptation and environmental change at the end of the Pleistocene. Council for British Archaeology Research Report 77 (Oxford 1991) 128-140.

1997: R. M. Jacobi, The »Creswellian« in Britain. In: J.-P. Fagnart / A. Thévenin (eds.), Le Tardiglaciaire en Europe du Nord-Ouest. Actes du 119e Congrès national des Sociétés historiques et scientifiques, Amiens 1994 (Paris 1997), 499-505.

2000: R. M. Jacobi, The Late Pleistocene archaeology of Somerset. In: C. J. Webster (ed.), Somerset Archaeology. Papers to mark 150 years of the Somerset Archaeological and Natural History Society (Taunton 2000), 45-52.

2004: R. M. Jacobi, The Late Upper Palaeolithic lithic collection from Gough's Cave, Cheddar, Somerset and human use of the cave. Proceedings of the Prehistoric Society 70, 1-92.

Jacobi et al. 1986: R. M. Jacobi / J. A. J. Gowlett / R. E. M. Hedges / R. Gillespie, Accelerator mass spectometry dating of Upper Palaeolithic finds, with the Poulton elk as an example. In: D. A. Roe (ed.), Studies in the Upper Palaeolithic of Britain and Northwest Europe. British Archaeological Report (International Series) 296 (Oxford 1986) 121-128.

Jacobi / Higham 2008: R. M. Jacobi / T. F. G. Higham, The »Red Lady« ages gracefully: New ultrafiltration AMS determinations from Paviland. Journal of Human Evolution 55, 898-907.

Jacobi / Higham / Bronk Ramsey 2006: R. M. Jacobi / T. F. G. Higham / C. Bronk Ramsey, AMS radiocarbon dating of Middle and Upper Palaeolithic bone in the British Isles: improved reliability using ultrafiltration. Journal of Quaternary Science 21, 557-73.

Kuzmin / Tankersley 1996: Y. V. Kuzmin / K. B. Tankersley, The colonisation of Eastern Siberia: An evaluation of the Palaeolithic Age Radiocarbon Dates. Journal of Archaeological Science 23, 577-85.

Laurie 2003: T. C. Laurie, Researching the prehistory of Wensleydale, Swaledale and Teesdale. In: T. G. Manby / S. Moorhouse / P. Ottaway (eds.), The Archaeology of Yorkshire: an assessment at the beginning of the 21st century. Yorkshire Archaeological Society Occasional Paper 3 (Leeds 2003), 223-253.

Law / Hedges 1989: I. A. Law / R. E. M. Hedges, A semi-automated bone pretreatment system and the pretreatment of older and contaminated samples. Radiocarbon 31, 247-253.

Lord et al. 2007: T. C. Lord / T. P. O'Connor / D. C. Siebrandt / R. M. Jacobi, People and large carnivores as biostratinomic agents in Lateglacial cave assemblages. Journal of Quaternary Science 22, 681-694.

Mangerud et al. 1974: J. Mangerud / S. T. Andersen / B. E. Berglund / J. J. Donner, Quaternary stratigraphy of Norden, a proposal for terminology and classification. Boreas 3, 109-126.

Megaw / Simpson 1979: J. V. S. Megaw / D. D. A. Simpson, Introduction to British prehistory: from the arrival of Homo sapiens to the Claudian invasion (Leicester 1979).

Moir 1932: J. R. Moir, Further Solutré implements from Suffolk. Antiquaries Journal 12, 257-261.

Muir Evans 1933: H. Muir Evans, The Maglemose harpoon. Proceedings of the Prehistoric Society of East Anglia 7 (1932) 131-132.

Murphy / Lord 2003: P. Murphy / T. C. Lord, Victoria Cave, Yorkshire, UK: new thoughts on an old site. Cave and Karst Science 30, 83-88.

Oakley / Campbell / Molleson 1971: K. P. Oakley / B. G. Campbell / T. I. Molleson, Europe. Catalogue of Fossil Hominids 2 (London 1971).

Pengelly 1868: W. Pengelly, Third report of the Committee for exploring Kent's Cavern, Devonshire. Report of the thirty-seventh meeting of the British Association for the Advancement of Science, Dundee 1867 (London 1868) 24-34.

1884: W. Pengelly, The literature of Kent's Cavern, part V. Report and Transactions of the Devonshire Association for the Advancement of Science, Literature and Art 16, 189-434.

Peterson 1955: R. L. Peterson, North American Moose (Toronto 1955).

Pettitt et al. 2003: P. B. Pettitt / W. Davies / C. S. Gamble / M. B. Richards, Palaeolithic radiocarbon chronology: quantifying our confidence beyond two half-lives. Journal of Archaeological Science 30, 1685-93.

Radley 1969: J. Radley, A note on four Maglemosian bone points from Brandesburton, and a flint site at Brigham. Antiquaries Journal 49, 377-378.

Reimer et al. 2004: P. J. Reimer / M. G. L Baillie / E. Bard / A. Bayliss / J. W. Beck / C. J. H. Bertrand / P. G. Blackwell / C. E. Buck / G. Burr / K. B. Cutler / P. E. Damon / R. L. Edwards / R. G. Fairbanks / M. Friedrich / T. P. Guilderson / A. G. Hogg / K. A. Hughen / B. Kromer / F. G. McCormac / S. Manning / C. Bronk Ramsey / R. W. Reimer / S. Remmele / J. R. Southon / M. Stuiver / S. Talamo / F. W. Taylor / J. van der Plicht / C. E. Weyhenmeyer, INTCAL04 terrestrial radiocarbon age calibration, 0-26 kyr BP. Radiocarbon 46, 1029-1058.

Richards et al. 2000: M. P. Richards / R. E. M. Hedges / R. M. Jacobi / A. P. Currant / C. B. Stringer, Gough's Cave and Sun Hole Cave human stable isotope values indicate a high animal protein diet in the British Upper Palaeolithic. Journal of Archaeological Science 27, 1-3.

Rose et al. 1980: J. Rose / C. Turner / G. R. Coope / M. D. Bryan, Channel changes in a lowland river catchment over the last 13,000 years. In: R. A. Cullingford / D. A. Davidson / J. Lewin (eds.), Timescales in Geomorphology (Chichester 1980) 159-175.

Salisbury 1988: C. R. Salisbury, Late Upper Palaeolithic artefacts from Lindale Low Cave, Cumbria. Antiquity 62, 510-513.

Saville 2004: A. Saville, The material culture of Mesolithic Scotland. In: A. Saville (ed.), Mesolithic Scotland and Its Neighbours: The Early Holocene Prehistory of Scotland, its British and Irish Context, and some Northern European Perspectives (Edinburgh 2004), 185-220.

Shotton 1972: F. W. Shotton, An example of hard-water error in radiocarbon dating of vegetable matter. Nature 240, 460-461.

Smith / Bonsall 1991: C. Smith / C. Bonsall, Late Upper Palaeolithic and Mesolithic chronology: points of interest from recent research. In: N. Barton / A. J. Roberts / D. A. Roe (eds.), The Late Glacial in north-west Europe: human adaptation and environmental change at the end of the Pleistocene. Council for British Archaeology Research Report 77 (Oxford 1991) 208-212.

Spriggs 1989: M. Spriggs, The dating of the Island Southeast Asian Neolithic: an attempt at chronometric hygiene and linguistic correlation. Antiquity 63, 587–613.

Spriggs / Anderson 1993: M. Spriggs / A. J. Anderson, Late colonisation of East Polynesia. Antiquity 67, 200-217.

Stapert / Johansen 1999: D. Stapert / L. Johansen, Flint and pyrite: making fire in the Stone Age. Antiquity 73, 765-777.

Stevens / Hedges 2004: R. E Stevens / R. E. M. Hedges, Carbon and nitrogen stable isotope analysis of northwest European horse bone and tooth collagen, 40,000 BP-present: Palaeoclimatic interpretations. Quaternary Science Reviews 23, 977-991.

Street / Terberger / Orschiedt 2006: M. Street / T. Terberger / J. Orschiedt, A critical review of the German Paleolithic hominin record. Journal of Human Evolution 51, 551-579.

Stringer 1986a: C. B. Stringer, The British fossil hominid record. In S. N. Collcutt (ed.), The Palaeolithic of Britain and its Nearest Neighbours: Recent Trends (Sheffield 1986), 59-61.

1986b: C. B. Stringer, Direct dates for the fossil hominid record. In: J. A. J. Gowlett / R. E. M. Hedges (eds.), Archaeological Results from Accelerator Dating. Oxford University Committee for Archaeology Monograph 11 (Oxford 1986), 45-50.

Tratman 1955: E. K. Tratman, Second report on the excavations at Sun Hole, Cheddar. The Pleistocene levels. Proceedings of the University of Bristol Spelaeological Society 7, 1954-1955, 61-70.

Tratman / Henderson 1928: E. K. Tratman / G. T. D. Henderson, First report on the excavations at Sun Hole, Cheddar. Levels above the Pleistocene. Proceedings of the University of Bristol Spelaeological Society 3, 1927, 84-97.

Walker / Coope / Lowe 1993: M. J. C. Walker / G. R. Coope / J. J. Lowe, The Devensian (Weichselian) Lateglacial palaeoenvironmental record from Gransmoor, East Yorkshire, England. Quaternary Science Reviews 12, 659-680.

Walker et al. 2003: M. J. C. Walker / G. R. Coope / C. Sheldrick / C. S. M. Turney / J. J. Lowe / S. P. E. Blockley / D. D. Harkness, Devensian Lateglacial environmental changes in Britain: a multi-proxy environmental record from Llanilid, South Wales, UK. Quaternary Science Reviews 22, 475-520.

Welin / Engstrand / Vaczy 1974: E. Welin / L. Engstrand / S. Vaczy,

Institute of Geological Sciences radiocarbon dates V. Radiocarbon 16, 95-104.

Westerby 1931: E. Westerby, Den mesolitiske Tid i Norden. Ymer 51, 41-58.

Wheeler 1978: A. Wheeler, Why were there no fish remains at Star Carr? Journal of Archaeological Science 5, 85-89.

Wymer 1975: J. J. Wymer, Two barbed points from Devil's Wood Pit, Sproughton. East Anglian Archaeology 1, 1-4.

Wymer / Jacobi / Rose 1975: J. J. Wymer / R. M. Jacobi / J. Rose, Late Devensian and Early Flandrian barbed points from Sproughton, Suffolk. Proccedings of the Prehistoric Society, 41, 235-241.

Wymer / Rose 1976: J. J. Wymer / J. Rose, The long blade industry from Sproughton, Suffolk and the date of the buried channel deposits at Sproughton. East Anglian Archaeology 3, 1-15.

Abstract

Improving the chronology of the human occupation of Britain during the Late Glacial

The paper presents direct radiocarbon dates on bone and antler samples from selected sites in Britain using the new ultrafiltration protocol. These include dates for the first occupation of Sun Hole, evidence for the hunting of red deer at Kent's Cavern during the Late Glacial and a single determination from Victoria Cave which is currently the earliest evidence for human presence in the Dales of north-west Yorkshire. We also report on the re-dated elk remains from Poulton-le-Fylde and, by implication, the two bone or antler barbed points found with the skeleton. Finally, details of new determinations are given for two previously dated barbed points from Sproughton in east Suffolk.

Key-words

Ultrafiltration protocol, Cheddar point, Late Magdalenian, barbed points

Acknowledgements

We would like to thank the following for allowing us to date material which is in their charge: Chris. Hawkes of the University of Bristol Spelaeological Society, Barry Chandler at Torquay Museum, Emma Heslewood of the Harris Museum and Art Gallery, Preston and Bob Entwistle at Ipswich Museum. Doug Stables made available the elk tooth from Bart's Shelter. We thank him for a long and fruitful collaboration. A major part of the text as well as the map and tables were prepared for publication by Silvia Bello of the Ancient Human Occupation of Britain Project and we owe her a great debt of thanks. The drawings of the flint artefacts from Sun Hole and of the barbed points from Poulton-le-Fylde are by Hazel Martingell. The barbed points from Sproughton were drawn by Jules Cross and the photograph of the metacarpal from Kent's Cavern is by Gwil Owen. We thank them for their skill. The time spent by R. M. J. on this paper was made possible by the Leverhulme Trust-funded Ancient Human Occupation of Britain Project. Radiocarbon dating is a team effort, and we acknowledge the care and hard work of all members of the Oxford Radiocarbon Accelerator Unit, University of Oxford, over the past 25 years.

OLIVIER BIGNON

REGIONAL POPULATIONS AND EXPLOITATION OF LARGE HERBIVORES IN THE PARIS BASIN DURING THE LATE GLACIAL: IN SEARCH OF AN INTEGRATED MODEL

This article uses archaeological data from the late Palaeolithic period in the Paris Basin. Well known Magdalenian sites such as Pincevent and Verberie, with the more recently investigated Tureau des Gardes and Grand Canton, occupy a predominant place in the study conducted here. Due to their exceptional richness, these sites enable the construction of an integrated model of the interactions between human societies and their environments from the Last Glacial Maximum to the start of the Holocene.

Knowledge of the environment that existed during the course of the Palaeolithic is still subject to debate and research, however, work by R. D. Guthrie has shed light on the unique nature of Pleistocene ecological communities and his concept of the Mammoth Steppe is today widely accepted and employed by specialists (Guthrie 1982; 1984; 1990; Barnosky et al. 2004). More than any other, the period that saw the end of the Palaeolithic in Europe affords precise information on the characteristic climatic variations and environmental components of this time. This provides a good reason for the choice of this period to develop a systematic methodology for the observation of environments and human societies. The first task is to model the mosaic pattern of the Mammoth Steppe, and the ecological foundations upon which these communities were based. Secondly, the developed model will be set against data from studies of the hunting tactics of the main Paris Basin hunter-gatherer societies at the end of the Palaeolithic. These studies demonstrate the need to combine palaeoenvironmental and socio-economic analysis and also the relevance of exploring these issues further.

Main characteristics of the Mammoth Steppe

In a brief summary of the Mammoth Steppe concept, three main characteristics can be cited. First, the Mammoth Steppe has been recognised as a vast biome (or macro-ecosystem), which developed over most of the Eurasian continent and much of North America (Guthrie 1982). Chronologically, the archaeological data signal its existence for at least the duration of the Upper Palaeolithic and up to the Holocene in the most northerly areas (Hopkins et al. 1982; Zimov et al. 1995; McPhee et al. 2002). This biome is essentially defined on the basis of its highly diversified animal and plant communities, evidencing a longstanding shared evolutionary history (Pimm 1994). Viewed individually, these specific configurations appear to combine different features of present-day biomes, in particular tundra and steppe (Chernov 1985). The ecological communities of the Mammoth Steppe are however quite unique, and have no strict present-day equivalent (Guthrie 1982; 1984; 1990).

The second characteristic of the Mammoth Steppe is its particular mode of ecological functioning. Only a few communities in the present-day African savannah possess such diversified plant and animal communities and so complex a structure in open landscapes. This is, for example, the case for the Serengeti Park, which has been studied and described as a successive grazing ecosystem (Bell 1970; 1971; McNaughton 1984; 1994) and used as a model to reconstitute the communities of the Mammoth Steppe (Guthrie 1982).

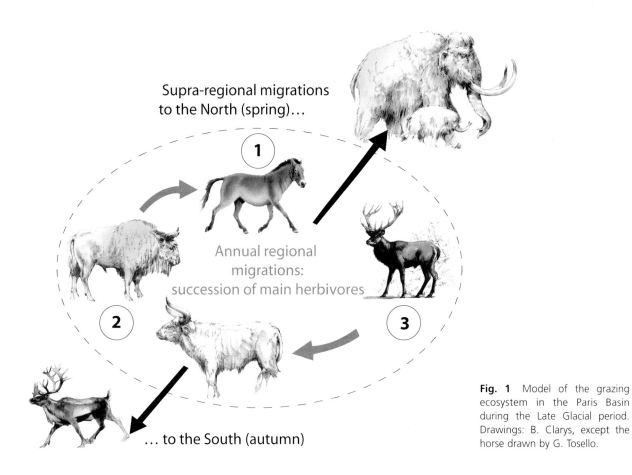

Supra-regional migrations
to the North (spring)…

Annual regional
migrations:
succession of main herbivores

… to the South (autumn)

Fig. 1 Model of the grazing ecosystem in the Paris Basin during the Late Glacial period. Drawings: B. Clarys, except the horse drawn by G. Tosello.

This model is necessarily analogical, since the specific Palaeolithic components are not the same as those of the Serengeti. However in both instances the complementary nature of animal diets, of animal migrations and of their interactions yields a grazing ecosystem and heterogeneous open landscapes.

The third characteristic of the Mammoth Steppe is the mosaic pattern of the landscape at a regional level. The complex layout pattern of the habitats corresponds to a complex interconnection of all the plant and animal species (Guthrie 1982; 1984). This author proposes a view of this structure in terms of a landscape mosaic, rather than the latitudinal layout of modern ecosystems.

Structuring and functioning of animal communities

The trophic networks show that the large herbivores have a direct impact on vegetation (the primary production of the ecosystem). This phenomenon is most marked in ecosystems with successive grazing patterns (McNaughton 1984; 1994). In this type of ecosystem the animal species capture the larger part of primary production flows and hence have a preponderant part in shaping landscapes (Naiman 1988).

Among the Mammoth Steppe populations, mammoth, reindeer, bison and horses are systematically observed in Upper Palaeolithic Eurasian faunas (Hopkins et al. 1982; Morel / Müller 1997; Costamagno 1999; Bignon 2003). For this reason, these animals should be viewed as recurrent species, an intrinsic part of the ecological organisation of Palaeolithic communities. The mammoth and the horse, both monogastric with a generalist diet, were certainly key species (Bond 1994; also known as »mega-herbivores« according to

Owen-Smith 1988). From an ecological viewpoint, these taxa probably had a major impact on plant species and a disproportionate effect on the persistence of all other species in these communities. Thus the animal species did not all have the same status and some, in particular the ruminants, can be viewed as »redundant« species in this type of grazing ecosystem (Lawton / Brown 1994). However, it should be noted that these animals underpinned the variability of the regional colonization of the Mammoth Steppe, and thus made a significant contribution to the mosaic pattern of its landscapes.

Present day successive grazing ecosystems are characterised by large herds and seasonal migrations, which are synchronised with the differential availability of plant parts suited to the various specific diets (Bell 1970; 1971). It is thus possible to infer that this type of phenomenon very probably also occurred in some regional Mammoth Steppe communities (Guthrie 1982; 1984; Bignon 2003). According to the scale of migrations, to diets, and to the body size of the herbivores on the Mammoth Steppe, an identikit or model of the communities in the Paris Basin can be constructed for the Late Glacial period (**Fig. 1**). On account of the variability in composition of the different regional populations, this type of model requires adjustment to each geographical context.

Regional community patterns in the Late Glacial in Europe

Good indications of the distribution of available plant resources among the herbivores on the Mammoth Steppe are provided by studies of the stable isotopes in collagen. Observations based on herbivores in south-west France or the Paris Basin in the Upper Palaeolithic have shown marked distinctions in grazing habits (Drucker 2006; Drucker / Bocherens / Billiou 2003). They indicate stable dietary adaptations, despite a continuously changing environment.

These results are further supported by the demonstration of a structuring on a regional scale of the populations of the key species in the Mammoth Steppe. Thus regional morphotypes among horses have been revealed by conventional and geometric morphometry in the Paris Basin, the Swiss plateau and in the Charente area of western France (Bignon 2003). To these regions can now be added Great Britain and Belgium (**Fig. 2**; Bignon / Cornette / Baylac in prep.). The skeletal parts studied were the following cranial and postcranial elements: upper and lower tooth sets, metapodial distal epiphyses (metacarpals and metatarsi) and ungual phalanges. All these skeletal parts were examined using conventional morphometry and the metapodials were also analysed by geometric morphometry (homologous landmark method: Bignon et al. 2005; Bignon / Eisenmann 2006). These studies have shown the existence of recurrent variability patterns at a regional scale, with the exception of ungual phalanges, which implies their common adaptation for lowland habitats (Bignon 2005a). In addition, the Paris Basin has the particular aspect of presenting two regional morphotypes, identified from equine jugal teeth and metapodials. Caution should therefore be applied in the use of the taxonomic label »*E. caballus arcelini*«. This name is, strictly speaking, associated with particular characteristics of the horses identified in the Magdalenian level at Solutré (Guadelli 1991); in a wider sense (*E. caballus arcelini, sensu lato*), the term refers to all horses in the Late Glacial period and incorporates their infra-species variability, reflected in the morphometric characteristics mentioned above.

In the Late Glacial, a fragmentation of the horse populations in Western Europe can be noted from one region to another. Similar regional morphotypes have been discovered in Western Europe for reindeer populations by way of studies using conventional morphometry. Indeed, the work by J. Weinstock (1997; 2000) has shown significant morphometric differences between the north and south of Germany, in association with Switzerland, Belgium and the Paris Basin. In addition, L. Fontana (2000) has recognized morphometric distinctions between the reindeer populations of the French Massif Central and the Languedoc-

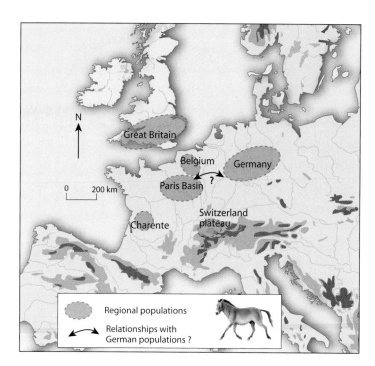

Fig. 2 Pattern of the regional horse populations during Late Glacial revealed by geometric morphometrics (Bignon et al. 2005; Bignon / Cornette / Baylac in prep.) Horse drawings: G. Tosello.

Roussillon area in southern France, pointing to the regional nature of their migrations. This data suggests markedly regionalised animal communities up to the end of the »Meiendorf/Bølling« period (around 12 000 BP). Osteological observations for the different Pleistocene mammoth taxa suggest that, under the effect of complex migratory phenomena, there was also a marked regional fragmentation of populations of these animals (Lister / Sher 2001). Indeed, although no studies on this aspect have been conducted for bison, the pattern of morphometric fragmentation is nevertheless attested for populations of three of the four key species. This phenomenon of relatively isolated regional groups of specific populations can cast light on the mosaic structure of landscape by revealing the outline of the distribution of regional communities. These observations also show that the pattern of communities of the Mammoth Steppe appears to have been fairly stable in the Late Glacial. The data also imply low levels of genetic exchange and hence high demographic density of key species. Indeed, bio-geographical observations of the flora and fauna of the Arctic also show a clear fragmentation of species' distribution areas into distinct regions (Chernov 1985). In arctic animals, such as reindeer (*Rangifer tarandus*) or musk ox (*Ovibos moschatus*), one of the most interesting features is that these species only remain in these extreme environments in the shape of large populations (Remmert 1980). Large numbers of individuals should be seen as a risk-reduction strategy in relation to the risks attendant upon small populations (Bennett 1999), these risks being stochastic, arising from demography, genetics and the environment and compounded by natural disasters. The viability of small fragmented populations is also highly improbable in terms of their very existence due to genetic erosion, as has been shown by several recent studies (Young / Clarke 2000).

The fragmentation of populations thus appears as a new significant feature of the Mammoth Steppe, evolving in a fairly autonomous manner at the regional scale. This hypothesis presupposes the underlying existence of strong co-evolutionary interactions among herbivores, plants and decomposers. Links of this type between population components necessarily presume a long shared evolutionary history (several thousand millennia) on a regional scale. At a continental scale, the existence of »habitat corridors« that could have connected the different regional population basins must be envisaged. These corridors may have enabled various species of animals (specialised or not) to reside in or transit through them, thus rendering biogeo-

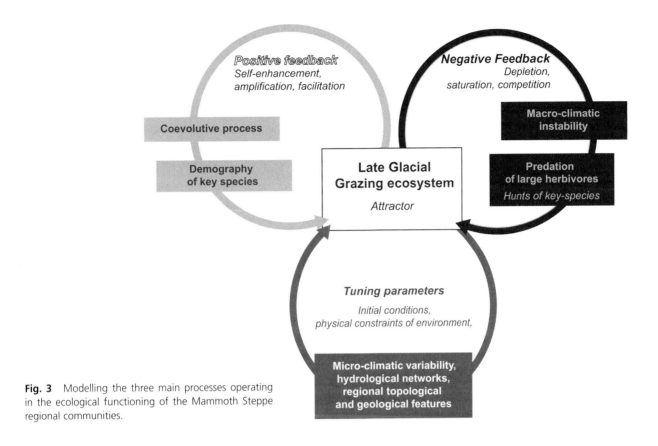

Fig. 3 Modelling the three main processes operating in the ecological functioning of the Mammoth Steppe regional communities.

graphical exchanges more fluid (Bennett 1999). As at the present day, these geographical corridors were certainly provided by the main channels of the hydrographic network, which follow topography and edaphic contexts and may have been connected to shelter zones.

Ecological modelling of regional communities in the mammoth Steppe

Biological systems are open systems in which the characteristics of self-organisation can emerge within a group of organisms or between groups, for instance in shoals of fish (Theraulaz / Spitz 1997; Camazine et al. 2001). Basically self-organisation is a process in which a structuring of the system on a global scale emerges solely from the numerous interactions occurring among the components of the system itself. Grazing ecosystems demonstrate characteristics of a self-organising system, in particular by a decentralized organisation of animal migrations succeeding each other in time and space. The crucial point is that this phenomenon arises entirely from multiple interactions among animals of several species, by information transfers between them at the local scale and without any reference to the global pattern. Thus the Mammoth Steppe biome should be viewed as a mosaic of regional populations, in which self-organisation is likely to have occurred during the emergence of successive grazing ecosystems. However, this type of ecosystem may have emerged recurrently in different locations in the northern areas of Europe, which offer at once extensive plains, well developed hydrological networks, and a topography favourable to the existence of shelter zones. In fact, the grazing ecosystems should be seen as an emergent property, also known as an »attractor«.

Modelling the modes of functioning of populations on the Mammoth Steppe requires consideration of the three main processes inherent in self-organising systems (**Fig. 3**; Camazine et al. 2001). Firstly positive feed-

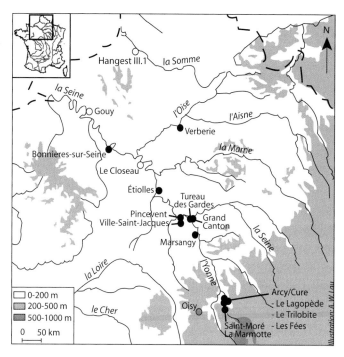

Fig. 4 Map of Paris Basin Late Glacial sites with faunal remains. Grey dot: Badegoulian site; black dots: Magdalenian sites; white dots: Azilian sites.

back is generally described as a process of growth, amplification or facilitation. Here the feedback can be seen in the co-evolutionary links between plant and animal species, and in the demographic amplification of the populations of key species.

Conversely, negative feedback is linked to processes of saturation, regulation, depletion or competition that occur in biological systems. In the case of the Mammoth Steppe, such processes are associated with the instability of macro-climatic phenomena and, more directly, with predation affecting the populations of large herbivores. As the Late Glacial super predators, from the ecological viewpoint, human hunters very regularly targeted key or recurrent species in the Mammoth Steppe (Bignon 2006a). This same observation can be generalised for the Upper Palaeolithic overall; human societies can be seen as a major regulator of grazing ecosystems on account of their ability to hunt the largest herbivores. In the systemic framework of this model, hunter-fauna interactions should be viewed as a more general co-evolutionary relationship between predator and prey, which may in fact have favoured the persistence or coexistence of such a wide range of herbivores (Blondel 1995).

Finally, the third process concerns tuning parameters. The source of variation among the several regional populations, these are essentially environmental parameters. This concept aims to give a picture of the significant impact on populations of various combinatory phenomena, such as micro-climatic variability or particular regional physical features such as the diversity and extent of hydrological networks and topo-geological characteristics.

Evolution of the last Palaeolithic societies in the Paris Basin: what can be learned?

The faunal composition at the Badegoulian site of Oisy in the Nevers region of France at around 16 000 BP shows that the Mammoth Steppe re-colonised the northern areas quite soon after the Last Glacial Maximum (**Fig. 4**; Bignon 2005b). Badegoulian hunters used individual hunting tactics, targeting reindeer and horses in a selective manner (**Fig. 5**). Results obtained from studies suggest human social groups that were restricted in numbers and very mobile, this appearing consistent with the patterns of production of stone tools in the Paris Basin and the Centre region of France (L. Chehmana, pers. comm.). This hypothesis is at present also applied on the basis of faunal remains to findings in south-west France (J.-C. Castel, pers. comm.).

Duing the Magdalenian period in the Paris Basin, horses were culled throughout the year (Bignon 2006a; 2006b). This regularity and the existence of collective tactics lead to the conclusion that horses were the main target of subsistence strategies (**Fig. 5**). It is only in the autumn that reindeer were particularly hun-

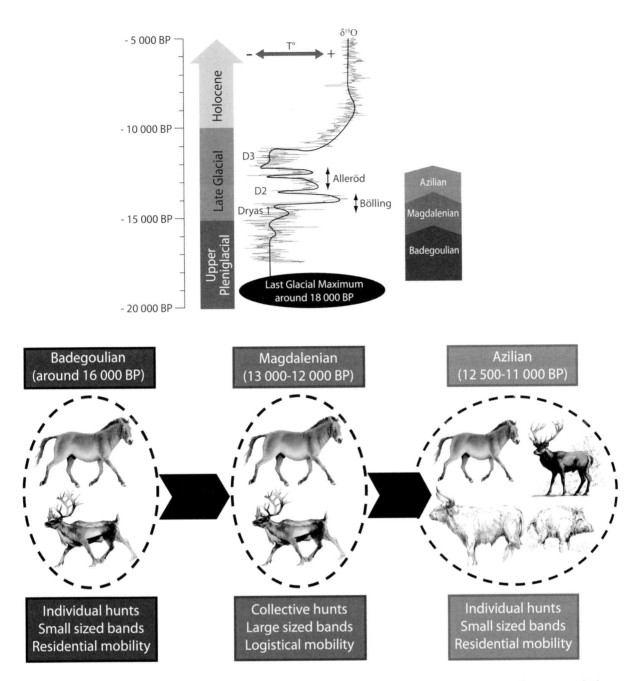

Fig. 5 Socioeconomic variability of the main cultural entities at the end of the Palaeolithic period Drawings: B. Clarys, except the horse drawn by G. Tosello.

ted in a complementary manner, at the time of their migration in large herds and again by collective tactics without selection. It is very probable that at this season stores were made for the winter period. Such storage strategies would explain the hunts and their particular place within the Magdalenian subsistence economy of the Paris Basin. The large number of hunters, their collective tactics, the culling and simultaneous processing of numerous carcasses and the storage of food all clearly suggest the existence of large social groups in the Paris Basin during the Magdalenian period. The huge butchering sites at Tureau des Gardes and Grand Canton (Julien / Rieu 1999; Bignon 2003) necessarily involved participation of the different components of the social body. The sites probably formed in the course of a succession of expeditions, mostly to hunt horses throughout the year, but particularly in spring and autumn. Since they possessed this logistic mobility, the Magdalenian groups may have adjusted to the alternating aggregation and dispersion patterns of their main prey, the horse (Bignon 2006a; 2006b; in press). This hypothesis seems to be supported by the adoption of a new tactic in level IV 0 at Pincevent (Bignon / Enloe / Bemilli 2006; Debout / Bignon / Enloe 2006): a shift from collective hunts targeting horses in autumn to individual tactics targeting reindeer in winter.

Studies of the early Azilians at Le Closeau identify a marked contrast in their hunting tactics in relation to the Magdalenians in the region (Bignon / Bodu 2006). The hunts organised by the Azilians targeted species other than those usually culled by the Magdalenians (deer, boar and even lion) in addition to horses and were also characterised by different hunting tactics for the latter species (Bignon / Bodu 2006). A series of observations suggestive of a certain anticipation of needs makes a logistic-type socio-economic organisation likely. This is seen in the remarkable investment in the structuring of concentrations 4 and 46, in the import of good quality exogenous flint, or again in the storage of food that was exported for later consumption. However, several arguments temper this first view in favour of a more mobile type of residential organisation (**Fig. 5**; Bodu / Debout / Bignon 2006). Firstly, the frequentation of Le Closeau by small social groups appears to be established on the basis of the small number of hunters, the low density of remains and only limited site modification. Secondly, individual hunts targeting horses with fairly low yields were repeated through the year, suggesting that hunting strategies consisted of more numerous and frequent hunting expeditions. The frequentation patterns in these occupations are also characterised by stays of short duration. It is probable that after occupation of Le Closeau the next stop was at a relatively short distance and formed part of a series of occupations of the same kind, possibly within a fairly small territory. In early Azilian times, there was therefore a shift towards individual hunting tactics (Bignon / Bodu 2006) and a return to highly mobile, small human groups (Bodu / Debout / Bignon Bodu 2006).

The emergence of the socio-economic model of the early Azilians might therefore be linked to a particular exploitation of the mosaic landscape in the Paris Basin. This environment, less open than the wide alluvial valleys of the Seine, may have enabled certain groups to adopt economic strategies different to those of the Magdalenians. These changes are mainly reflected by changes in hunting tactics and in main hunting targets. Moreover, once again it can be concluded that hunting behaviour and the mobility of hunter-gatherers were closely linked with the aggregation-dispersion patterns of the animal populations and the structuring of the environment (Mauss 1950; Torrence 1983). The extension of Azilian groups in the Allerød could be connected with the progressive extension of this »niche« exploited by the early Azilians.

Despite these major socio-economic changes it is remarkable that the exploitation of high-yielding (large) herbivores remains a constant feature (Bridault / Bignon / Bemilli 2003). The successive changes in social patterns at the end of the Upper Palaeolithic do not appear to be governed by climatic fluctuations alone (**Fig. 5**). This socio-economic fluidity could express the evolution of hunter-gatherer cultural variability during the course of the Palaeolithic. If these cultural entities were not able to escape climatic and environmental parameters, the particular genius or skill of each was in using such situations to their advantage and it is this that underpins the dynamics of their ways of life.

Nevertheless, the disappearance of the Mammoth Steppe after 12 000 BP in Europe can be seen as a veritable ecological disaster (Barnosky et al. 2004). It resulted in a homogenisation and a decrease of biodiversity in latitudinal macro-ecosystems, which stabilised with the beginning of the Holocene. This radical change in ecosystems and landscapes is thought to be the result of a redistribution of co-evolutionary alliances in favour of the large ruminants (Graham / Lundelius 1984). After 12 000 BP, the horse seems to be less represented by faunal remains in the Paris Basin. The phenomenon could also relate to human hunting, which, by targeting harem groups, could have seriously damaged the reproductive potential of the horse population (Bignon 2006b). After exercising a regulatory function, it is possible that humans, via hunts targeting key species, became a contributory factor to the deterioration of the Mammoth Steppe. Today, this hypothesis is plausible in the context of the Paris Basin, but it is not the only hypothesis possible. Indeed, the appearance of a wider main river channel from the Allerød period onwards may have drowned the valley floors (Pastre et al. 2000), thus depriving horses of the well-endowed habitats in which they had previously found most of their subsistence (Bignon 2003; 2005).

Conclusion

Our theoretical contribution is an attempt to model both the main characteristics of the Mammoth Steppe and the role played by human societies at the end of the Upper Palaeolithic. The application of a model of this nature must nevertheless take into account various limitations connected with the practice of zooarchaeology. This concerns for instance the bias introduced by taphonomic processes, and in particular the different states of preservation of the different animal remains (to the detriment of the representation of smaller species) or the bias arising from the statistical presentation of archaeological data (which is processed in the form of supposedly representative samples). Despite these difficulties, the foundations of our model do seem sound enough to constitute a theoretical matrix for the better understanding of the Mammoth Steppe and the variability of grazing ecosystems during the Palaeolithic. Indeed, other work based on a macro-ecological approach to the question of the large mammals in the Upper Palaeolithic has confirmed the relevance of this type of approach (Brugal / Yravedra Sainz de los Torros 2005-2006).

References

Barnosky et al. 2004: A. D. Barnosky / P. L. Koch / R. S. Feranec / S. L. Wing / A. B. Shabel, Assessing the causes of the Late Pleistocene Extinctions on the Continents. Science 306, 70-75.

Bell 1970: R. H. V. Bell, The use of the herb layer by grazing ungulates in the Serengeti. In: A. Watson (ed.), Animal populations in relation to their food resources (Oxford 1970) 111-127.

1971: R. H. V. Bell, A grazing ecosystem in the Serengeti. Scientific American 225/1, 86-93.

Bennett 1999: A. F. Bennett, Linkages in the landscape. The role of corridors and connectivity in wildlife conservation. International Union for Conservation of Nature and Natural Resources (Cambridge 1999).

Bignon 2003: O. Bignon, Diversité et Exploitation des équidés au Tardiglaciaire en Europe occidentale - Implications pour les stratégies de subsistance et les modes de vie au Magdalénien et à l'Azilien ancien du Bassin parisien. Thèse de doctorat, Université Paris X (Nanterre 2003).

2005a: O. Bignon, Habitat préférentiel et connectivité des chevaux tardiglaciaires d'Europe occidentale (Equus caballus arcelini, Guadelli 1991). Archaeofauna 14, 267-284.

2005b: O. Bignon, La faune. In: P. Bodu / L. Chehmana / G.

Debout (eds.), Le gisement badegoulien du Mont-St-Aubin Oisy (Nièvre) – Document final de synthèse de fouille programmée (autorisation tri-annuelle 2003-2005) (Nanterre 2005) 61-81.

2006a: O. Bignon, Vers une nouvelle compréhension du mode de vie au Magdalénien dans le Bassin parisien: de l'exploitation des chevaux aux stratégies de subsistance. Gallia Préhistoire 48, 181-206.

2006b: O. Bignon, La chasse des chevaux au Magdalénien dans le Bassin parisien: reconstruction des interactions prédateurs-proies, implications socio-économiques. In: I. Sidéra (ed.), La Chasse – Pratiques et symboliques. 2e Colloque de la Maison René-Ginouvès »Archéologie et Ethnologie« (Paris 2006) 167-179.

in press: O. Bignon, L'autre «Civilisation du Renne» ... pour une réinterprétation des stratégies cynégétique au Magdalénien dans le Bassin parisien. In: S. Beyries / V. Vaté (eds.), Actes des XXVIIe rencontres internationales d'Archéologie et d'Histoire d'Antibes 2006. Les Civilisations du renne d'hier et d'aujourd'hui: approches ethno-historiques, archéologiques et anthropologiques (Antibes in press).

Bignon / Bodu 2006: O. Bignon / P. Bodu, Stratégie cynégétique et mode de vie à l'Azilien ancien dans le Bassin parisien: les apports de l'exploitation des chevaux du Closeau (niveau inférieur; Rueil-Malmaison, Hauts-de-Seine). L'Anthropologie 110/3, 401-417.

Bignon / Cornette / Baylac in prep.: O. Bignon / R. Cornette / M. Baylac. From bones to behaviours: a morphometrical approach of horse palaeoecology. In: M. Street / E. Turner, The faunal remains from Gönnersdorf. Monographien des RGZM (Mainz, in prep.).

Bignon / Eisenmann 2006: O. Bignon / V. Eisenmann, Western European Late Glacial horse diversity and its ecological implications. In: M. Mashkour (ed.), Equids in the Ancient World Vol. III – Proceedings of 9th ICAZ »Equid Session« (Durham, GB, 2002) (Oxford 2006) 161-171.

Bignon / Enloe / Bemilli 2006: O. Bignon / J. G. Enloe / C. Bemilli, Chapitre II. 1. Étude archéozoologique de l'unité T125: originalité de la chasse des rennes et des chevaux. In: P. Bodu / M. Julien / B. Valentin / G. Debout (eds.), Un dernier hiver à Pincevent – Les Magdaléniens du niveau IV 0. Gallia Préhistoire 48, 18-35.

Bignon et al. 2005: O. Bignon / M. Baylac / J.-D. Vigne / V. Eisenmann, Geometric morphometrics and the population diversity of Late Glacial horses in Western Europe (Equus caballus arcelini): Phylogeographic and anthropological implications. Journal of Archaeological Science 32, 375-391.

Blondel 1995: J. Blondel, Biogéographie. Approche écologique et évolutive (Paris 1995).

Bodu / Chehmana / Debout 2005: P. Bodu / L. Chehmana / G. Debout (eds.), Le gisement badegoulien du Mont-St-Aubin Oisy (Nièvre) – Document final de synthèse de fouille programmée (autorisation tri-annuelle 2003-2005) (Nanterre 2005) 61-81.

Bodu / Debout / Bignon 2006: P. Bodu / G. Debout / O. Bignon, Variabilité des habitudes tardiglaciaires dans le Bassin parisien: l'organisation spatiale et sociale de l'Azilien ancien du Closeau. Bulletin de la Société préhistorique française 103/4, 711-728.

Bond 1994: W. J. Bond, Keystone species. In: E.-D. Schulze / H. A. Mooney (eds.), Biodiversity and ecosystem function (New York 1994) 237-253.

Bridault / Bignon / Bemilli 2003: A. Bridault / O. Bignon / C. Bemilli, L'exploitation du cheval à la fin du Tardiglaciaire dans le Bassin parisien. In: S. Costamagno / V. Laroulandie (eds.), Mode de vie au Magdalénien: apports de l'archéozoologie - XIVe Colloque international U.I.S.P.P. Liège 2001. British Archaeological Reports (International Series) 1144 (Oxford 2003) 33-45.

Brugal / Yravedra Sainz de los Torros 2005-2006: J.-P. Brugal / J. Yravedra Sainz de los Torros, Essai sur la biodiversité des associations de grands mammifères à la fin du Pléistocène dans le sud-ouest de l'Europe. Munibe 57/1, 139-162.

Camazine et al. 2001: S. Camazine / J.-L. Deneubourg / N. R. Franks / J. Sneyd / G. Thelauraz / B. Bonabeau, Self-Organization in Biological Systems. Princeton Studies in Complexity (Princeton 2001).

Chernov 1985: Y. I. Chernov, The living tundra. Studies in Polar Research (Cambridge 1985).

Costamagno 1999: S. Costamagno, Stratégies de chasse et fonction des sites au Magdalénien dans le Sud de la France. Thèse de Doctorat Université de Bordeaux I (1999).

Debout / Bignon / Enloe 2006: G. Debout / O. Bignon / J. G. Enloe, Chapitre III. 1. Répartition des témoins animaux: une gestion de l'espace rythmée par les saisons? In: Bodu, P., Julien, J., Valentin, V., Debout, G. (eds.), Un dernier hiver à Pincevent – Les Magdaléniens du niveau IV 0. Gallia Préhistoire 48, 134-135.

Drucker 2006: D. Drucker, Teneurs en carbone-13 et en azote-15 du collagène de grands mammifères du site d'Étiolles. In: M. Olive (ed.), Étiolles - Rapport triennal 2004-2006 (Nanterre 2006) 57-63.

Drucker / Bocherens / Billiou 2003: D. Drucker / H. Bocherens / D. Billiou, Evidence for shifting environmental conditions in Southwestern France from 33 000 to 15 000 years ago derived from carbon-13 and nitrogen-15 natural abundances in collagen of large herbivores. Earth and Planetary Science Letters 216, 163-173.

Fontana 2000: L. Fontana, La chasse au renne au Paléolithique supérieur dans le Sud-Ouest de la France: nouvelles hypothèses de travail. Paleo 12, 141-164.

Graham / Lundelius 1984: R. W. Graham / E. L. Lundelius, Coevolutionary disequilibrium and Pleistocene extinctions. In: P. S. Martin / R. G. Klein (eds.), Quaternary Extinctions: A prehistoric revolution (Arizona 1984) 223-249.

Guadelli 1991: J.-L. Guadelli, Les chevaux de Solutré (Saône et Loire, France). In: J.-P. Raynal / D. Miallier (eds.), Datation et caractérisation des milieux pléistocènes. Cahiers du Quaternaire 16, 261-336.

Guthrie, 1982: R. D. Guthrie, Mammals of the mammoth steppe as paleoenvironmental indicators. In: D. M. Hopkins / J. V. Matthews Jr. / C. E. Schweger / S. B. Young (eds.), Paleoecology of Beringia (New York 1982) 307-328.

1984: R. D. Guthrie, Mosaïcs, Allelochemics and Nutrients: An Ecological Theory of Late Pleistocene Megafaunal Extinctions. In: P. S. Martin / R. G. Klein (eds.), Quaternary Extinctions. A prehistoric revolution (Arizona 1984) 259-298.

1990: R. D. Guthrie, Frozen Fauna of the Mammoth Steppe: The story of Blue Babe (Chicago 1990).

Hopkins et al. 1982: D. M. Hopkins / J. V. Matthews Jr. / C. E. Schweger / S. B. Young (eds.), Paleoecology of Beringia (New York 1982).

Julien / Rieu 1999: M. Julien / J.-L. Rieu, Occupations du Paléolithique supérieur dans le Sud-Est du Bassin parisien. Éditions de la Maison des Sciences de l'Homme. Documents d'Archéologie Française 78 (Paris 1999).

Lawton / Brown 1994: J. H. Lawton / V. K. Brown, Biodiversity and Ecosystem Function. In: E.-D. Schulze / H. A. Mooney (eds.),

Biodiversity and ecosystem function (New York 1994) 255-270.

Lister / Sher 2001: A. M. Lister / A. V. Sher, The origin and evolution of the woolly mammoth. Science 294, 1094-1097.

Mauss 1950 (reed. 1993): M. Mauss, Sociologie et anthropologie (Paris 1950).

McNaughton 1984: S. J. McNaughton, Grazing lawns: animals in herbs, plant form and coevolution. The American Naturalist 124/6, 863-886.

1994: S. J. McNaughton, Biodiversity and function of grazing ecosystems. In: E.-D. Schulze / H. A. Mooney (eds.), Biodiversity and ecosystem function (New York 1994) 361-383.

McPhee et al. 2002: R. D. E. McPhee / A. N. Tikhonov / D. Mol / C. De Marliave / H. van der Plicht / A. D. Greenwood / C. Flemming / L. Agenbroad, Radiocarbon chronologies and extinction dynamics of the late Quaternary mammalian megafauna of the Taimyr Peninsula, Russian Federation. Journal of Archaeological Science 29, 1017-1042.

Morel / Müller 1997: P. Morel / W. Müller, Étude archéozoologique (secteur 1). Hauterive-Champréveyres 11. Un campement magdalénien au bord du lac de Neuchâtel. Archéologie neuchâteloise 23 (Neuchâtel 1997).

Naiman 1988: R. J. Naiman, Animal influences on ecosystem dynamics. BioScience 38/11, 750-752.

Owen-Smith 1988: R. N. Owen-Smith, Megaherbivores. The influence of very large body size on ecology (Cambridge 1988).

Pastre et al. 2000: J.-F. Pastre / C. Leroyer / N. Limondin-Lozouet / C. Chaussé / M. Fontugne / A. Gebhardt / C. Hatte / V. Krier, Le Tardiglaciaire des fonds de vallée du Bassin parisien (France). Quaternaire 11/2, 107-122.

Pimm 1994: S. L. Pimm, Biodiversity and the balance of nature. In: E.-D. Schulze / H. A. Mooney (eds.), Biodiversity and ecosystem function (New York 1994) 347-359.

Remmert 1980: M. Remmert, Arctic animal ecology (Berlin 1980).

Theraulaz / Spitz 1997: G. Theraulaz / F. Spitz, Auto-organisation et comportement (Paris 1997).

Torrence 1983: R. Torrence, Time budgeting and hunter-gatherer technology. In: G. Bailey (ed.), Hunter-gatherer economy in Prehistory: a European perspective (Cambridge 1983) 11-22.

Watson 1970: A. Watson (ed.), Animal populations in relation to their food resources (Oxford 1970).

Weinstock 1997: J. Weinstock, Late Paleolithic reindeer populations in Central and Western Europe. In: M. Kokabi / J. Wahl (eds.), Actes du Colloque International d'Archéozoologie, Konstanz 1994. Anthropozoologica 25-26, 383-388.

2000: J. Weinstock, Demography through osteometry: sex ratios of reindeer and hunting strategies in the Late Glacial site of Stellmoor, Northern Germany. Archaeozoologia 11/1-2, 187-198.

Young / Clarke 2000: A. G. Young / G. M. Clarke, Conclusions and future directions: what do we know about the genetic and demographic effects of habitat fragmentation and where do we go from here? In: A. G. Young / G. M. Clarke (eds.), Genetics, demography and viability of fragmented populations (Cambridge 2000) 361-366.

Zimov et al. 1995: S. A. Zimov / V. I. Chuprynin / A. P. Oreshko / F. S. Chapin III / J. F. Reynolds / M. C. Chapin, Steppe-Tundra Transition: A Herbivore-Driven Biome Shift at the End of the Pleistocene. The American Naturalist 146/5, 765-794.

Abstract / Résumé

Regional populations and exploitation of large herbivores in the Paris Basin during the Late Glacial: in search of an integrated model
This article undertakes an exploration of ecological communities in Europe at the end of the Upper Palaeolithic. The aim of this work is to provide a first approach to the construction of an integrated model of the interactions between human societies and their environments. Because of the amount of climatic, environmental and socio-cultural data available and its precision, the period extending from the last glacial maximum (around 18 000 BP) to the start of the Holocene (around 10 000 BP) is the best suited for this enterprise. The study uses the basis of the Mammoth Steppe concept and the regional context of the Paris Basin to illustrate the approach.

Populations régionaux et l'exploitation des grandes herbivores dans le bassin parisien au tardiglaciaire: Recherche d'une modèle intégrée
Cet article amorce une réflexion sur les peuplements écologiques de l'Europe à la fin du Paléolithique supérieur. L'ambition de ce travail est de proposer une première approche pour construire un modèle intégré des interactions

entre les sociétés humaines et leurs environnements. Du fait de la précision et de l'importance des données climatiques, environnementales et socioculturelles, la période allant du dernier maximum glaciaire (vers 18 000 BP) jusqu'au début de l'Holocène (vers 10 000 BP) est la meilleure pour mener à bien notre objectif. Nous nous appuierons sur les fondements du concept de la steppe à mammouth, ainsi que du contexte régional du bassin parisien pour illustrer notre démarche.

Key words / Mots clés

Paris Basin, human societies, Mammoth Steppe, Late Glacial;
bassin parisien, sociétés humaines, steppe à mammouth, tardiglaciaire.

Acknowledgements

Thanks to Angela Verdier for the translation of this paper and to Anita W. Lau who has been very helpful in producing the illustrations.

REBECCA MILLER · PIERRE NOIRET

RECENT RESULTS FOR THE BELGIAN MAGDALENIAN

Over the past 25 years, data concerning the Belgian Magdalenian have been recovered through the systematic excavation of cave sites located in the Meuse Valley and along tributaries of the Meuse in the Ardennes region and at open-air sites in Flanders. Recent syntheses include the analysis of Magdalenian chronology (Charles 1994; 1998), a study of the cluster of cave sites in the Lesse Valley (Stutz 1993; Teheux 1994) and critical analyses of the timing and processes of the Magdalenian colonization of Belgium and northern Europe (Charles 1996; Germonpré 1997; Housley et al. 1997; López Bayón 2000; Street et al. 1994). The most recently excavated sites include Chaleux (Otte 1994), Bois Laiterie (Otte / Straus 1997) and Trou Da Somme. The latest excavation at the latter site contributes new information to the discussion of Magdalenian re-colonization and settlement practices in Belgium.

Trou Da Somme

Trou Da Somme is located at the base of the Massif de la Roche-al-Rue near Waulsort, on the west bank of the Meuse river, 5 km west of Chaleux and other Lesse River sites. The site consists of two caves: the upper cave (TDS II), formerly occupied by the Da Somme family during the 19th century, and the lower cave (TDS I), which contains Late Magdalenian archaeological deposits (**Fig. 1**).

It was first excavated in 1954 by Verheyleweghen (1958; 1959) and subsequently by Léotard in 1988 (Léotard 1988; 1993), López Bayón in 1997 (López Bayón et al. 1997; 1998) and Miller in 1998 (Miller et al. 1998; Otte et al. 1999).

The stratigraphic sequence in TDS I is summarized as follows (**Fig. 2**): Sterile dolomitic sand (stratum 6) forms the base of the stratigraphic sequence. It is overlain by a uniform silty clay layer containing the Magdalenian occupation (stratum 5). Despite its overall uniformity, stratum 5 is characterized by a degree of disturbance, including pockets of dolomitic sand along the cave walls (stratum 4), and a large bad-

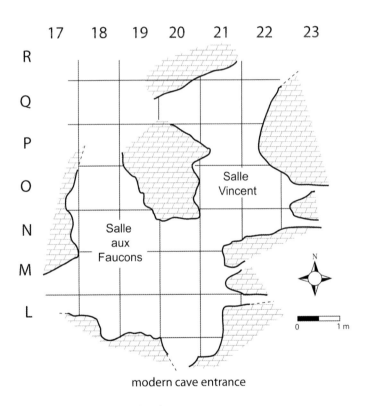

Fig. 1 Trou Da Somme, site plan.

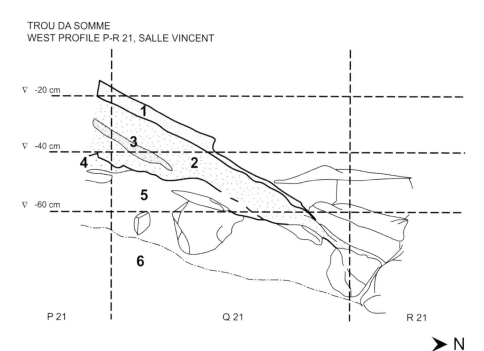

TROU DA SOMME
WEST PROFILE P-R 21, SALLE VINCENT

Fig. 2 Trou Da Somme, stratigraphic sequence.

∇ -20 cm

∇ -40 cm

∇ -60 cm

P 21   Q 21   R 21

➤ N
to back of cave

ger den and other smaller, sub-modern, burrows of small mammals (vole and shrew) grouped as stratum 3. The deposits are capped by a thick stalagmitic layer, the lower part of which is porous (stratum 2) and the upper part a finely laminated stalagmitic floor (stratum 1), varying in thickness from 3 to 30 cm.

Belgian Magdalenian chronology

Largely as a result of Charles' (1994) doctoral research on Late Magdalenian chronology in the Ardennes, we have a fairly complete series of radiometric dates for the Belgian sequence ranging from early dates around 16 100 BP[1], but with questionable archaeological association, to 10 700 BP (**Fig. 3**).

Dates of 16 130 ± 250 (Lv-1558) and 16 270 ± 230 BP (Lv-1385) from Trou des Blaireaux (Vaucelles), layer III/1, were obtained on shed antler, but this material was not the result of human accumulation and a correlation with the rare lithics cannot be proven (Housley et al. 1997, 32-33). The earliest dates associated with human presence come from layer III/2 at this site (Lv-1433: 13 930 ± 120 BP) and Verlaine in the Ourthe Valley in eastern Belgium (Lv-690: 13 780 ± 220 BP). These fall within the Dryas I. The majority of dates are found during the »Bølling« climatic optimum, ranging from 13 330 ± 160 BP (OxA-4200) at Trou des Blaireaux to 12 150 ± 150 BP (Lv-686) at Coléoptère, while Trou du Frontal yielded a late date of 10 720 ± 120 BP (Lv-1135). The dates obtained show continuity in the occupation or re-occupation of sites such as Chaleux and Coléoptère over a period of several centuries.

Recent dates for Trou Da Somme also indicate re-occupation of this site, although post-depositional processes have made it impossible to identify separate occupation horizons. The date of 12 815 ± 75 BP (OxA-8308) makes the site penecontemporaneous with early occupations at Chaleux (OxA-4912: 12 860 ± 140 BP) and Trou du Frontal (OxA-4917: 12 800 ± 130 BP), while a second date (OxA-4199: 12 240 ± 130 BP) is penecontemporaneous with a later occupation at Chaleux (Lv-1568: 12 370 ± 170 BP).

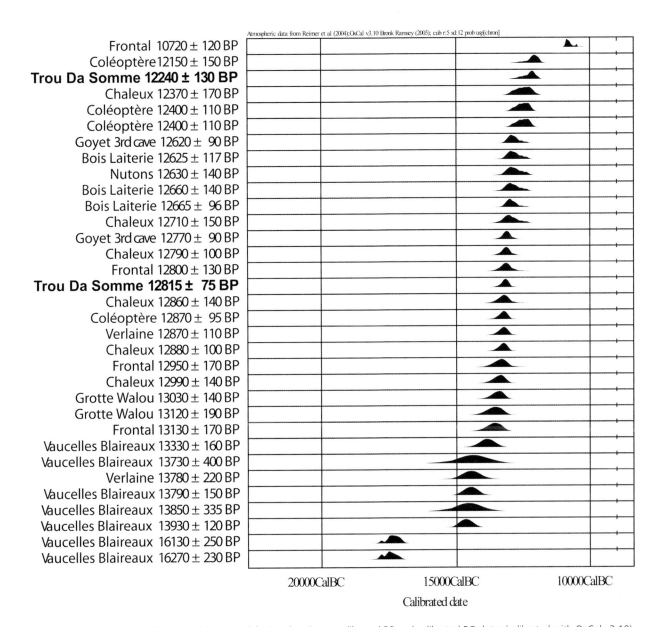

Fig. 3 Radiocarbon dates for the Belgian Magdalenian showing uncalibrated BP and calibrated BC dates (calibrated with OxCal v3.10).

Belgian Magdalenian site distribution (Fig. 4)

Two open-air Magdalenian workshop sites are known north of the Meuse, at Orp (**Fig. 4, 1**) on the Brabant Plateau (Vermeersch et al. 1987; Vermeersch 1991) and Kanne (**Fig. 4, 2**) in the province of Limburg near the Dutch border (Vermeersch / Lauwers / Van Peer 1985). Magdalenian cave sites form two occupation clusters. The Meuse Valley group of sites is primarily concentrated between Hastière and Namur, (**Fig. 4, 4-9**), but also includes Vaucelles (**Fig. 4, 3**) on the French border near Givet (Bellier / Cattelain 1983), the Goyet caves on the Samson River (**Fig. 4, 10**) (Germonpré 1996; Germonpré / Sablin 2002) and Engis (**Fig. 4, 11**) near Liège. Engis, however, could be considered rather to be part of the eastern cluster, the Ourthe Valley group. This smaller group of sites, including Verlaine, Coléoptère and Walou Cave, is concentrated south and east of Liège (**Fig. 4, 12-14**).

Fig. 4 Location of the principal Magdalenian sites in Belgium. – **1** Orp, – **2** Kanne, – **3** Trou des Blaireaux, – **4** Trou Da Somme, – **5** Trou du Frontal, – **6** Trou des Nutons, – **7** Chaleux, – **8** Trou Magrite, – **9** Bois Laiterie, – **10** Grottes de Goyet, – **11** Engis, – **12** Verlaine, – **13** Grotte du Coléoptère, – **14** Grotte Walou.

Most stratified Belgian cave sites containing Mousterian and/or Aurignacian occupations also contain Magdalenian horizons (Trou Magrite, Goyet, Engis). However, the most of Magdalenian sites contain only a single occupation of this period or are overlain by more recent Late Glacial occupations (e.g. Grotte de Coléoptère). The Magdalenian population thus appears to have occupied the same territory as preceding Middle and Early Upper Palaeolithic populations, but to have exploited it differently. The addition of uniquely Magdalenian cave sites represents an increase in the number of caves that were previously unoccupied and thus a slightly higher density in occupation of the territory. Magdalenian sites vary in function and duration of occupation. They include larger sites such as Chaleux, Magrite and Goyet, which may have served as base camps, as well as smaller sites such as Trou Da Somme, Frontal, Nutons and Bois Laiterie, which may have been short-term camps for specialized activities. This seems to indicate an increase in familiarity with the territory occupied during the Magdalenian, with exploitation of caves within the known territory which were not previously exploited during the Middle and Early Upper Palaeolithic.

Re-colonization models

After a period of abandonment of northwest Europe during the Last Glacial Maximum, Magdalenian groups began to recolonize the region. López Bayón (2000) proposes a dual stage process for Magdalenian re-colonization of Belgium: an initial phase during the Dryas I characterized by short-term occupations, followed by the establishment of regular occupation/re-use of longer-term sites in Belgium during the »Bølling«. In his model, Magdalenian populations arrived from the northeast, with links to populations in the Rhine Valley. Other researchers propose migration from southwest to northeast and thus movement from the Paris Basin to the Meuse Basin and then on to the Rhine Basin (e.g. Rensink 1993). Teheux (1994) suggests an origin for the Belgian Magdalenian in the »Magdalénien à navettes« sites of northern France, citing similarities between Chaleux and La Garenne (Creuse, France).

Raw material exploitation

Research on raw material exploitation and lithic sources for the western Meuse Valley group contributes to the question of recolonization or, at least, to the development of contacts between the western Belgian group and the Paris Basin after settlement of the upper Meuse Valley in Belgium. Two of the most commonly used lithic raw material sources at the western Belgian sites indicate exploitation of high quality Belgian flint (**Fig. 5a**) found to the north and northwest of the main concentration of Magdalenian sites and good quality silicified limestone (**Fig. 5b**) located to the west and southwest near Charleville-Mézières, France. Macroscopic comparison of flint from the cave sites of Trou Da Somme and Bois Laiterie and the open-air workshop sites of Orp and Kanne suggests that the fine-grained, white-patinated flint from the cave sites is similar to that from Orp. The flint at Kanne, in eastern Belgium near the Dutch border, is quite different, particularly with respect to cortical characteristics, and does not seem to have been transported to the western group sites. The white-patinated flint at Trou Da Somme appears to be identical to Bois Laiterie type 10.

The source of a second raw material, silicified limestone, is located in the Champagne region of France, near Charleville-Mézières, following the Meuse upstream into France (pers. comm., University of Liège). The term »silicified limestone« is

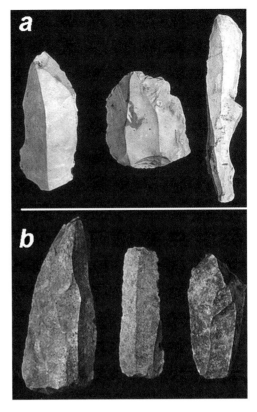

Fig. 5 Trou Da Somme. Main lithic raw materials. – **a** flint, – **b** silicified limestone.

that used by Penisson, but the material is actually a form of coarser-grained flint, mottled gray, opaque and matte, which does not patinate. This material is dominant at Trou Da Somme, comprising 57.2 % of the entire lithic assemblage. It is also present at Bois Laiterie, Chaleux and Frontal, but in lower frequencies (fine-grained flint is dominant at these sites).

Other raw materials, including other kinds of good quality flint, probably also from north of the Meuse, local quartzite and sandstone, have a minor presence at Trou Da Somme (each less than 5 % of the lithic assemblage).

Differences in reduction and tool production strategies can be observed in the Trou Da Somme assemblage structure, in response to differences in availability and quality of lithic raw materials exploited (**Table 1**). Technological activity at Trou Da Somme was focused on the reduction of small, prepared cores (mainly silicified limestone) and the resharpening of transported tools (patinated flint). When assemblage structure is examined in more detail, it can be seen that the main differences in reduction strategies are linked to blade and bladelet production. More blades were made on silicified limestone (45.5 % versus 35.0 %) and more bladelets on patinated flint (15.2 % versus 9.4 %). Crested blades are also more common on silicified limestone, and flakes more common on flint.

The inter-site distribution of raw materials suggests that the Meuse River acted as a conduit for Magdalenian population movement from the Paris Basin to western Belgium. Groups would have followed the Meuse Valley up- and downstream, transporting silicified limestone from near Charleville-Mézières and obtaining flint north of the Meuse once in Belgium. The eastern Ourthe Valley group may have had con-

Debitage class	white patinated flint		silicified limestone		Total
	n	%	n	%	
trimming flakes	18	7.6%	78	12.1%	96
shatter	4	1.7%	6	0.9%	10
flakes	85	35.9%	180	27.9%	265
blades	83	35.0%	294	45.5%	377
crested blades	1	0.4%	14	2.2%	15
bladelets	36	15.2%	61	9.4%	97
cores	1	0.4%	3	0.5%	4
burin spalls	5	2.1%	2	0.3%	7
tablettes		0.0%	1	0.2%	1
angular debris	2	0.8%	3	0.5%	5
platform renewal flakes	2	0.8%	4	0.6%	6
Total	237	100.0%	646	100.0%	883

Table 1 Trou Da Somme, assemblage structure.

nections with the Kanne workshop and Magdalenian populations in western Germany (e. g. Gönnersdorf and Andernach). However, the presence of fossil marine shells at sites in both Belgian clusters suggests affinities and/or contact between them, and thus a broader range of contacts extending from the Paris Basin to the Rhine Basin via Belgium.

Tools

A total of 199 tools was recovered, with backed bladelets most common (n=48), followed by end scrapers (n=27), pièces esquillées (n=26) and pieces with continuous retouch on one or both edges (n=25). Two multiple perçoirs of Chaleux type support a connection between Trou Da Somme and Chaleux. When broken down according to the two most common raw materials, it is evident that raw material characteristics influenced choices for different kinds of tools (**Table 2**). For most tool classes, silicified limestone and pati-

Tool class	patinated flint		silicified limestone		other flint
	n	%	n	%	n
slightly retouched	5	8.5	5	5.0	4
continuously retouched pieces	7	11.9	13	12.9	4
backed bladelets	18	30.5	25	24.8	3
burins	6	10.2	12	11.9	5
truncated pieces	2	3.4	6	5.9	3
borers	4	6.8	7	6.9	3
multi-borers (Chaleux type)	1	1.7	0	0.0	1
endscrapers	3	5.1	19	18.8	4
notches/denticulates	1	1.7	2	2.0	2
sidescrapers	0	0.0	1	1.0	0
splintered pieces	12	20.3	11	10.9	2
Total	49	100.0	92	100.0	31

Table 2 Trou Da Somme, tool frequencies for flint and silicified limestone.

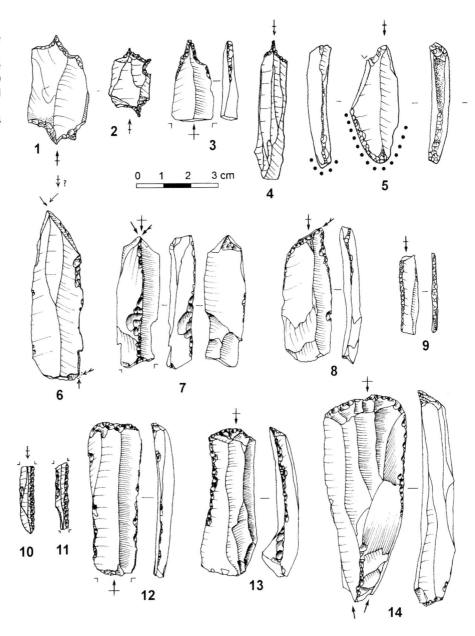

Fig. 6 Trou Da Somme, tools. Flint (1-9): – **1-2** Chaleux-type multi-perçoirs, – **3-4** perçoirs, – **5** retouched blade with edge smoothing, – **6-8** burins, – **9** backed bladelet. Silicified limestone (10-14): – **10-11** backed bladelets, – **12-14** end scrapers.

nated flint were exploited similarly. However, flint was preferred for backed bladelets (30.5 % versus 24.8 %) and pièces esquillées (20.3 % versus 10.9 %), and silicified limestone for end scrapers (18.5 % versus 5.1 %). Such preferences may be linked to variability in quality between the two materials - relative facility of producing bladelets on flint versus silicified limestone (quality with respect to reduction), to the relative durability of silicified limestone during activities using end scrapers, or to the relative susceptibility to splintering of flint during use (quality with respect to function). The range of tools and techniques corresponds well to the typical panoply of the northern Magdalenian in its late phase (**Fig. 6**). Such lithic tools were accompanied by tools made on bone (e.g., sagaies) to which they were directly linked by the fitting of armatures or indirectly by the necessity of mechanical preparation.

Factorial correspondence analysis (CA) and ascendant hierarchical classification (AHC) were carried out based on the percentages of tool classes at ten Belgian Magdalenian sites to explain, at least in part, vari-

Site	endscrapers		burins		borers		truncated tools		backed tools		composites	
	n	%	n	%	n	%	n	%	n	%	n	%
Chaleux (1865; 1985-88)	279	8.6	492	14.7	703	21.2	174	5.1	864	28.7	116	3.6
Coléoptère B	17	14.5	13	11.1	10	8.5	7	6.0	67	57.3	1	0.9
Frontal	16	9.3	37	21.5	32	18.6	20	11.6	46	26.7	9	5.2
Kanne	9	10.6	35	41.2	3	3.5	3	3.5	7	8.2	2	2.4
Nutons	8	14.8	9	16.7	13	24.1	5	9.3	17	31.5	0	0.0
Orp-east	53	12.1	220	50.2	14	3.2	14	3.2	36	8.2	8	1.8
Orp-west	22	15.4	66	46.2	7	4.9	5	3.5	2	1.4	8	5.6
Trou da Somme	27	13.6	24	12.1	16	8.0	11	5.5	48	24.1	0	0.0
Verlaine	23	11.1	21	10.1	19	9.2	14	6.8	80	38.7	4	1.9
Bois Laiterie (YSS)	21	8.6	35	14.3	18	7.4	23	9.4	89	36.5	2	0.8

Table 3 part 1   Typological tool frequencies and percentages by tool class for the main Belgian Magdalenian sites. Data sources: Chaleux (1865; 1985-88): Dewez 1987; Cabboi 1994; Teheux 1997. Coléoptère B: Dewez 1987. Frontal: Dewez 1987. Kanne: Vermeersch / Lauwers / Van Peer 1985. Nutons: Dewez 1987. Orp-East and Orp-West: Vermeersch et al. 1987. Trou Da Somme: Miller et al. 1998. Verlaine: Dewez 1987. Bois Laiterie: Straus / Orphal 1997.

ability between the sites (**Table 3**). Tool groups include end scrapers, burins, perçoirs (including becs, zinken, micro-perçoirs and multiple perçoirs), truncated tools, backed tools (primarily backed bladelets, but also backed blades and (very few) Azilian or Creswello-Hamburgian points), composite tools, pièces esquillées, retouched blades and flakes, and notches/denticulates. The class »diverse«, present in publications for several sites, was excluded from the analysis.

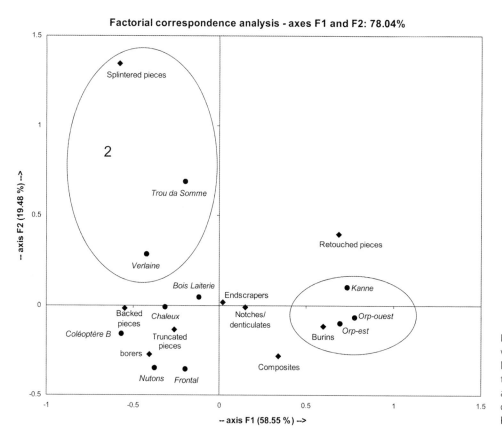

Fig. 7 Variability between ten Belgian Magdalenian sites shown by factorial correspondence analysis (CA) using percentages of tool classes: Factors F1 and F2.

Table 3 part 2 For table caption see Table 3 part 1. Site	splintered pieces		retouched tools		notches/ denticulates		others		Total	
	n	%	n	%	n	%	n	%	n	%
Chaleux (1865; 1985-88)	189	5.8	104	3.7	229	7.1	42	1.5	3192	100
Coléoptère B	0	0.0	2	1.7	0	0.0	0	0.0	117	100
Frontal	1	0.6	0	0.0	11	6.4	0	0.0	172	100
Kanne	0	0.0	21	24.7	5	5.9	0	0.0	85	100
Nutons	0	0.0	0	0.0	2	3.7	0	0.0	54	100
Orp-east	0	0.0	53	12.1	26	5.9	14	3.2	438	100
Orp-west	0	0.0	24	16.8	8	5.6	1	0.7	143	100
Trou da Somme	26	13.1	25	12.6	5	2.5	17	8.5	199	100
Verlaine	18	8.7	10	4.8	14	6.8	4	1.9	207	100
Bois Laiterie (YSS)	2	0.8	36	14.8	16	6.6	2	0.8	244	100

78.04 % of the variability between sites is explained by factors F1 and F2 (**Fig. 7**). First, F1 distinguishes between three sites (Kanne, Orp-East and Orp-West) and all other sites, which could reflect differences between these open-air sites (group 1) and cave sites, or workshop sites of group 1 and sites with other functions, including habitation sites and short-term hunting camps. F1 also opposes burins and backed tools. Referring to **Table 3**, group 1 is correlated with a high percentage of burins, while cave sites tend to have

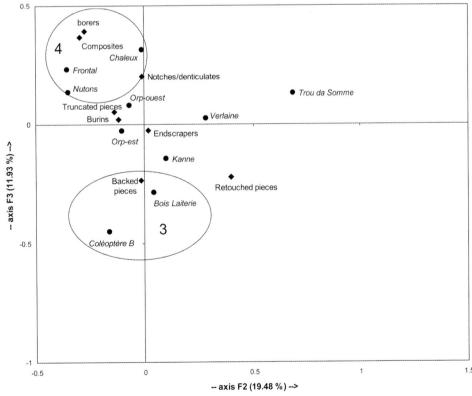

Fig. 8 Variability between ten Belgian Magdalenian sites shown by factorial correspondence analysis (CA) using percentages of tool classes: Factors F2 and F3.

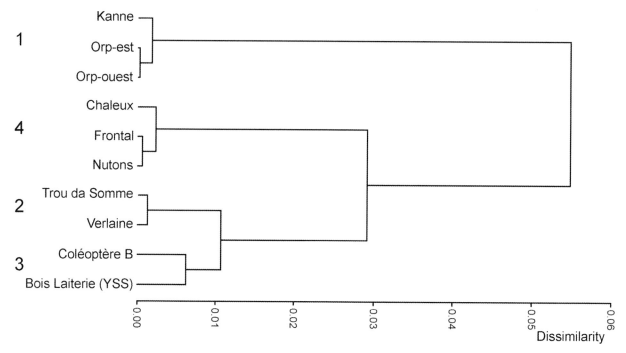

Fig. 9 Dendrogram summarizing the results of ascendant hierarchical classification for ten Belgian Magdalenian sites.

more backed pieces (ranging from 24-57 %). F2 shows a clear opposition between burins and pièces esquillées. It also opposes group 2 (Trou Da Somme, Verlaine) with all other sites. The group 1 sites each have greater than 40 % burins in their toolkits and no pièces esquillées. Group 2, in contrast, contains sites with splintered pieces (13.1 % at TDS and 8.7 % at Verlaine) and the lowest percentages of burins; Chaleux is the only other site with splintered pieces (5.8 %).

The combination of factors F2 and F3 (**Fig. 8**) explains 31.41 % of the variability between sites. F3 separates the cave sites into groups 3 (Bois Laiterie, Coléoptère B) and 4 (Chaleux, Frontal, Nutons) and also separates backed tools and perçoirs. Referring to again to table 3, Coléoptère B has the highest percentage of backed tools (57.3 %). The group 4 sites have the highest percentages of perçoirs, ranging from 18.6 % - 24.1 %; all other sites contain less than 10 %.

End scrapers, truncated tools, composites and notches/denticulates do not play a significant role in this classification of Belgian Magdalenian sites.

In sum then, F1 separates three sites (group 1) from other sites (groups 2 - 4); F1 and F2 separate group 1 sites from group 2 sites; and F3 separates group 3 sites from group 4 sites. On the basis of factorial correspondence analysis of tool classes, the ten analyzed Magdalenian sites form four groups:

Group 1: Kanne, Orp-East, Orp-West burins
Group 2: Trou Da Somme, Verlaine splintered pieces
Group 3: Bois Laiterie, Coléoptère B backed tools
Group 4: Chaleux, Frontal, Nutons perçoirs

Ascendant hierarchical classification (χ^2 distance, Ward criterion) on the first four factors (F1-F4) produces a dendrogram summarizing these results (**Fig. 9**). As shown by F1, group 1 differs from all other groups, and the dendrogram indicates that this is the most dissimilar contrast between groups of sites. This distinction would separate open-air and cave sites, or workshops versus sites with other functions. The group 4 sites (Chaleux, Frontal and Nutons) are quite similar and geographically close in the Lesse River valley. Chaleux is likely separated from the other two sites by the much larger size of the lithic assemblage, which itself reflects differences in site function (habitat). Group 4 is separated from groups 2 and 3 by the elevated percentage of perçoirs. Although found in the western and eastern groups respectively, the group 2 sites (Trou Da Somme and Verlaine) are similar in percentage for nearly all tool classes as well as toolkit size. Finally, the group 3 sites (Bois Laiterie and Coléoptère B) are separated from group 2 by their higher percentage of backed tools.

Fossil marine shells

Fossil marine shells, dating to the Tertiary and probably coming from the Paris Basin, have been recovered from most Belgian Magdalenian sites, in both the western (Chaleux, Bois Laiterie, Trou Da Somme, Frontal, Trou Magrite, Trou des Nutons and Goyet) and eastern (Coléoptère B, Verlaine) groups. Certain species are common both to Chaleux, which contained the highest number of shells, and other sites: *Bayania lactea*, *Glycimeris pulvinata* and *Hipponyx cornucopia*.

A single perforated fossil shell (*Bayania lactea*) was recovered from Trou Da Somme in 1997. This species is also found at other Magdalenian sites, including Chaleux, Coléoptère B and four specimens at Bois Laiterie. The double perforation was made by pressure and rotation while the same type of shell at Bois Laiterie was perforated by abrasion (López Bayón et al. 1996; Lejeune 1997).

It is of interest that such fossils are found both at Chaleux and the smaller cave sites, indicating a level of importance attributed to such objects. They may reflect notions of ethnic identity and territory, marking even short-term sites as belonging to the same settlement system. 64 fossils of a dozen different species were recovered from Chaleux and even Bois Laiterie, a small cave unsuitable for long-term occupation, contains eight fossils representing five different species. The type found at Trou Da Somme (*Bayania lactea*) is also found at both these sites, as well as at Trou Magrite and Coléoptère B. With respect to Paris Basin sites, Marsangy also has an example of *Bayania*; Étiolles and Bois Laiterie both have *Campanile giganteum*; Pincevent and Verberie have *Turritella* sp. in common with Chaleux, Frontal, Goyet and Verlaine, and *Ancillaria* sp. in common with Chaleux.

Plaques

Plaques of psammite, schist and sandstone have been found at several Magdalenian sites and Trou Da Somme is no exception. 290 fragments of stone plaques were recovered from both chambers, most often vertically oriented, indicating post-depositional movement, probably due to mudflow from the upper cave to the lower cave (see López Bayón et al. 1997). Refitting of 53 fragments in 22 series was possible. Three pairs were found inside the cave, each in close proximity, probably broken in situ without much subsequent disturbance. Another series joins pieces from the two chambers of TDS I, reflecting a greater degree of displacement. A series of five fragments gives an indication of the originally much larger size of the plaques. The transport of such plaques to the cave, probably for paving, reflects a significant degree of investment in making the site more habitable.

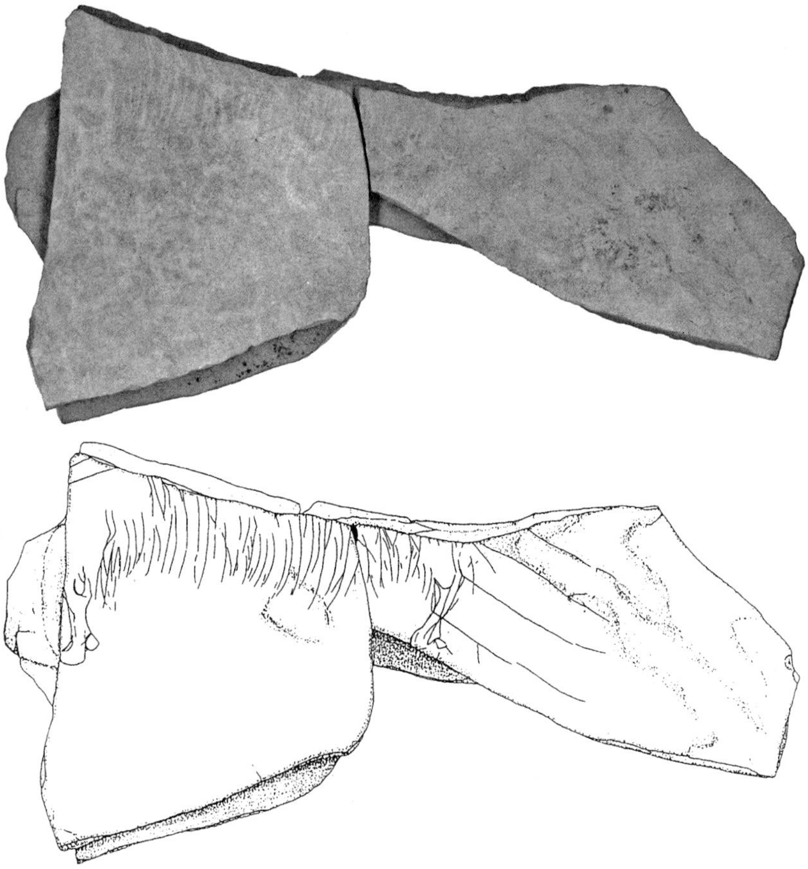

Fig. 10 Trou Da Somme: Engraved plaque.

Engraved plaque

Engraved plaques have also been found in Belgian Magdalenian contexts, often figurative and sometimes with abstract incised lines (possibly due to butchery rather than representing art), and including Trou Da Somme. Engraved plaques at Chaleux depict aurochs and reindeer, a plaque from Frontal depicts a bison, and an engraved reindeer antler from Nutons also depicts a bison, among other motifs (see Lejeune 1987). Two refitted fragments of an engraved plaquette were recovered from Trou Da Somme (**Fig. 10**). The drawing shows the left side of an animal with the front and back limbs and a series of curved lines representing the hair coat hanging from the belly. A series of four rectilinear lines is directed toward the rear limb, one of which is in contact with the limb and another which crosses it. Initial interpretation considered the engraving to represent a rhinoceros or bison rather than aurochs, a caprid, equid or mammoth (Lejeune 1993). However, a more recent interpretation takes into account zooarchaeological criteria and rejects interpretation as rhinoceros or bison: rhinoceros because this species has three digits on the fore- and hind limbs and a marked convex ventral line and bison because it has shorter hair and the ratio between bison limb and body length is disproportionate with that depicted (López Bayón et al. 1997, 74). Other taxa - gracile herbivores, carnivores and aurochs – are also rejected based on limb length and other biomorphological traits. Instead, a series of traits, including short limb length, a long hair coat that entirely covers the animal, hair that begins at the stifle and continues to the thigh, so that only the lower half of the limb lacks hair making details of the fetlock and dew-claw clearly visible, supports the hypothesis that the animal represented is musk ox (*Ovibos moschatus*), a species regularly found at Late Glacial sites in the region, Trou Da Somme included. At Goyet, a date of 12 620 ± 90 BP (GrA-3238) was obtained on musk ox bone.

I. López Bayón also proposes an interpretation of the scene represented based on ethology. The musk ox is less mobile and is less limited by environmental constraints than reindeer. At the end of the Late Glacial, faced with the progressive disappearance of reindeer, Magdalenian hunters would have adapted their hunting strategy to include musk ox. The defensive strategy of musk ox is to form a closed circle, facing outwards, to protect calves inside the circle. If the number of individuals is small, a defensive line is formed instead of a circle. While this would have made it difficult for hunters to attack calves and females, inexperienced and old males are expelled from the herd during the rutting season (August-September) and could have been more easily hunted.

Bone industry

A single fragment of a sagaie made of reindeer antler was recovered in 1988 and a sample from this artefact was used to obtain the date of 12 240 ± 130 BP (OxA-4199) (Charles 1994). The »grooving and splitting« technique used is comparable to that observed on the sagaies recovered at Bois Laiterie (López Bayón et al. 1997).

Discussion

A series of elements is regularly present at the western Belgian Magdalenian sites: use of psammite plaques for paving, presence of fossil shells of various kinds, engraved plaques and other mobile art, a developed antler and bone industry including sagaie points, needles and polishers, exploitation of the same lithic raw material sources. Even the smaller cave sites, such as Trou Da Somme, Bois Laiterie and Frontal, contain plaque paving, fossil shells and mobile art, suggesting both investment in such sites for probable regular re-use and the cultural importance of fossil shells and engravings even at sites of short-term occupation. Lithic sources indicate movement along the Meuse corridor from the Champagne region in France to the plateaus of Belgium. Such elements also link the Belgian sites with groups in the Paris Basin and Rhine Valley and indicate a degree of coherence in terms of population movement and/or contact at an interregional scale.

Note

1 All dates are given in uncalibrated years BP.

References

Bellier / Cattelain 1983: C. Bellier / P. Cattelain, Fouilles au »Trou des Blaireaux« à Vaucelles (Doische - Prov. Namur). Campagnes 1981-1982. Notae Praehistoricae 3, 42-49.

Cabboi 1994: S. Cabboi, Les fouilles récentes. III.5.4. Outillage. In: M. Otte (dir.), Le Magdalénien du Trou de Chaleux (Hulsonniaux-Belgique). E.R.A.U.L. 60 (Liège 1994) 111-140.

Charles 1994: R. Charles, Towards a New Chronology for the Lateglacial Archaeology of Belgium. Part II: Recent Radiocarbon Dates from the Oxford AMS System. Notae Praehistoricae 13, 31-39.

1996: R. Charles, Back into the North: the radiocarbon evidence for the human recolonisation of the northwest Ardennes after the last glacial maximum. Proceedings of the Prehistoric Society 62, 1-19.

1998: R. Charles, Late Magdalenian chronology and faunal exploitation in the north-western Ardennes. British Archaeological Reports (International Series) 737 (Oxford 1998).

Dewez 1987: M. Dewez, Le Paléolithique Supérieur Récent dans les Grottes de Belgique. Publication d'Histoire de l'Art et d'Archéologie de l'Université Catholique de Louvain LVII (Louvain-la-Neuve 1987).

Germonpré 1996: M. Germonpré, Preliminary results on the nammals of the Magdalenian upper horizon of Goyet (Belgium). Notae Praehistoricae 16, 75-85.

1997: M. Germonpré, The Magdalenian upper horizon of Goyet and the late Upper Palaeolithic recolonisation of the Belgian Ardennes. Bulletin de l'Institut Royal des Sciences Naturelles de Belgique, Sciences de la Terre 67, 167-182.

Germonpré / Sablin 2002: M. Germonpré / M. Sablin, Preliminary results on the large bovids of the Belgian Magdalenian. Notae Praehistoricae 22, 71-73.

Housley et al. 1997: R. A. Housley / C. S. Gamble / M. Street / P. Pettitt, Radiocarbon evidence for the late glacial human recolonisation of northern Europe. Proceedings of the Prehistoric Society 63, 25-54.

Lejeune 1987: M. Lejeune, L'art mobilier paléolithique et mésolithique en Belgique (Treignes-Viroinval 1987).

1993: M. Lejeune, Découverte d'une plaquette gravée dans le Magdalénien du Trou Da Somme (Massif de Roche-al-Rue, Waulsort, Belgique). Notae Praehistoricae 12, 1993, 53-57.

1997: M. Lejeune, L'art mobilier magdalénien final de la Grotte du Bois Laiterie. In: M. Otte / L. G. Straus (eds.), La grotte du Bois Laiterie. E.R.A.U.L. 80 (Liège 1997) 293-318.

Léotard 1988: J.-M. Léotard, Occupation magdalénienne au Trou Da Somme, massif de Roche-al-Rue (Waulsort). Notae Prahistoricae 8, 1988, 17-23.

1993: J.-M. Léotard, Hastière-Waulsort: Trou Da Somme. Chronique de l'Archéologie Wallonne 1, 1993, 101.

López Bayón 2000: I. López Bayón, La recolonisation tardiglaciaire de la Belgique. In: B. Valentin / P. Bodu / M. Christiansen (eds.), L'Europe centrale et septentrionale au Tardiglaciaire: confrontation des modèles régionaux de peuplement. Actes de la table-ronde internationale de Nemours 1997. Mémoires du Musée de préhistoire d'Île-de-France 7 (Nemours 2000) 139-149.

López Bayón et al. 1996: I. López Bayón / E. Teheux / L. G. Straus / J.-M. Léotard, Pointes de sagaies au Magdalénien du Bois Laiterie (Profondeville, Namur). Préhistoire Européenne 8 (Liège 1996) 125-141.

1997: I. López Bayón / J.-M. Léotard / M. Otte / Y. Quinif / V. Ancion / Ph. Lacroix / R. Miller / P. Noiret, Nouvelles recherches dans le site magdalénien du Trou da Somme (Hastière). Notae Praehistoricae 17, 63-75.

1998: I. López Bayón / J.-M. Léotard / M. Otte / Ph. Lacroix / V. Ancion, Le Trou da Somme (Hastière): état de la question. Actes de la Sixième Journée d'Archéologie Namuroise 1998 (Gembloux 1998) 19-32.

Miller et al. 1998: R. Miller / J.-M. Léotard / M. Otte / I. López Bayón / Ph. Lacroix / V. Ancion, Trou Da Somme: Excavation Report 1998. Notae Praehistoricae 18, 51-63.

Otte 1994: M. Otte (dir.), Le Magdalénien du Trou de Chaleux (Hulsonniaux-Belgique). E.R.A.U.L. 60 (Liège 1994).

Otte et al. 1999: M. Otte / J.-M. Léotard / R. Miller / I. López Bayón / Ph. Lacroix / V. Ancion, Trou Da Somme: Rapport de fouilles 1998. Namur. Actes de la Septième Journée d'Archéologie Namuroise (Gembloux 1999) 31-47.

Otte / Straus 1997: M. Otte / L. G. Straus (eds.), La grotte du Bois Laiterie. E.R.A.U.L. 80 (Liège 1997).

Rensink 1993: E. Rensink, Moving into the North: Magdalenian Occupation and Exploitation of the Loess Landscapes of Northwestern Europe (Leiden1993).

Straus / Orphal 1997: L. G. Straus / J. Orphal, The Bois Laiterie Magdalenian Lithic Industry. In: M. Otte / L. G. Straus (eds.), La grotte du Bois Laiterie. E.R.A.U.L. 80 (Liège 1997) 219-256

Street et al. 1994: M. Street / M. Baales / B. Weninger, Absolute Chronologie des späten Paläolithikums und Frühmesolithikums im nördlichen Rheinland. Archäologisches Korrespondenzblatt 24, 1994, 1-28.

Stutz 1993: A. Stutz, Settlement Patterns in Late Glacial Northwestern Europe: The Example from the Lesse Valley Magdalenian. B.A. thesis Harvard University, Cambridge MA (1993).

Teheux 1994: E. Teheux, Le Magdalénien de la Vallée de la Lesse. Mémoire de licence, University of Liège (1994).

1997: E. Teheux, Approche écologique, économique et sociale du Magdalénien de la vallée de la Lesse (Belgique). In: J.-P. Fagnart / A. Thévenin (eds.), Le Tardiglaciaire en Europe du Nord-Ouest. Colloque Amiens 1994 (Paris 1997) 367-380.

Verheyleweghen 1958: J. Verheyleweghen, Occupation magdalénienne avec dallage sur les berges de la Meuse à Waulsort. Archéologie 2, 417.

1959: J. Verheyleweghen, Untitled. Bulletin de la Société Spéléologique de Namur 1, 11.

Vermeersch 1991: P. Vermeersch, TL dating of the Magdalenian sites at Orp, Belgium. Notae Praehistoricae 10, 27-29.

Vermeersch / Lauwers / Van Peer 1985: P. Vermeersch / R. Lauwers / P. Van Peer, Un site magdalénien à Kanne. Archaeological Belgica 1,17-54.

Vermeersch et al. 1987: P. Vermeersch / N. Symens / J. Vynckier / G. Gikselings / R. Lauwers, Orp, site magdalénien de plein air. Archaeologica Belgica 3, 7-56.

Abstract / Résumé

Recent results for the Belgian Magdalenian

This paper presents the Belgian Magdalenian from the perspective of recent results from the cave site of Trou Da Somme and places the latter in relation to the other known Belgian Magdalenian sites, including caves in Middle Belgium (Chaleux, Bois Laiterie, Goyet, etc.) and open-air sites in Flanders (Orp, Kanne). Emphasis is placed on site function, chronology and lithic raw material procurement. Additionally, an engraved plaque found at Trou Da Somme will be discussed.

Résultats récents pour le Magdalénien Belge

On présente le Magdalénien belge du point de vue des récents résultats obtenus du site du Trou Da Somme, en le mettant en relation aux autres sites magdaléniens, dont des grottes en Wallonie (Chaleux, Bois Laiterie, Goyet,…) et des sites de plein air en Flandres (Orp, Kanne). On discute la fonction du site, la chronologie et l'économie lithique. De plus, on présente des données concernant une plaquette gravée provenant du Trou Da Somme.

Key-words

Magdalenian, Belgium, art, typology, recolonization models.

Acknowledgments

Fieldwork was made possible in 1997 and 1998 by subsidies from the Minister of the Walloon Region (96/12789 and 97/14056). Thanks to all of the students who participated in the excavation.

MARTA POŁTOWICZ-BOBAK

MAGDALENIAN SETTLEMENT IN POLAND IN THE LIGHT OF RECENT RESEARCH

The Magdalenian technocomplex is one of the best known and best described taxonomical units of the European Palaeolithic. The sites belonging to this cultural complex were already the subject of interest during the earliest period of Palaeolithic research due to the abundance and variety of the archaeological sources. G. Ossowski initiated research on the Magdalenian sites in Poland, working at the most famous Palaeolithic site in the Maszycka Cave at the end of the 19th century (Kozłowski et al. 1995). In the first half of the 20th century, a Magdalenian presence was recognized in Upper Silesia (Cyprzanów, Śmicz, Bliszczyce?: Kozłowski 1964). Some limited Magdalenian finds were discovered in Little Poland, including part of the finds from the Okiennik Cave, which is known mainly for the rich Middle Palaeolithic inventory (Kozłowski / Kozłowski 1977), or the sites in caves near Krakow (Dr. Majer's Cave, Na Łopiankach Cave: Kozłowski 1960). The artefacts from the Puchacza Skała in Krakow-Czestochowa Jurassic Upland (The Jura) unearthed at the turn of the century (Kowalski et al. 1965) were also described as Magdalenian. For many years the bone harpoon from Przemyśl found during World War II was the only trace of the easternmost Magdalenian settlement (Kozłowski 1977).

The development of research into the Magdalenian in Poland was continued after World War II. In the 1950s and 1960s, archaeological work was carried out at sites in Grzybowa Góra (Schild 1965) and Mały Antoniów (Sawicki 1960) and again in the Maszycka Cave (Kozłowski et al. 1995), among others. In the 1970s the long-term excavations at the site in Brzoskwinia commenced (Sobczyk 1993). The first Magdalenian site in the Carpathians was discovered in Sromowce Wyżne-Kąty in the Pieniny (Kozłowski 1987). Many more sites were discovered and surveyed from the 1980s onward. At the turn of the 21st century very important Magdalenian remains were recognized in different parts of southern Poland, mainly in Silesia (sites in Dzierżysław: Połtowicz 2000; Ginter et al. 2002; 2005; Sowin: Furmanek / Rapiński 2003, Broniszowice: Krawczyk / Płonka / Wiśniewski 2004) and in south-eastern Poland (Klementowice-Kolonia, Hłomcza, Wilczyce, Uście Gorlickie, Grodzisko Dolne: Połtowicz 2006 with further references). Sites with small inventories were also discovered in caves in the Krakow-Czestochowa Jurassic Upland (Cyrek 1999). The above-mentioned findings and the state of research provide the basis to propose a new synthesis and characterization of the Magdalenian Poland.

Chronology

Today, a number of absolute dates are available for a few sites, which were surveyed mainly within the last 20 years. The increasing number of dates has somewhat changed our view of Magdalenian settlement chronology in Poland (**Table 1**).

The complex from the Maszycka Cave undoubtedly provides the earliest evidence of Magdalenian settlement. This site, being the best known of all Magdalenian sites in Poland, yielded lithic and bone inventories linked with the Middle-Magdalenian facies à navettes. The ^{14}C dates determined for the site (15 490 ± 310 BP: Ly-2454; 14 250 ± 240 BP: Ly-2453) differ by over 1 000 radiocarbon years. Today it seems more

Site	Lab. no.	14C BP	Bibliography
Dzierżysław	GdA-69 (AMS)	13500±80	Ginter et al. 2002; 2005
Dzierżysław	GdA-193 (AMS)	13370±80	Ginter et al. 2002; 2005
Dzierżysław	GdA-70 (AMS)	13220±70	Ginter et al. 2002; 2005
Dzierżysław	Poz-10136 (AMS)	14150±70	unpublished report by T. Goslar
Dzierżysław	Poz-10135 (AMS)	13180±60	unpublished report by T. Goslar
Hłomcza	TL	13500±2000	Łanczont et al. 2002
Hłomcza	TL	14600±2300	Łanczont et al. 2002
Krucza Skała cave	Lod-407	11400±200	Cyrek 1999
Maszycka cave.	Ly-2454	15490±319	Kozłowski et al. 1995
Maszycka cave.	Ly-2453	14520±240	Kozłowski et al. 1995
Mosty	Lod-107	11290±280	Cyrek 1986a
W Zalasie cave	OxA-6591 (AMS)	12530±110	Kozłowski / Pettitt 2001
W Zalasie cave	OxA-6625 (AMS)	12820±80	Kozłowski / Pettitt 2001
Wilczyce	Ua-15720	11400±135	Fiedorczuk / Schild 2000
Wilczyce	Ua-15721	8415±100	Fiedorczuk / Schild 2000
Wilczyce	Ua-15722	11665±135	Fiedorczuk / Schild 2000
Wilczyce	Ua-15723	11890±105	Fiedorczuk / Schild 2000

Table 1 Radiometric dating of Magdalenian sites in Poland.

probable that the Magdalenian settlement should be linked with the earlier date (Kozłowski et al. 1995). This is earlier than the dates obtained for the other sites by several hundred years. The settlement in the Maszycka Cave can be interpreted as the first »pioneering« penetration of the eastern part of Central Europe by Magdalenian hunters, who ventured far beyond the borders of the range of this technocomplex of that time. It is interesting that in spite of the progress in research and the increase in available resources, no analogous and chronologically similar sites have been found so far in the area between the Krakow-Czestochowa Jurassic Upland and the territory of France, from which the closest analogies are known (Allain et al. 1985).

The first main phase of Magdalenian settlement in Central Europe took place in the period before the Bølling interstadial, after the Epe interstadial. We know of three sites from Poland (Dzierżysław, Wilczyce and Hłomcza) with absolute dates indicating that they were occupied in the early Dryas. However, Hłomcza has only provided TL-dates (Łanczont et al. 2002) which are disputed by some researchers. Two of the settlements are located at the eastern border of the Magdalenian culture range. It should be also emphasized that the sites at Dzierżysław and Wilczyce are base camp sites with rich inventories, which probably were re-occupied several times. Hłomcza is a site with few finds, apparently representing the remains of a single stay (Valde-Nowak / Muzyczuk 2000). Recent absolute dating of the Moravian sites of Balcarova, Žitneho and Nova Dratenicka (Valoch / Neruda 2005), as well as the Kniegrotte in Thuringia (Höck 2000) also suggest the presence of Magdalenian communities in the eastern part of Central Europe in Dryas I.

The range of Magdalenian settlement and the nature of the sites dated to Dryas I allow us to propose two important theses. The sites indicate that Magdalenian settlement already attained its maximum eastern extension in the period preceding the main wave of settlement into the western part of Central Europe. Moreover, this settlement was not restricted to short (hunting?) stays, although this type prevailed, but it also demonstrates a more stable and permanent character, reflected by rich inventories found at the camp

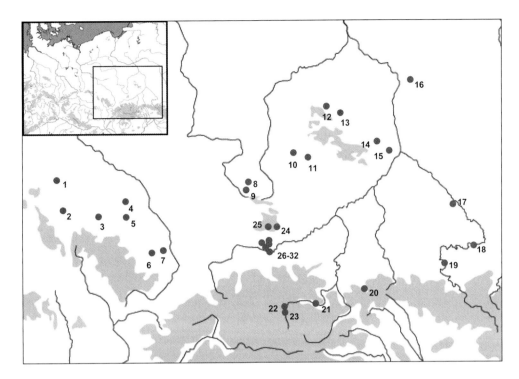

Fig. 1 Magdalenian sites in Poland (redrawn after a draft by D. Bobak). – 1 Grodziszcze 7, – 2 Ławica, – 3 Broniszowice 2, – 4 Sowin, – 5 Śmicz B, – 6 Dzierżysław, – 7 Cyprzanów 3, – 8 Krucza Skala Cave, – 9 Okiennik Cave, – 10 Kozłow 4, – 11 Mosty, – 12 Mały Antoniów, – 13 Grzybowa Góra, – 14 Mały Gawroniec 1, – 15 Wilczyce, – 16 Klementowice-Kolonia, – 17 Grodzisko Dolne, – 18 Przemyśl 2, – 19 Hłomcza, – 20 Uście Gorlickie, – 21 Sromowce Wyżne-Kąty, – 22 Podczerwone 1, – 23 Koniówka 1, – 24 Maszycka Cave, – 25 Puchacza Cave, – 26 Brzoskwinia, – 27 Gaik I Cave, – 28 Gaik II Cave, – 29 Dr. Majera Cave, – 30 Na Łopiankach Cave, – 31 Wołowice, – 32 Zalasie Cave.

sites. The eastern part of Central Europe belonged to the important settlement areas in the early phase of re-colonisation of the Central European Uplands, although at that time, as well as in the earlier phase, these areas constituted the periphery of Magdalenian settlement territory.

The most important and the most intense wave of Magdalenian settlement took place during the Bølling interstadial. The majority of the sites should be dated to this period, even if we assume that some of them should be dated to the earlier periods, as in case of some sites mentioned above. The territory of Bohemia was probably inhabited for the first time at the same period (Vencl 1991). Although most of the Polish sites are attributed to the Bølling period, this is only proven by absolute dating at a few sites.

The presence of Epi-Magdalenian groups, which settled in Poland and neighbouring regions is shown by a number of radiometrically dated sites. Of the Polish sites, that at Mosty (Cyrek 1986a) and cave sites in the Jura (Krucza Skała cave: Cyrek 1999) should be mentioned. In the past, the sites of Sromowce Górne-Kąty and Grzybowa Góra (Kozłowski 1987) were linked with the Allerød. Due to the lack of absolute dating, only typological arguments were taken into account, i.e. the presence of short end scrapers and a backed blade. The new dating determined for the inventory from Balcarova skala in Moravia (Valoch / Neruda 2005) shows very clearly that such forms were present in Central Europe even much earlier. The classic examples from Central Europe are layers 3 and 4 from the Kůlna Cave (Valoch 1988). It is believed that only few Magdalenian groups survived until the Allerød period.

Magdalenian settlement was represented in Poland for a period of about 3 000 years. Apart from the episode from the Maszycka Cave, we are probably dealing here with the continuous migration of communities from Dryas I until the Allerød period. On the basis of the number of discovered sites it can be assumed that Magdalenian settlement in Poland was not very intensive and that the areas covered by it always constituted the borderland of the region penetrated by Magdalenian hunters. The new Magdalenian sites discovered in recent years may be able to verify this interpretation.

Arrangement and variety of sites

Magdalenian sites are dispersed throughout almost the entire region of southern Poland (**Fig. 1**). Certain areas (»settlement centres«), in which the traces of the Magdalenian settlement are grouped, can be distinguished as follows: Silesia (sites at Dzierżysław, Śmicz, Bliszczyce?, Cyprzanów, Sowin), Little Poland (including Brzoskwinia, Wołowice, the Puchacza Cave, Dr. Majer's Cave, the Na Łopiankach Cave and the Zalas Cave) and south-eastern Poland (Grodzisko Dolne, Wilczyce, Przemyśl, Hłomcza) (approximately 40 sites in total). These centres are surrounded by areas where no traces or hardly any traces of Magdalenian settlement were discovered. Single sites were found in the region of the Carpathian Mountains (Sromowce Wyżne-Kąty) and the Sudetes (Broniszowice: Krawczyk / Płonka / Wiśniewski 2004), as well as in regions situated further to the north, at the boundary of the Central European Uplands and Lowlands (Klementowice-Kolonia: Jastrzębski / Libera 1988; Mosty: Cyrek 1986a; Grzybowa Góra: Schild 1965). There are no larger concentrations of settlement traces in any of these regions, unlike in Moravia and Central Germany. Even the largest concentration of sites in the Krakow-Czestochowa Jurassic Upland cannot be compared with the intensity of settlement in the neighbouring regions. The sites in south-eastern Poland and in Silesia are quite dispersed. Nevertheless, they should be treated as settlement micro-regions. The majority of the very diverse sites occupying relatively small areas are known only from the Jura. It makes this region somewhat similar to the classic karst of the Moravian Krass. Its characteristic feature is the lack of larger base camps.

During the whole Magdalenian period the settlement range did not extend beyond the Central European Uplands, although during the warm Bølling and Allerød interstadials it did reach the borderland between the Central European Uplands and the Lowlands (Klementowice-Kolonia, Mosty, Grzybowa Góra).

Settlement occurred at both open-air sites and caves, the latter of which are found only in the Jura, which could be explained by the natural morphology of the terrain. It should be mentioned that Magdalenian sites in caves have not yet been found in the Carpathians or the Sudetes, which may merely be a consequence of insufficient research.

Settlement structure seems to be quite complex. In all settlement micro-regions the sites with inventories not exceeding 1 000 artefacts prevail. They correspond to short-term, seasonal camp sites. All the large camp sites with a greater number of finds are located outside the Jura, beyond the area with the biggest site cluster. What is more, all Magdalenian sites with thousands of flint artefacts from the Krakow region are workshops (Brzoskwinia, Wołowice). Other than these, only small sites interpreted as short-term camps are known.

Large, long-term and/or re-settled base camp sites, such as those located in Silesia (Dzierżysław) and in south-eastern Poland (Klementowice-Kolonia, Wilczyce) are very rare on Polish territory. On the other hand, it is interesting that just these large sites are dated to the period preceding the Bølling interstadial (Wilczyce, Dzierżysław) and also that they are found in the easternmost areas (Klementowice, Wilczyce). The settlement pattern known from Moravia or Thuringia, characterised by the presence of large central sites surrounded by smaller »satellite« sites, is not observed in Poland. The observed pattern of site type and location may confirm the hypothesis presented above that Polish territory constituted a peripheral zone settled mainly during short-term seasonal expeditions.

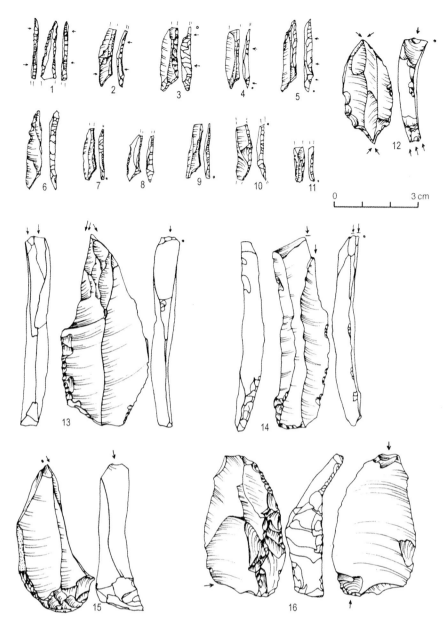

Fig. 2 Dzierżysław site. Lithic tool types (after Ginter et al. 2005).

The number of lithic workshop sites in Poland is quite low and includes Sowin in Silesia, and also Brzoskwinia and Wołowice, both in Little Poland. Imports of Krakow Jurassic flint were recognized at sites situated to the south and north of the area of their mining. To the south, finds from Moravia (Bednarz 1998) and individual items from the Gudenus Cave in Austria (Cyrek 1986b) have been discovered. There is no evidence of more intensive raw material export in the south of Poland. Numerous Jurassic flint imports were found at sites of Mosty and Grzybowa Góra, located north of the outcrops of Krakow Jurassic flint (Połtowicz 2005, also further information). The identification at other sites of imports of erratic raw material, such as that processed at Sowin, is very difficult.

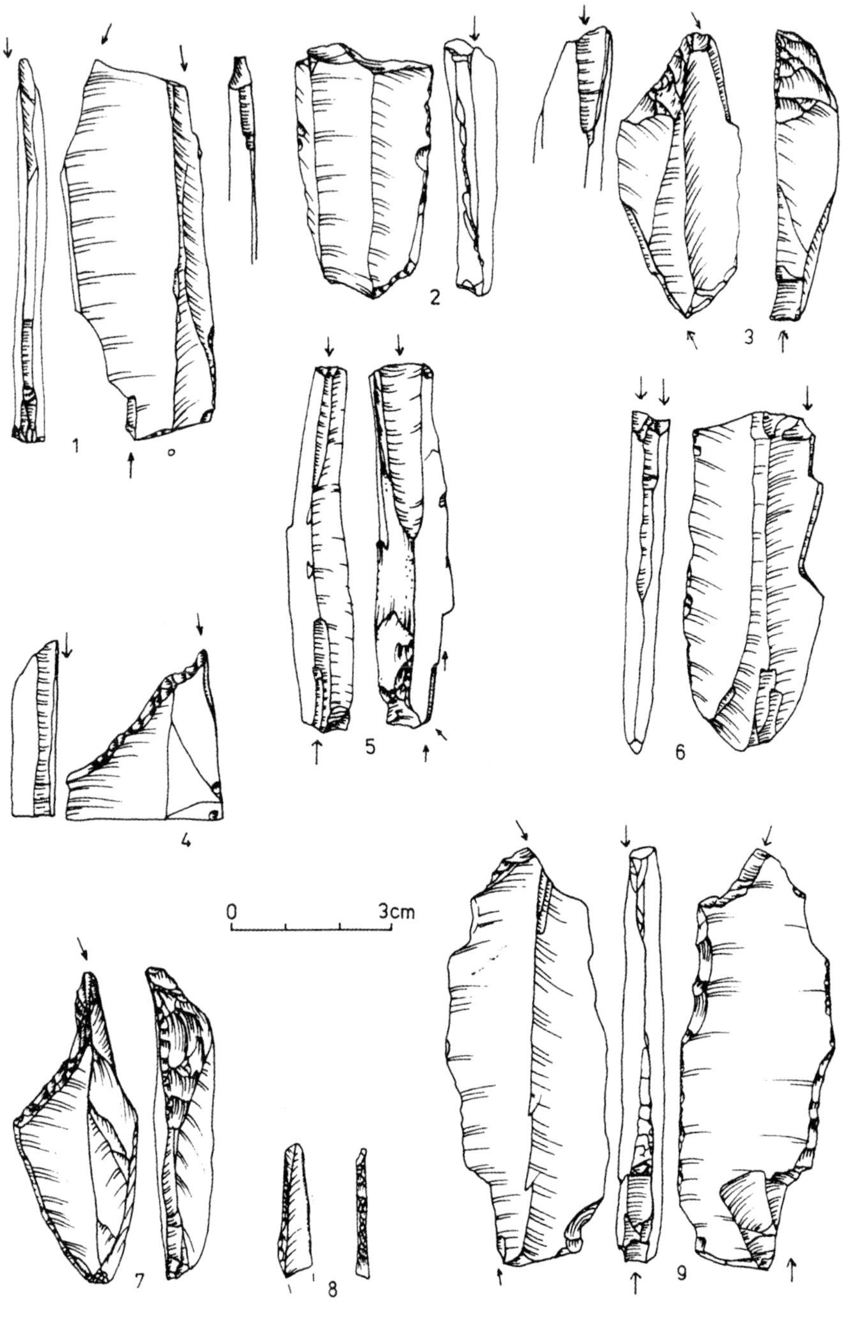

Fig. 3 Hłomcza site. Lithic tool types (after Valde-Nowak / Muzyczuk 2000).

Inventories

In a paper from 1987 J. K. Kozłowski proposed a division of the Polish Magdalenian, distinguishing several facies on the basis of the lithic inventories. This division reflects the enormous variety of the inventories. In principle, almost each site could be regarded as representing a distinct type. Analogies were pointed out from sites in other parts of Europe, mainly Central Europe, to the specific types of tools in the Polish inventories. Subsequent research developments and the increase in the number of discovered sites now allow these previous conclusions to be supplemented.

Undoubtedly, the variety of the inventories is very clear. An attempt to distinguish the various complexes by their characteristic tool types can be made. These show analogies to regions located further west, inclu-

Fig. 4 Wilczyce site. Lithic tool types (after Fiedorczuk / Schild 2000).

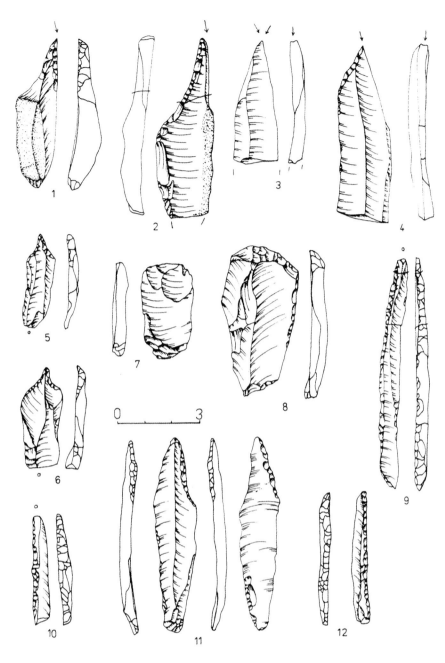

ding those typical for the Magdalenian technocomplex. One of the most characteristic complexes is the one containing triangles from Dzierżysław (Silesia), which corresponds to the facies with geometric microliths known from Western and Central Europe (**Fig. 2**). Similarly distinct are the complexes with Lacan type burins, recognized at the sites of Hłomcza (**Fig. 3**) and Wilczyce (**Fig. 4**), or those with »Langbohrer« perforators known from Klementowice Kolonia (**Fig. 5**). The characteristic forms found in all these inventories find their equivalents in lithic complexes from Central Europe (facies with triangles: Kniegrotte in Thuringia and Hranice in Czech Silesia; complexes with Lacan type burins: Oelknitz in Thuringia, Pekarna in Moravia; »Langbohrer« complexes: Nebra in Thuringia, Malomefiice-Borky in Moravia). The sites of Sromowce Wyżne-Kąty and Grzybowa Góra also call for attention. In both inventories arched backed blades were pre-

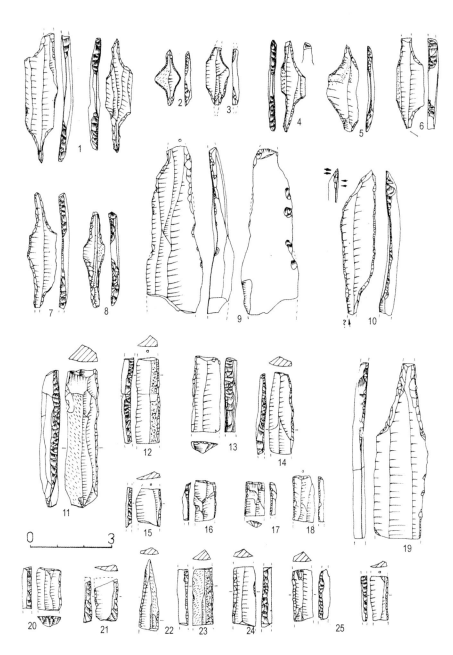

Fig. 5 Klementowice-Kolonia site. Lithic tool types (after Jastrzębski / Libera 1988).

sent, which in the past was seen as a basis for dating them to the Allerød period. Today it seems more likely that both inventories should be dated to the Bølling period.

The occurrence of a tool type characteristic for a specific »facies« of the Magdalenian does not preclude the presence of other forms (e.g. Lacan burins and »Langbohrer« perforators occur together at Malomefiice-Borky I), which is why it seems that they cannot be interpreted as the distinguishing features of different groups. Moreover, inventories with the specific forms which might serve to distinguish a specific »facies« are never »identical« (or even very similar to each other) regarding the typology of the tools, e.g. the complexes with triangles from Dierżysław, Poland and from Kniegrotte, Germany.

It seems that despite attempts to sub-divide the Magdalenian technocomplex in Central Europe, we cannot distinguish different and separate facies, but only identify the common features or characteristic forms found at the various sites which are typical for the Magdalenian in Central Europe. A differentiation of the French Magdalenian was suggested previously by B. Bosselin and F. Djindjan (1988). It seems that a similar (or maybe even greater) differentiation is also present in the Central Europe Magdalenian province. At the same time, it is possible to recognize common features of the inventories (technology, tool types), which are dispersed across vast areas and over a long period of time. It might be suggested that these similarities may be interpreted by taking into account the role of tradition, manifested in the long-term preservation of the style and form of the products, and also by considering the equivalent function of sites and models of adaptation to environmental conditions, which were no less important and perhaps even decisive factors in the production of specific tool and inventory types.

Raw material distribution

The southern part of Poland is a region with rich flint resources. In Silesia, they take the form of erratic flint derived from moraine deposits of earlier glaciations. In Little Poland the material is mainly Krakow Jurassic flint and in south-eastern Poland a few varieties of material are found, mainly Świeciechow, chocolate and erratic flint. The Magdalenian hunters never had any problems with the good quality raw material supplies. It is apparent that local raw materials constitute almost all the material processed by knapping at nearly all the sites. The inventories from Sromowce Wyżne-Kąty (Kozłowski 1987) and Uście Gorlickie (Valde-Novak 1998) are manufactured on chert. In case of the site of Sromowce Wyżne, chert is a readily available local raw material. The community at the settlement of Uście Gorlickie imported this raw material from the nearest available sources.

The presence of imported raw materials at Polish sites is poorly recognized. The rare finds of radiolarite at the sites of Dzierżysław, Brzoskwinia, Mosty and Wilczyce are the easiest to interpret (Połtowicz 2005, also further information). In most cases determination of their origin is problematic. Such radiolarite may come from the Pieniny region or further away in Slovakia, from regions beyond the areas occupied by Magdalenian people.

The Krakow Jurassic flint exploited at the sites of Mosty and Grzybowa Góra (36.6% and 80% respectively) was also imported. In both cases, the distance between the camp sites and the outcrops of Krakow Jurassic flint exceeds 100 km. It was not brought in single pieces taken »for the journey« but as the result of a planned strategy of ensuring raw material supplies. Imported raw materials were also used at Klementowice-Kolonia, where more than 20% of the inventory was made of chocolate flint imported from the south, from a location approximately 70 km distant.

All these sites provide evidence of connections (migrations?) along a south-north axis, between the southern and northern parts of the southern Polish Uplands as well as between areas lying on opposite sites of the Carpathians and the Sudetes. The latter contacts are mainly demonstrated by the presence of Polish raw material imports at Moravian sites (Bednarz 1998). This situation is characteristic of the Magdalenian sites dated to Dryas I and Bølling periods.

Isolated artefacts made of Volhynian flint, outcrops of which are located east of the limits of the Magdalenian range, are found at some sites in south-eastern Poland (Klementowice-Kolonia: Jastrzębski / Libera 1988; Grodzisko Dolne: Czopek 1999).

Another picture is drawn by the analysis of the directions of origin of imported artefacts found at the Maszycka Cave (Kozłowski et al. 1995). Many raw materials originate from regions located to the west, sometimes coming from far-distant areas, e. g. »Plattensilex« (chert) from the Altmühl river valley and possibly Upper Danube flint. Raw materials also originate in regions to the east of the site (Volhynian and chocolate flint) and, to a lesser degree, to the south (raw materials from the Pieniny region). The directions of origin of these imports show the other orientation of migrations of these »pioneers« of Magdalenian settlement in Poland, connecting the western and the eastern ranges of Magdalenian culture.

Conclusion

The areas of Magdalenian settlement in Poland mark the northern and eastern extremes of the range of this technocomplex. The number of the sites represents a long period of time; by far the most sites are represented by limited material and were probably settled only once, suggesting that the region formed the periphery of the area settled by Magdalenian people. However, the traces of dwelling in the Maszycka cave and sites dated to the Dryas I stadial prove that the territory of Poland was penetrated by this cultural group from the very beginning of the period of Magdalenian settlement in Central Europe.

The areas of Poland covered by Magdalenian settlement are bordered to the southeast and to the east by regions settled by communities belonging to the other contemporary taxonomical unit – the Epigravettian. Raw materials found in Magdalenian contexts in Poland obtained from regions beyond the eastern extension of this culture (Volhynian flint) and possibly from the territory of Slovakia (radiolarite?) suggest that contacts between communities of the two cultures cannot be ruled out. However, it appears that there are no lithic typological arguments which might confirm this hypothesis. It is possible that even if such contacts existed, they were not very intensive and that both cultures had already established their respective configuration, so that any such relationship had no impact on the character of lithic inventories.

The Magdalenian settlement areas of Poland constitute the borderland of this cultural complex and, at the same time form an integral part of its south-eastern European province. All the basic features of material culture as well as of settlement strategy correspond directly to models known from other, more »classic« regions of Magdalenian settlement. Magdalenian finds from the territory of Poland thus show in an exceptional way the cultural homogeneity and uniformity of the Magdalenian technocomplex.

References

Allain et al. 1985: J. Allain / R. Desbrosse / J. K. Kozłowski / A. Rigaud / M. Jeannet / A. Leroi-Gourhan, Le Magdalénien à navettes. Gallia Préhistoire 28, 37-124.

Bednarz 1998: M. Bednarz, Polskie surowce krzemienne w materiałach magdaleńskich z Morawskiego Krasu. Światowit 41 B, 307-322.

Bosselin / Djindjan 1988: B. Bosselin / F. Djindjan, Un essai de structuration du Magdalénien français à partir de l'outillage lithique. Bulletin de la Société Préhistorique Française 85, 304-331.

Cyrek 1986a: K. Cyrek, Magdaleńskie obozowiska w Górach Świętokrzyskich (Mosty, stanowisko 13). Acta Archaeologica Carpathica 25, 11-55.

1986b: K. Cyrek, Die Technologie des Magdalenischen Stein-Komplexes aus der Gudenushöhle. Mitteilungen der österreichischen Arbeitsgemeinschaft für Ur- und Frühgeschichte 36, 7-24.

1999: K. Cyrek, Menschliche Penetration der Höhlen im mittleren Teil der Krakowska-Częstochowska Hochebene zwischen 18. und dem 11. Jahrtausend (von Interstadial Lascaux bis zum Interstadial Allerød). Folia Quaternaria 70, 269-288.

Czopek 1999: S. Czopek, Pradzieje Polski południowo-wschodniej (Rzeszów 1999).

Fiedorczuk / Schild 2000: J. Fiedorczuk / R. Schild, Wilczyce – A new late Magdalenian site in Poland. In: B. Bratlund / B. Eriksen (eds.), Recent studies in the Final Palaeolithic of the European plain. Proceedings of a U.I.S.P.P. Symposium, Stockholm 1999. Jutland Archaeological Society Publications 39 (Århus 2002) 91-100.

Furmanek / Rapiński 2003: M. Furmanek / A. Rapiński, Wstępne wyniki badań ratowniczych górnopaleolitycznego stanowiska w Sowinie pow. nyski. Śląskie Spotkania Archeologiczne 13, 11.

Ginter et al. 2002: B. Ginter / M. Połtowicz / M. Pawlikowski / S.

Skiba / J. Trąbska / A. Wacnik / M. Winiarska-Kabacińska / P. Wojtal, Dzierżysław 35 – stanowisko magdaleńskie na przedpolu Bramy Morawskiej. In: J. Gancarski (ed.), Starsza i środkowa epoka kamienia w Karpatach polskich (Krosno 2002) 111-145.

2005: B. Ginter / M. Połtowicz / M. Pawlikowski / S. Skiba / J. Trąbska / A. Wacnik / M. Winiarska-Kabacińska / P. Wojtal, Dzierżysław 35 – ein neuer Fundplatz des Magdalénien in Oberschlesien. Archäologisches Korrespondenzblatt 35, 431-446.

Höck 2000: Ch. Höck, Das Magdalénien der Kniegrotte. Weimarer Monographien zur Ur- und Frühgeschichte 35 (Stuttgart 2000).

Jastrzębski / Libera 1988: S. Jastrzębski / J. Libera, Stanowisko późnomagdaleńskie w Klementowicach – Kolonii w świetle badań 1981-1982. Sprawozdania Archeologiczne 39, 9-52.

Kowalski et al. 1965: K. Kowalski / J. K. Kozłowski / M. Krysowska / A. Wiktor, Badania osadów schroniska w Puchaczej Skale w prądniku Czajowskim, pow. Olkusz. Folia Quaternaria 20.

Kozłowski 1960: J. K. Kozłowski, Pradzieje powiatu krakowskiego (Kraków 1960).

1964: J. K. Kozłowski, Paleolit na Górnym Śląsku (Wrocław 1964).

1987: J. K. Kozłowski, Le Magdalénien en Pologne. In: J. Ph. Rigaud (ed.), Le Magdalénien en Europe. E.R.A.U.L. 38 (Liège 1987) 31-49.

Kozłowski / Kozłowski 1977: J. K. Kozłowski / S. K. Kozłowski, Epoka kamienia na ziemiach polskich (Warszawa 1977).

Kozłowski / Pettitt 2001: J. K. Kozłowski / P. B. Pettitt, Absolute dating of the Polish Magdalenien. Fontes Archaeologici Posnaniensis 39, 31-35.

Kozłowski et al. 1995: S. K. Kozłowski / E. Sachse-Kozłowska / A. Marshack / T. Madeyska / H. Kierdorf / A. Lasota-Moskalewska / G. Jakubowski / M. Winiarska-Kabacińska / Z. Kapica / A. Wierciński, Maszycka Cave. A Magdalenian site in southern Poland. Jahrbuch des RGZM 40, 1993 (1995) 115-252

Kozłowski 1977: S. K. Kozłowski, Harpun ze stanowiska Przemyśl II. Acta Archaeologica Carpatica 17, 139-143.

Krawczyk / Płonka / Wiśniewski 2004: M. Krawczyk / T. Płonka / A. Wiśniewski, Nowe stanowisko magdaleńskie w Broniszowi-

cach st. 2 na Górnym Śląsku. Śląskie Sprawozdania Archeologiczne 46, 235-240.

Łanczont et al. 2002: M. Łanczont / T. Madeyska / A. Muzyczuk / P. Valde-Nowak, Hłomcza – stanowisko kultury magdaleńskiej w Karpatach polskich. In: J. Gancarski (ed.), Starsza i środkowa epoka kamienia w karpatach polskich (Krosno 2002) 147-187.

Połtowicz 2000: M. Połtowicz, Sprawozdanie z I sezonu badań ratowniczych na stanowisku Dzierżysław 35, gmina Kietrz. Badania archeologiczne na Górnym Śląsku i ziemiach pogranicznych w 1997, 20-29

2005: M. Połtowicz, Wykorzystanie i dystrybucja surowców kamiennych w paleolicie Polski południowo – wschodniej. In: M. Kuraś (ed.), Archeologia Kotliny Sandomierskiej, Rocznik Muzeum Regionalnego w Stalowej Woli 4, 2006, 187-197.

2006: M. Połtowicz, The eastern borders of the Magdalenian culture range. Analecta Archaeologica Ressoviensia 1, 11-28.

2007: M. Połtowicz, The Magdalenian period in Poland and neighbouring areas. Archaeologia Baltica 7, 21-27.

Sawicki 1960: L. Sawicki, Stanowisko otwarte madleńskie Antoniów Mały. Z badań czwartorzędu w Polsce 9, 171-208.

Schild R. 1965, Nowy przemysł cyklu madleńskiego w Polsce. Archeologia Polski 10, 115-150.

Sobczyk 1993: K. Sobczyk, The Late Palaeolithic Flint Workshops at Brzoskwinia-Krzemionki near Kraków. Prace Archeologiczne 55 (Kraków 1993).

Valde-Nowak 1998: P. Valde-Nowak, Z badań najstarszego osadnictwa w Karpatach Polskich. In: J. Gancarski (ed.), Dzieje Podkarpacia 2 (Krosno 1998) 39-54.

Valde-Nowak / Muzyczuk 2000: P. Valde-Nowak / A. Muzyczuk, Magdalenien Settlement at Hłomcza (Polisch Carpathians). Acta Archaeologica Carpathica 35, 1999-2000 (2000) 5-32.

Valoch 1988: K. Valoch, Die Erforschung der Kůlna-Höhle1961-1976. Anthropos 24 (Brno 1988).

Valoch / Neruda 2005: K. Valoch / P. Neruda, K chronologii moravského magdalénienu. Archeologické rozhledy 57, 459-476.

Vencl 1991: S. Vencl, Bemerkungen zum Magdalénien in Böhmen. Anthropologie 29, 1991, 85-93.

Abstract

Magdalenian settlement in Poland in the light of recent research

The paper considers the timing and distribution of Magdalenian occupation in Poland. Evidence from Maszycka cave and other sites proves that the territory of Poland was penetrated by the Magdalenian from the very beginning of the period of settlement of Central Europe by this cultural group. Southeast and east of areas with Magdalenian occupation there is evidence for Epigravettian settlement. Raw material distribution studies show that there may have been some contact between groups within these two major taxonomical units, although the degree of interaction and cultural influence may have been fairly minimal. This underlines the remarkable cultural homogeneity and uniformity of the Magdalenian technocomplex through time.

Key-words

Magdalenian, Epigravettian, lithic raw material, technocomplex

Acknowledgement

I would like to thank Jadwiga Szczupak for the English translation of the text.

JACEK KABACIŃSKI · IWONA SOBKOWIAK-TABAKA

BIG GAME VERSUS SMALL GAME HUNTING – SUBSISTENCE STRATEGIES OF THE HAMBURGIAN CULTURE

The emergence of the society of the Hamburgian culture in the northern part of the European Lowlands at the beginning of the Late Glacial climatic warming around 12 700 cal BC (Greenland-Interstadial 1e – Meiendorf/Bølling-Interstadial: Björck et al. 1998) instigated a permanent process of recolonisation of this area. At its maximum range it covered the area of the northern Netherlands, northern Germany, southern Denmark and western Poland. Of particular importance is the increment of data during the last few years, testifying to the permanent, relatively compact Hamburgian occupation in Denmark (Jels, Slotseng, Sølbjerg, Køge Bugt: Holm 1996; 2003; Petersen 2006) and central-western Poland (Mirkowice, Łęgoń, Krągola, Myszęcin: Chłodnicki / Kabaciński 1997; Burdukiewicz 1999; Kabaciński et al. 1999; 2002; Kabaciński / Kobusiewicz 2007). The end of the Hamburgian occupation of the European Lowlands is related to the so called Havelte phase and occurred most probably about 12 000 years ago, as indicated by a date obtained from Ahrenshöft (AAR-2784:12 030 ± 60 BP; Clausen 1997).

So far more than 130 Hamburgian sites are recognised and, if we include assemblages with single elements typologically related to the Hamburgian culture including surface finds, we obtain a number of more than 150 sites (Burdukiewicz 1987; Eriksen 1999; Terberger / Lübke 2004; Bobrowski / Sobkowiak-Tabaka 2006). Only six sites have produced archaeozoological data enabling the reconstruction of subsistence strategies of the society of the Hamburgian culture (**Fig. 1**).

The aim of our paper is to show that the Hamburgian subsistence strategy was more complex than is usually presented. In order to achieve it we:

1) Review the main economic strategies.

2) Present and partially verify archaeozoological data on which they are based.

3) Introduce premises from the domain of settlement palaeogeography and present new archaeozoological data indicating the necessity of at least partial modification of current economic hypotheses.

Economic strategies of the Hamburgian hunter-gatherers

It is commonly accepted that Hamburgian economic strategy was based on seasonal migrations of people following migrating reindeer, which were the fundamental food source for the Hamburgian societies (most often termed »reindeer hunters«). All sites situated in the Ahrensburg Tunnel Valley have been interpreted as seasonal camps of reindeer hunters and a number of hypotheses have been suggested which attempt to provide models for both Hamburgian and Ahrensburgian settlement. However, despite many years of study, authors have not been able to agree on the season of the year when the hunters exploited the migrating herds of reindeer. D. A. Sturdy (1975) interpreted remains of reindeer antlers from the sites of the Ahrensburg Valley as derived from winter camps and the sites themselves were supposed to represent »the seasonal, autumn-winter facies« of the Magdalenian (Sturdy 1975).

K. Bokelmann (1979) also interprets the sites in the area of the Ahrensburg Valley as winter camps. According to him, the decisive role in food procurement was played by autumn massacres of reindeer cros-

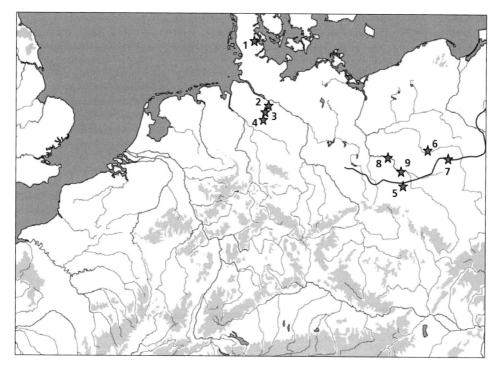

Fig. 1 Hamburgian sites with archaeozoological data: – 1 Slotseng (Denmark), – 2 Poggenwisch (Germany), – 3 Stellmoor (Germany), – 4 Meiendorf (Germany), – 5 Olbrachcice (Poland), – 6 Mirkowicze (Poland). Hamburgian sites in Poland located in the young moraine landscape: – 6 Mirkowicze, – 7 Kragola, – 8 Myszęcin, – 9 Liny.

sing the Elbe towards the north, and by spring massacres to the west of this river, a model which is supported by a large number of sites in this area. The summer pastures could have been situated in the Netherlands and in winter the hunters consumed food from supplies hoarded earlier (Bokelmann 1979).

A. Rust and G. Tromnau interpreted the Hamburgian sites in northern Germany in a completely different way, believing them to be the remains of summer camps. In this model the lowland area of northern Germany was the ultimate destination of spring migrations to summer pastures, whereas in winter the reindeer stayed in the south or south-west (Rust 1943; Tromnau 1976).

These radically different interpretations of the season when the Hamburgian groups stayed in the area of the Ahrensburg Valley result from the difficulties in obtaining unequivocal data on the seasonality of occupation on the basis of the analysed animal remains. The analysis of the faunal material from Stellmoor alone shows that reindeer were present there throughout the entire year (Bratlund 1996a). They were hunted both in autumn and spring, whereas in summer horses and birds were killed. According to B. Bratlund (1996a), swans, geese and probably horses were hunted in late summer, before a group moved to strategic camps in autumn (Meiendorf, Stellmoor AbH, Poggenwisch), where mostly reindeer were hunted. In fact, the analyses of B. Bratlund suggest that on the available data we can describe neither the directions nor the extent of reindeer migrations on the European Lowlands (Bratlund 1996a).

Furthermore, the area of England and the northern part of the shelf linking the British Isles with the mainland are claimed to have been the destination of migration by reindeer and groups of people during the spring-summer season. In winter people were supposed to have moved south to areas today underwater and to Belgium, the Netherlands and parts of northern Germany (Campbell 1977). However, until now there are no convincing arguments to support this hypothesis[1].

The Hamburgian sites from Poland and eastern Denmark essentially challenge the theory proposing seasonal migrations of people to the Lowland, following the seasonally migrating herds of reindeer, and indicate rather that Hamburgian groups spent the whole year on the European Lowlands. The migrations of the Hamburgian societies, if they did exist, took place between the regions of open tundra in the east and park-

or woodland tundra in the west (Campbell 1977; Kozłowski 2004). In fact, sites from Poland have so far never been taken into account when hypotheses on the economic strategies of Hamburgian groups have been formulated.

Archaeozoological data

Up to the beginning of the 1990s the only sites to provide archaeozoological data, the basis for the reconstruction of the subsistence strategies of the societies of the Hamburgian culture, were three sites in the Ahrensburg Tunnel Valley located at the Meiendorf pond, at Stellmoor and at Poggenwisch. These data are today complemented by much more modest assemblages from Olbrachcice, Slotseng and Mirkowice.

Meiendorf

The faunal remains from the site at Meiendorf (Rust 1937) comprised bones of several mammal and bird species (Krause 1937; Krause / Kollau 1943). A number of these were subsequently lost during the Second World War, the remaining finds being re-examined by B. Bratlund (1996a). The mammal faunal collection comprised material representing a minimum of 71 reindeer (*Rangifer tarandus*) – 1 931 surviving specimens after Bratlund (1996a) – and also far fewer remains of horse (*Equus* sp.), hare (*Lepus* sp.), red fox (*Vulpes* sp.), wolverine (*Gulo gulo*), also possibly badger (*Meles meles*) after Bratlund (1996a) and Russian desman (*Desmana moschata*). The bird species include grouse (*Lagopus lagopus*), swan (*Cygnus* sp.), goose (*Branta leucopsis* and *Anser* sp.), duck/merganser (Anatidae), spotted crake (*Porzana porzana*), common crane (*Grus grus*) and gull (*Larus marinus* or *Larus hyperboreus*).

Traces of anthropogenic modification on the above mentioned bones have been described by Bratlund (1994; 1996a). A high proportion of the larger bird bones was in the form of modified artefacts (bone tubes), the majority identified as whooper swan (Bratlund 1996a). Most identified birds species usually live near water and not all of them must have been hunted by the Hamburgian settlers. In another explanation, they (and the desman) could simply have been elements of the background fauna (Bratlund 1994).

Stellmoor

The deposits recorded from the kettle hole at the neighbouring site at Stellmoor (Krause / Kollau 1943; Bratlund 1996a), located only 800 m to the north-east of the Meiendorf site, produced bones of at least 41 reindeer (1 904 surviving specimens: Bratlund 1996a) and small numbers of finds identified as ground squirrel (*Citellus rufescens / Spermophilus superciliosus*) and hare (*Lepus* sp.), together with the bird species swan (*Cygnus* sp.), goose (*Anser* sp.), duck (Anatidae), grouse (*Lagopus lagopus*) and dunlin (*Calidris alpina*). An underlying layer of gyttja yielded bones of Norway lemming (*Lemmus lemmus*). A number of disturbances in the deposition of layers were recorded at the site and a degree of admixture of the Hamburgian fauna with specimens from the far larger overlying Ahrensburgian assemblage cannot be totally ruled out (Bratlund 1996a).

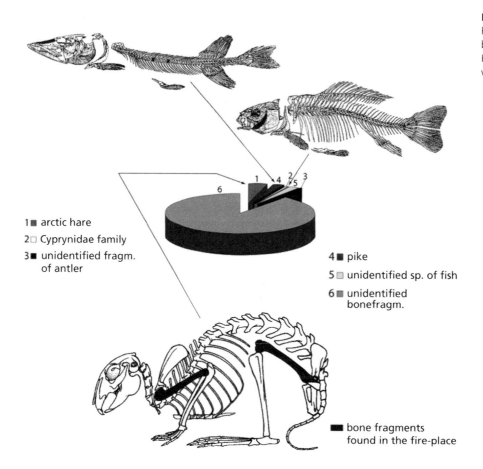

Fig. 2 Mirkowice, site 33. Frequency of animal and fish bones from the hearth (after Kabaciński et al. 1999; Makowiecki 2003).

1 ▪ arctic hare
2 □ Cyprynidae family
3 ▪ unidentified fragm. of antler

4 ▪ pike
5 ▫ unidentified sp. of fish
6 ▪ unidentified bonefragm.

▪ bone fragments found in the fire-place

Poggenwisch

The deposits at the site of Poggenwisch, situated about a kilometre to the north-east of Meiendorf, yielded remains of at least 15 reindeer and also bones of polecat (*Mustela putorius*), ground squirrel (*Citellus major/rufescens*), swan (*Cygnus olor?*), grouse (*Lagopus lagopus?*) and pike (*Esox lucius*) (Herre / Requate 1958; Bratlund 1996a).

It must be emphasised that the research of B. Bratlund (1996a) shows that extreme caution is necessary in the interpretation of the finds from Meiendorf and Stellmoor. At the site at Stellmoor, Hamburgian material could have been mixed with a number of Ahrensburgian elements, due to the impossibility of conclusive separation of the two occupation layers present at the site. This is clearly demonstrated by the fact that one of the dated antlers documented as related to the Hamburgian culture, gave a result of Younger Dryas (and hence Ahrensburgian) age (Fisher / Tauber 1987). Moreover, the loss for both sites of many of the bones of the rarely occurring species during World War 2 means that the faunal lists of supposedly represented taxa cannot be controlled or treated as conclusive. What is more, revision of the palynological analysis conducted at type localities, including Meiendorf (De Klerk 2004) shows that phases and oscillations distinguished on the basis of analysis of pollen profiles have no chronostratigraphic importance and revealed a number of inaccuracies during previous analyses of the above mentioned sites (De Klerk 2004).

Slotseng

The Danish site of Slotseng is situated about 5 km to the south-east of the Jels site and was excavated in 1985-1991 and 1993. In 2000 the kettle hole deposit was recorded to a depth of about 5 m. Due to favourable conditions, organic remains were preserved, namely pollen, twigs, insects, together with bones of reindeer and worked antler. In 2001 a thoracic vertebra of a reindeer was recovered with a Havelte point driven into it. The site also yielded single bones of birds and fish (Holm 2003).

Olbrachcice

In the mid-1970s, at the site at Olbrachcice, a number of burnt flint artefacts and other traces of fire, together with a large number of tiny burnt bones, were recorded at the base of feature no. 1 in the flint concentration of the Hamburgian culture (Burdukiewicz 1975; 1976). Cursory examination of the remains carried out by T. Czyżewska revealed that they belonged to mammals and that some of the bones, which could be analysed macroscopically, can be identified with high probability as the remains of reindeer (Burdukiewicz 1976). As neither the results of the research overall, nor the detailed analysis of the discussed bones have been published, results of this initial analysis cannot be treated as final.

Mirkowice

In the mid-1990s a hearth was registered within concentration number 1 at the site 33 at Mirkowice. It was built mostly of stones contained stone tools (a grinding stone, two hammer stones and a couple of fragments of plaques). The centre of the hearth and its immediate surroundings produced three flint perforators and 147 very tiny, burnt animal bones. These included six bones of arctic hare (*Lepus* sp.), fish bones identified as four bones of pike (*Esox lucius*) and a fragment belonging to a fish of the Cyprinidae family. An unidentified fragment of antler, one vertebra and two bones of unidentified species of fish were also found. 132 bone fragments cannot be determined taxonomically (**Fig. 2**) (Kabaciński et al. 1999; Makowiecki 2003).

A thick detritus gyttja deposit assigned to the first oscillation of the Late Glacial Interstadial (GI-1e/ Meiendorf-Bølling) produced a few thousand bones of fishes, among them pike, river perch (*Perca fluviatilis*), fish of the Cyprinidae and Salmonidae families (the latter most probably brown trout (*Salmo trutta*), birds, for example grouse (*Lagopus lagopus*) and common crane (*Grus grus*), small mammals, reptiles and amphibians (Kabaciński et al. 1999; Makowiecki 2003)[2]. Although the bones from the detritus gyttja are not directly connected with the Mirkowice settlement, they enrich the otherwise narrow database for the local Late Glacial fauna.

Pike have high tolerance regarding the water temperature during spawning-time and are widespread. They were therefore a significant element of the diet of prehistoric societies (Makowiecki 2003). Almost all of the above mentioned Mirkowice species (including ones recorded in the gyttja) are freshwater fish, which are the easiest to catch during the spawning period in spring, that is to say from April to May (pike, perch), or even to July (fish of the Cyprinidae family). These observations in conjunction with the fish remains from the hearth suggest that the site at Mirkowice was occupied in spring or possibly in early summer.

An AMS radiocarbon date of 12 290 ± 70 BP (GrA-17715) obtained on burnt bone from the hearth is one of a few direct dates related to the Hamburgian culture (Kabaciński / Schild 2005).

This review of the bone material recorded at sites of the Hamburgian culture reveals a clear dichotomy. On the one hand, there are sites with a massive dominance of reindeer (the attribution of which to the Hamburgian culture is however by no means always certain, e.g. Stellmoor). On the other hand, at the site of Mirkowice the fauna is dominated by small species, primarily fish.

Paleoecological framework of the Hamburgian occupation

According to B. Bratlund, Hamburgian societies hunted mainly large mammals, specifically horse and reindeer, and very rarely exploited birds. For this reason, they would not have been able to survive in the young moraine zone where this type of mammal (particularly horse) did not occur (Bratlund 1994; 1996b). However, in the light of the data presented here, it seems that not only did the Hamburgian settlers quickly cross the above mentioned environmental barrier, but they could adapt perfectly to the new conditions and find alternative sources of food, leaving behind early traces of occupation. This is confirmed not only by the Hamburgian settlement at Slotseng, but also by discoveries made over the last few years in Poland. The site at Mirkowice is located in the young moraine zone about 80 km to the north of the moraines of the Leszno-Brandenburg phase (Kabaciński et al. 1999; 2002). The recently excavated site at Krągola is situated in the area where the Warta ravine traverses moraines of the Poznań phase of the Vistulian (Kabaciński / Kobusiewicz 2007). A site at Myszęcin, discovered in 2005 (**Fig. 1**), is located about 40 km to the north-west of the site of Liny (Kobusiewicz 1973), in the moraine zone of the Poznań phase of the late glaciation. Up to now, excavations by J. Kabaciński have produced nine rich flint concentrations over an area of about 2 ha, with research still in progress (Kabaciński / Kobusiewicz 2008). Taking into consideration finds from Mecklenburg-Vorpommern, which suggest the possibility of Hamburgian occupation also in this region (Terberger / Lübke 2004), the hypothesis put forth by B. Bratlund should be regarded as outdated.

In any consideration of the economic strategies of Late Glacial societies, including the Hamburgian, we have to remember one further aspect, namely the use of plant food by hunter-gatherers. Outside the northern lowland zone, gathering has been confirmed among, for example, Magdalenian communities at coastal sites in Spain. Predominantly fruits were collected, mostly stone-pine nuts (Kozłowski 2004). In Santa Maira cave in Spain, the late Magdalenian and Final Palaeolithic layers yielded among other plant remains, a large number of acorns, charred fruit of rowan (*Sorbus*) and blackthorn (*Prunus spinosa*) and plants of the legume family e.g. *Lens nigricans* and everlasting pea (*Lathyrus latifolia*) (Aura et al. 2005). Acorns are a perfect source of carbohydrates, fat and fibres. Their procurement does not require any particular skills and their processing and storage are simple. Ethnographic analogies confirm that fresh fruit of rowan was consumed and also dried. The same applies to the plants of the legume family, the fruit of which was mostly dried (Aura et al. 2005).

Further possibilities have also opened up with increased awareness of a new source of information, namely fragments of charred parenchymatous tissue originating from the vegetative parts of plants. With this type of analysis, a list of species used in the diet of hunter-gatherers, including the area of the European Lowlands, is in the process of completion (Kubiak-Martens 2005). At the site of Całowanie, located in the central part of the Polish Lowland, the late Palaeolithic layer yielded charred seeds of Russian thistle (*Salsola kali*), a seed of bogbean (*Menynanthes trifoliata*) and charred achenes of plants of the sedge family, including beaked sedge (*Carex rostrata*) and *Carex extensae*. *Salsola kali* seeds are very rich in protein (44.9 g per 100 g) and may have been collected for food. The seeds of the bogbean were usually not treated as a food source, but their rootstocks are known to have been consumed in exceptional conditions by the people from the sub-arctic zone. The raw sweet stem bases or bulbs of the sedge were eaten by indigenous peoples of Canada. The bulbs and fleshy leaves bases were gathered in spring and summer (Kubiak-Martens 1996). The early Mesolithic sites at Całowanie, Łajty and Tłokowo produced fragments of rootstocks of knotweed (*Polygonum*), which were eagerly consumed, raw and scorched in the fire, by the peoples of northern Scandinavia, north-eastern Siberia, Greenland and Alaska, and of cattail (*Typha* sp.), the rootstock and sprouts of which were valued especially due to their large amounts of contained starch (Kubiak-Martens 2005). Another possible food resource is indicated at Pincevent in the Paris Basin and Champréveyres in Switzerland, where egg shells were registered, including duck eggs (Kozłowski 2004).

Conclusions

In the light of the data presented above, the picture of subsistence strategies of Hamburgian societies seems much more complex than it has appeared until recently. Reindeer hunting remains beyond doubt a significant element of the economy, as is demonstrated by, among other factors, the finds from Meiendorf, Poggenwisch and Stellmoor. On the other hand, the faunal remains from Mirkowice give a completely different picture; the subsistence of the Hamburgian people occupying the site was based mostly on fishing and the hunting of smaller animals. The collected data from Germany, Denmark and Poland could represent elements of the same overall strategy, in which diversification resulted, for example, from the seasonality of different economic activities. However, there is no convincing data to confirm this specifically although we can now clearly discuss different economic strategies used by different Hamburgian groups.

New data on the Hamburgian settlement from the area of Poland show unambiguously that both the old and young moraine landscapes were intensively used. It therefore seems that the economic strategies adopted by the Hamburgian societies were exceptionally flexible, enabling the groups of hunters to function in different (although not as radically different as sometimes described) ecosystems.

In the light of the presented data it should be acknowledged that while the term »reindeer hunters« is still correct in conjunction with the Hamburgian, it only describes local or seasonal preferences, and should not be implied to define the entire economic strategy adopted by Hamburgian societies.

Notes

1   Investigations of the bottom of the North Sea within the North Sea Project have not so far brought the anticipated results which would prove the coexistence in the area (today submerged) of people and reindeer or specific data on reindeer hunting (Glimmerveen / Mol / van der Plicht 2006).

2   A detailed study of faunal remains from the gyttja has been carried out by B. Bratlund and will be published elsewhere.

References

Aura et al. 2005: J. E. Aura / Y. Carrión / E. Estrelles / G. P. Jordá, Plant economy of hunther-gatherer groups at the end of the last Ice Age: plant macroremains from the cave Sant Maira (Alacant, Spain) c.a. 12 000-9 000 B.P. Vegetation History and Archaeobotany 14, 542-550.

Björck et al. 1998: S. Björck / M. J. C. Walker / L. C. Cwynar / S. Johnsen / K.-L. Knudsen / J. J. Lowe / B. Wohlfarth / INTI-

MATE Members, An event stratigraphy for the Last Termination I in the North Atlantic region based on the Greenland ice-core record; a proposal by the INTIMATE group. Journal of Quaternary Science 13/4, 283-292.

Bobrowski / Sobkowiak-Tabaka 2006: P. Bobrowski / I. Sobkowiak-Tabaka, How far to the East did the Hamburgian reach? Archaeologia Baltica 7, 11-20.

Bokelmann 1979: K. Bokelmann, Rentierjäger am Gletscherrand in Schleswig-Holstein? Offa 36, 12-22.

Bratlund 1994: B. Bratlund, A survey of the Subsistence and Settlement Pattern of the Hamburgian Culture in Schleswig-Holstein. Jahrbuch des RGZM 41, 59-93.

1996a: B. Bratlund, Hunting Strategies in the Late Glacial of Northern Europe. A Survey of the Faunal Evidence. Journal of World Prehistory 10, 1-48.

1996b: B. Bratlund, Archaeozoological Comments on Final Palaeolithic Frontiers in South Scandinavia. In: L. Larsson (ed.), The Earliest Settlement of Scandinavia and its relationship with neighbouring areas. Acta Archaeologica Lundensia Series in 8°, 24 (Stockholm 1996) 23-33.

Burdukiewicz 1975: J. M. Burdukiewicz, Z badań sondażowych stanowisk paleolitycznych i mezolitycznych w dolinie Kopanicy (rejon Olbrachcic i Sieldlnicy, pow. wschowski). Śląskie Sprawozdania Archeologiczne 27, 5-12.

1976: J. M. Burdukiewicz, Sprawozdanie z badań wykopaliskowych stanowiska kultury hamburskiej w Olbrachcicach koło Wschowy. Śląskie Sprawozdania Archeologiczne 18, 5-8.

1987: J. M. Burdukiewicz, Późnoplejstoceńskie zespoły z jednozadziorcami w Europie Zachodniej (Wrocław 1987).

1999: J. M. Burdukiewicz, Nowe ślady osadnictwa schyłkowopaleolitycznego w Łęgoniu koło Wschowy. Śląskie Sprawozdania Archeologiczne 41, 411-414.

Campbell 1977: J. B. Campbell, The Upper Palaeolithic of Britain. A Study of Man and Nature in the Late Ice Age (Oxford 1977).

Chłodnicki / Kabaciński 1997: M. Chłodnicki / J. Kabaciński, Mirkowice. Another Settlement of the Hamburgian Culture at the Polish Plain. Przegląd Archeologiczny 45, 5-23.

Clausen 1998: I. Clausen, Neue Untersuchungen an späteiszeitlichen Fundplätzen der Hamburger Kultur bei Ahrenshöft, Kr. Nordfriesland (ein Vorbericht). Archäologische Nachrichten aus Schleswig-Holstein 8, 1997 (Schleswig 1998) 8-49.

De Klerk 2004: P. de Klerk, Changes in vegetation and environment at the Lateglacial – Holocene transition in Vorpommern (Northeastern Germany). In: T. Terberger / B. V. Eriksen (eds.), Hunters in a changing world. Environment and Archaeology of the Pleistocene-Holocene Transition (ca. 11 000-9 000 B.C.) in Northern Central Europe. Workshop of the U.I.S.P.P.-Commission XXXII at Greifswald 2002. Internationale Archäologie, Arbeitsgemeinschaft, Symposium, Tagung, Kongress 5 (Rahden / Westfalen 2004) 27-42.

Eriksen 1999: B. V. Eriksen, Late Palaeolithic settlement in Denmark – how do we read the record? Folia Quaternaria 70, 157-173.

Fischer / Tauber 1987: A. Fischer / H. Tauber, New C-14 Datings of Late Palaeolithic cultures from northwestern Europe. Journal of Danish Archaeology, 5, 1986 (1987) 7-13.

Glimmerveen / Mol / van der Plicht 2006: J. Glimmerveen / D. Mol / J. van der Plicht, The Pleistocene reindeer of the North Sea – initial palaeontological data and archaeological remarks. Quaternary International 142-143, 242-246.

Herre / Requate 1958: W. Herre / H. Requate, Die Tierreste der paläolithischen Siedlungen Poggenwisch, Hasewisch, Borneck und Hopfenbach bei Ahrensburg. A. Rust (ed.), Die jungpaläolithischen Zeltanlagen von Ahrensburg (Neumünster 1943) 23-27.

Holm 1996: J. Holm, The Earliest Settlement of Denmark. In: L. Larson (ed.), The Earliest Settlement of Scandinavia and its Relationship with neighbouring areas, Acta Archaeologica Lundensia Series in 8°, 24 (Stockholm 1996) 43-59.

2003: J. Holm, Rentierjäger im Norden. Archäologie in Deutschland 3, 54-56.

Kabaciński et al. 1999: J. Kabaciński / B. Bratlund / L. Kubiak / D. Makowiecki / R. Schild / K. Tobolski, The Hamburgian Settlement at Mirkowice. Recent Results and Research Perspective. Folia Quaternaria 70, 211-238.

Kabaciński / Kobusiewicz 2007: J. Kabaciński / M. Kobusiewicz, Settlement of the Hamburgian culture at Krągola, Stare Miasto parish. In. M. Kobusiewicz / J. Kabaciński (eds.), Studies in the Final Palaeolithic Settlement of the Great European Plain (Poznań 2007) 21-51.

2008: J. Kabaciński / M. Kobusiewicz, New Hamburgian occupations in the Central-Western Poland. In: Z. Sulgostowska / A. J. Tomaszewski (eds.), Man – Millennia – Environment: Studies in honour of Romuald Schild (Warsaw 2007) 171-184.

Kabaciński / Schild 2005: J. Kabaciński / R. Schild, The Hamburgian Site at Mirkowice: A Chronological Framework. Fontes Archaeologici Posnanienses 41, 15-18.

Kabaciński et al. 2002: J. Kabaciński / R. Schild / B. Bratlund / L. Kubiak-Martens / K. Tobolski / K. van der Borg / A. Pazdur, The Late Glacial sequence at the Hamburgian site at Mirkowice: stratigraphy and geochronology. In: B. V. Eriksen / B. Bratlund (eds.), Recent studies in the Final Palaeolithic of the European plain. Proceedings of a U.I.S.P.P. Symposium, Stockholm 1999. Jutland Archaeological Society Publications 39 (Århus 2002) 109-116.

Kobusiewicz 1973: M. Kobusiewicz, Problems Concerning Hamburgian Culture in Central Europe. Przegląd Archeologiczny 21, 65-92.

Kozłowski 2004: J. K. Kozłowski, Świat przed »rewolucją« neolityczną (Kraków 2004).

Krause 1937: W. Krause, Die eiszeitlichen Knochenfunde von Meiendorf. In: A. Rust (ed.), Das altsteinzeitliche Rentierjägerlager Meiendorf (Neumünster 1937) 48-63.

Krause / Kollau 1943: W. Krause / W. Kollau, Die steinzeitlichen

Wirbeltierfaunen von Stellmoor in Holstein. In: A. Rust, Die alt- und mittelsteinzeitlichen Funde von Stellmoor (Neumünster 1943) 49-59.

Kubiak-Martens 1996: L. Kubiak-Martens, Evidence for possible use of plant foods in Palaeolithic and Mesolithic diet from the site of Całowanie in the central part of the Polish Plain. Vegetation History and Archaeobotany 5, 33-38.

2005: L. Kubiak-Martens, Rozpoznawanie organów spichrzowych roślin jako źródła pożywienia. In: M. Lityńska-Zając / K. Wasylikowa (eds.), Przewodnik po badaniach archeobotanicznych (Poznań 2005) 301-320.

Makowiewcki 2003: D. Makowiewcki, Historia ryb i rybołówstwa w holocenie na Niżu Polskim w świetle badań archeoichtiologicznych (Poznań 2003).

Petersen 2006: P. V. Petersen, White Flint and Hilltops – Late Palaeolithic Finds in Southern Denmark. In: K. M. Hansen / K. B. Pedersen (eds.), Across the western Baltic. Proceedings from an archaeological conference in Vordingborg. Sydsjællands Museums Publikationer I (Vordingborg 2006) 57-74.

Rust 1937: A. Rust, Das altsteinzeitliche Rentierjägerlager Meiendorf (Neumünster 1937).

1943: A. Rust, Die alt- und mittelsteinzeitlichen Funde von Stellmoor (Neumünster 1943).

Sturdy 1975: D. A. Sturdy, Some reindeer economies in prehistoric Europe. In: E. S. Higgs (ed.), Paleoeconomy (Cambridge 1975) 55-95.

Terberger / Lübke 2004: T. Terberger / H. Lübke, Hamburger Kultur in Mecklenburg-Vorpommern? Bodendenkmalpflege in Mekklenburg-Vorpommern, Jahrbuch 52, 15-34.

Tromnau 1976: G. Tromnau, Rentierjäger der Späteiszeit in Norddeutschland (Hildesheim 1976).

Abstract

Big game versus small game hunting – subsistence strategies of the Hamburgian culture

A generally accepted idea concerning the subsistence strategies of Hamburgian communities assumes that they primarily hunted large mammal species – reindeer and horse. In the present paper we discuss the results of latest studies on the Hamburgian economy, which show that another, independent economic strategy was also employed. This was based on hunting small mammals, fishing and fowling. At the same time, the paper falsifies the hypothesis that there was an absence of settlement activity by Hamburgian groups in northern European freshly deglaciated areas, i.e. north of Late Vistulian terminal moraines. New data on above subjects are presented.

Key-words

Late Glacial, Hamburgian Culture, faunal remains, subsistence strategies.

MARC DE BIE · MARIJN VAN GILS · KOEN DEFORCE

HUMAN OCCUPATION IN A LATE GLACIAL LANDSCAPE: THE FEDERMESSERGRUPPEN SITE COMPLEX AT LOMMEL MAATHEIDE (BELGIUM)

The extensive Federmessergruppen site of Lommel Maatheide in northern Belgium has long been known as a rich find spot of final Palaeolithic artefacts (Hamal-Nandrin / Servais / Louis 1935; Verheyleweghen 1956; Vermeersch 1975; Geerts 1984; Creemers / Carolus 1989). Polluting industrial activities on this spot in the first half of the 20th century destroyed the vegetation cover and instigated wind erosion of the sandy soil, caused tens of thousands of artefacts to re-surface. Since the 1930s, thousands of retouched tools have been collected during field walking and by uncontrolled »excavations«. In Schwabedissen's landmark publication on the Federmessergruppen, they served as the type-tool assemblage for the Belgian region (Schwabedissen 1954, 49-50). Unfortunately, the location and context of these collections have never been registered properly.

Fig. 1   Aerial view of the project area in early 2004, when the dump cover was being removed: – **A** Perimeter of the Late Glacial lake that drained into a small river westwards. Today part of this area is still marshland, and some small fens are preserved (the so-called Blokwaters). – **B** Location of the Late Glacial sand ridge bordering the northern side of the lake. Photo: Sibelco n.v.. Drawing: N. Van Gemert.

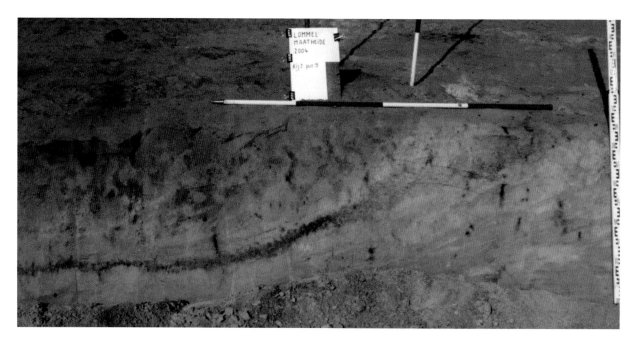

Fig. 2   View of the Usselo soil where it rapidly surfaces. Note the rich presence of charcoal in the top of the soil horizon.

In the 1970s, the area was used as dumping ground in order to stop the erosion and re-deposition of sand. With the removal of this dump cover in 2003, the terrain finally became available for proper geoarchaeological research. Three years of fieldwork have now provided excellent new insights into the location, extension, stratigraphy and preservation of this Federmessergruppen site complex, as well as the geographical and palaeoecological contexts of the settlement (De Bie / Gullentops / Van Gils 2003; De Bie / Van Gils 2005; 2006; Van Gils / De Bie 2005). This paper discusses some of the main results.

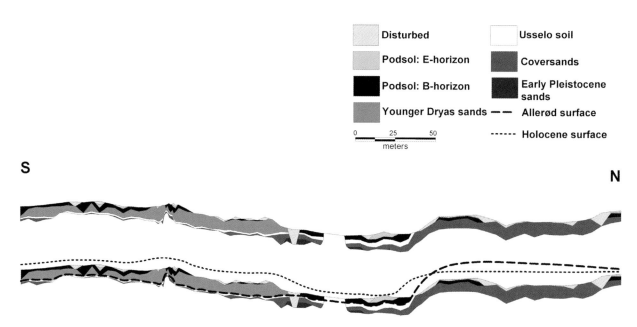

Fig. 3   Stratigraphy of the section through the valley, near the outlet of the Late Glacial lake (above), with reconstruction of the (asymmetrical) Allerød topography and the (symmetrical) Holocene surface (below).

M. De Bie · M. Van Gils · K. Deforce - Human occupation in a Late Glacial landscape

Fig. 4   View of the sampled peat deposit, covered by sands during the Younger Dryas.

A Late Glacial landscape: Geomorphology and Pedology

The site of Lommel Maatheide, formerly also referred to as Lommel Blokwaters, is situated in the sandy Campine region in northern Belgium. Maatheide is the toponym of a vast dry sandy plain with heath vegetation. The Blokwaters are a cluster of water bodies to the south of this heath plain (**Fig. 1A**). These fens are embedded in a larger marshy depression, which is also the source of the small river Rietreienloop, draining to the west, into the Meuse basin.

The general structure of the landscape at Lommel Maatheide still somewhat reflects the Late Glacial situation, when a sand ridge was formed on the northern edge of a Late Glacial fen (**Fig. 1B**). This dune stabilised during the Late Glacial interstadial and an Usselo soil developed. This paleosol could be registered throughout the valley, providing an opportunity to study its various aspects (Palmans 2006). In the depression of the Blokwaters, the Allerød soil continues as a peat layer.

During the subsequent Younger Dryas stadial, when the vegetation largely disappeared again, the ridge partly deflated. This explains the abrupt surfacing of the Usselo soil on the southern edge of the sand ridge (**Fig. 2**), as well as the heavy wind-gloss on most Federmessergruppen artefacts and the lack of small chips in the assemblages found on top of the (former) ridge. To the south, the re-activated Younger Dryas sands covered the Usselo soil and the Late Glacial peat. During the Holocene, new soil formation took place on top of these sands, eventually generating the current podsol.

A section across the valley near the outlet of the fen nicely illustrates the changes of the Late Glacial topography (**Fig. 3**). The stratigraphic profile shows an asymmetric valley during the Allerød, with a relatively steep slope onto the ridge in the north and a very gently rising southern slope. The shape of the northern ridge itself can only be estimated. During the Younger Dryas, aeolian activity changed the topography drastically, eroding the northern ridge and covering the southern slope. Remains of the podsol allow an estimate of the original Holocene surface, showing a more or less symmetric valley nowadays.

First Palaeoecological results: Palynology

To reconstruct the local environmental conditions at the time of the occupation of the site during the Allerød interstadial, several palaeoecological studies are being conducted on the thin peat deposit that occurs to the south of the Final Palaeolithic site. These studies include radiocarbon dating, the analysis of pollen, beetles, bryophytes and other botanical macro remains. At present, only the preliminary results of the palynological analysis are available.

The analysed peat deposit is situated some 100 m from the main occupation of the site and is covered by a ca. 1 m thick sand deposit. At this point, the peat is only 20 cm thick and consists mainly of mosses (**Fig. 4**). The results of the pollen analysis show an evolution of the vegetation considered to be characteristic for the Allerød oscillation in northern Belgium and the southern Netherlands (Munaut 1967; Verbruggen 1979; Hoek 1997; Bos 1998). The arboreal vegetation is dominated by *Betula* in the lower part of the peat deposit and *Pinus* in the upper part. Other trees and shrubs occurring in the pollen diagram are *Juniperus*, *Salix* and *Populus*. The herbaceous vegetation is dominated by Cyperaceae and Poaceae and further characterised by dwarf-shrubs and herbs like *Artemisia*, *Calluna vulgaris*, *Empetrum nigrum* and *Helianthemum*.

The high amounts of both macroscopic remains of mosses and microscopic remains of colonies of *Botyococcus braunii* and *Pediastrum* and spores of *Spirogyra* indicate the presence of a shallow lake.

The strong decrease in arboreal vegetation at the top of the deposit illustrates the climatic deterioration at the end of the Allerød. The evolution towards an open vegetation type caused by a more severe climate is also demonstrated by the increase in wind-blown sand in the peat towards the top of the deposit, finally resulting in a cessation of peat growth.

The general increase of microscopic charcoal fragments towards the upper part of the peat deposit must probably be linked with the increased presence of *Pinus*. Short term fluctuations of microscopic charcoal on the other hand might be linked with human activities in the area.

The results of this pollen analysis are very similar to the pollen diagram of the nearby site of Lommel Weyerkense Bergen (Mullenders / Gullentops / Crevecoer 1958).

A Federmessergruppen site complex

More than 70 surface concentrations on the (former) ridge north of the valley, a stretch of land of some 100 m wide and more than 1 km long, show that Lommel Maatheide repeatedly attracted Final Palaeolithic and Mesolithic residents (**Fig. 5**). The gaps in between these scatters are presumably due to recent destruction, as testified by the disappearance of the podsolic soils here, rather than to a lack of occupation. The site most probably continued further to the east and west, but these areas are presently used as industrial locations and for sand-quarrying, making further research impossible.

With the exception of two isolated scatters, intensive sampling of the Late Glacial deposits of the southern slope of the valley yielded no Federmessergruppen finds, showing that Allerød occupation was systematically located to the north of the water. However, small Mesolithic scatters were found on both sides of the depression, always associated with the podsol.

On top of the northern ridge, the remaining Federmessergruppen scatters are generally preserved in a Holocene podsolic soil, having been eroded from their primary stratigraphical position. However, three isolated concentrations, excavated slightly to the north and south of the ridge, were still preserved in the Usselo soil (**Fig. 5, 1-3**). Unfortunately, one of them was affected by ploughing in connection with the past dump activities (**Fig. 5, 1**), but the others are clearly *in situ*, even though iron illuviation of the podsol has

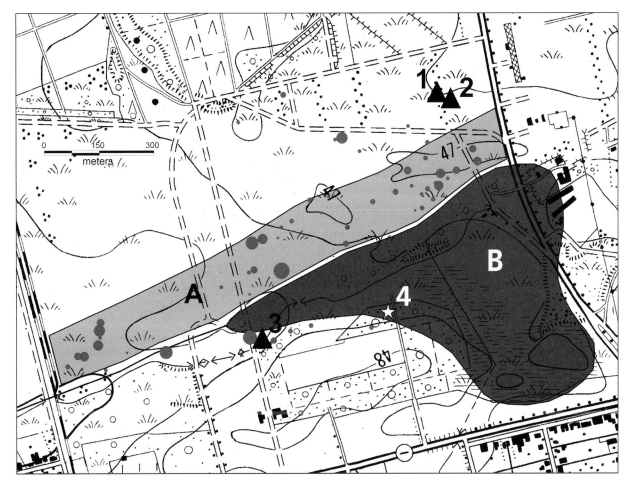

Fig. 5 Distribution of the artefact loci (represented as grey dots) across the landscape: – **A** Late Glacial dune. – **B** Late Glacial lake. – **1** locus LB60. – **2** locus LB01. – **3** locus LB 57A. – **4** location of peat sample used for palynology.

masked the visual characteristics of the Usselo soil in relation to one of them (**Fig. 5, 3**). The vertical distribution of the artefacts in these *loci* was restricted to the 10 cm thick Usselo soil and the artefacts showed exceptional freshness and adhering sediment, suggesting that they had not been displaced since the Younger Dryas.

Characteristics of the lithic industry

The assemblages collected during the three recent field seasons are characterized by a well elaborated laminar production and dominated by the three main tool groups of the Federmessergruppen industries: laterally modified laminar pieces, end scrapers and burins. In addition, a respectable number of borers and becs was retrieved.

The laterally modified laminar pieces are mostly typical Federmesser points (**Fig. 6, 1-6**). Curved backed points are clearly dominant although sometimes specimens with a slightly angled back were observed. The scraper assemblage is dominated by rather long and robust endscrapers on blades (**Fig. 6, 7-10**). One is made on an extensively elaborated crested blade and double endscrapers are also present. The burins are

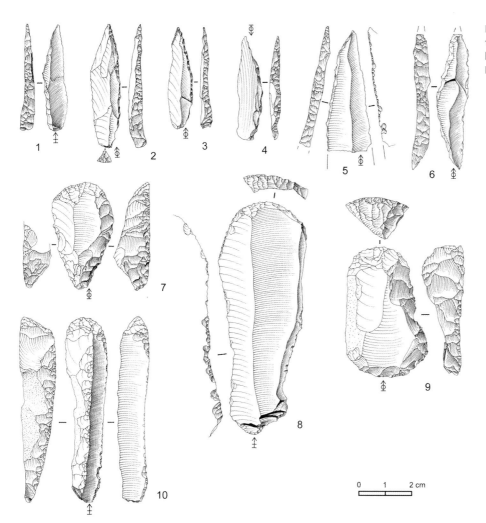

Fig. 6 Tools collected during the latest field seasons. – **1-6** backed points, **7-10** scrapers. Drawings: M. Van Meenen.

often made on elongated blades (**Fig. 7, 1-4**). The burin blow is generally delivered to the right side of a burin platform prepared by truncation. The narrow burin end is reminiscent of burins in the Magdalenian tradition and may reflect an early variant of the Federmessergruppen groups. The edges are repeatedly retouched, a common attribute for Federmessergruppen burins in this region (De Bie 2007). Multiple burins are clearly represented. Another indication of a possibly rather early phase of the Federmessergruppen tradition are perhaps the relatively thick, robust becs that are quite common at Lommel Maatheide (**Fig. 7, 6-8**). The assemblage largely confirms the characteristics of earlier finds (Verheyleweghen 1956; Geerts 1984). Moreover, similar raw materials were used and the artefacts carry the same wind gloss, showing that they most likely originate from the same location and context. This sheds new light on the vast but poorly registered collection of finds from Lommel.

The tool assemblage is typical of the Federmessergruppen known in the Campine area (De Bie / Van Gils 2006). Site complexes of this period generally consist of large campsites. Some of the well preserved artefact distributions at Lommel can tentatively be interpreted as habitations, presumably around a hearth (**Fig. 8**), while other, more peripheral *loci* may represent shorter-term working spots.

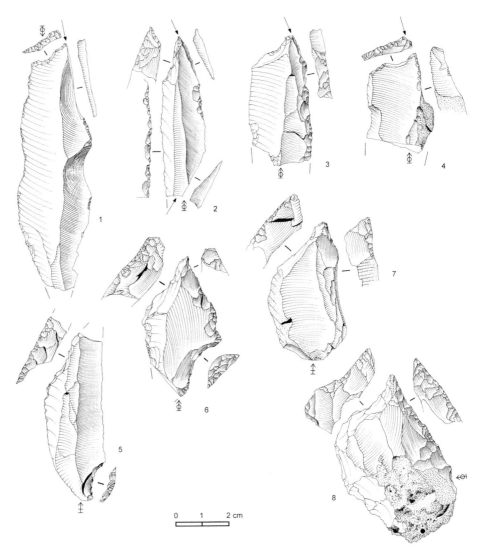

Fig. 7 Tools collected during the latest field seasons. – **1-4** burins. – **5** truncated tool. – **6-8** becs. Drawings: M. Van Meenen.

One of these, a well preserved isolated scatter to the north of the ridge, yielded exclusively burins as formal tools (**Fig. 5, 2**), Refitting has shown that these have been manufactured and resharpened on the spot, and that the concentration is the result of a single, probably rather short, occupation. Although microwear analysis is still underway, as a preliminary interpretation this scatter can be considered a small one-time working area where burins were manufactured and used, presumably for working bone or antler.

Discussion

Archaeological, geomorphological, and palaeoecological research at Lommel is providing new insights into the palaeoenvironmental context of the Federmessergruppen site complex. The results at Lommel Maatheide also provide ideas on the land use system employed by the final Palaeolithic hunter-gatherer societies. The Late Glacial sand ridge along the open water repeatedly attracted people of the Federmessergruppen. From this dry location they had a good view across the water southward and found

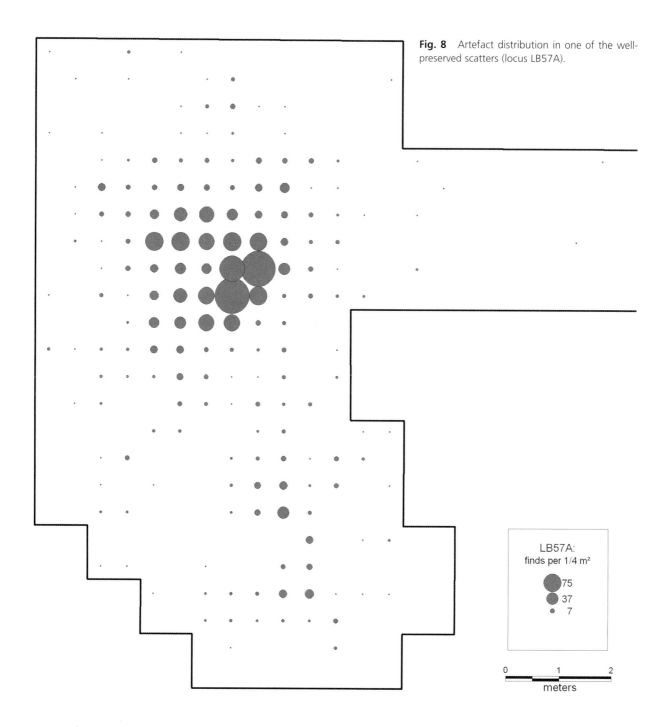

Fig. 8 Artefact distribution in one of the well-preserved scatters (locus LB57A).

LB57A:
finds per 1/4 m²

75
37
7

0   1   2
meters

many of the available resources nearby. The Federmessergruppen may have selected locations such as Lommel Maatheide to exploit the diversity of these rich biotopes.

The deliberate choice of location on the northern side of the water is a recurrent feature seen in the Campine region. At Lommel, this seems to be the result of the absence of dry ground to the south, rather than a conscious preference for the sunny northern slope. When the valley became symmetrical after the Younger Dryas, with sands covering the marshland in the south, Mesolithic camps started to occupy both banks of the then somewhat smaller lake.

At many of the Final Palaeolithic and Mesolithic sites in the region, such suitable camping ground to the south of the water is lacking. This can be explained by the geomorphology of the Campine region, which had most of its current topography defined by Late Glacial sand dunes. These dunes moved slowly through

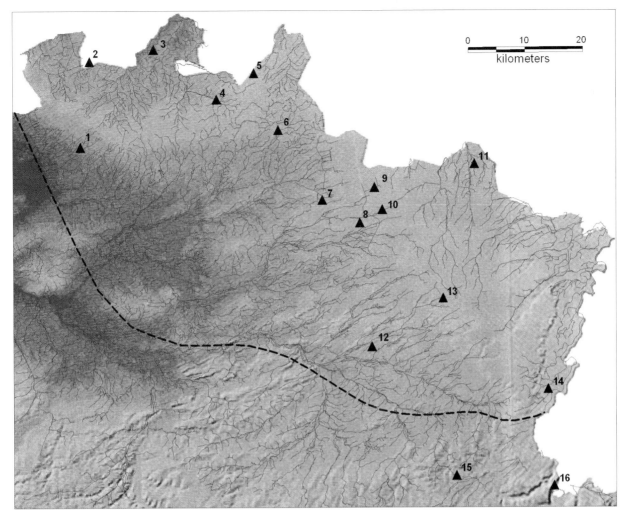

Fig. 9 Distribution of the currently known Federmessergruppen settlement sites in northern Belgium. The dashed line delimits the sandy Campine region. – **1** Brasschaat Ankerhof, – **2** Nieuwmoer De Maatjes, – **3** Meer Meirberg, – **4** Merksplas Hoekeinde, – **5** Weelde Eindegoorheide, – **6** Oud-Turnhout Vliegveld, – **7** Mol Achterdonk, – **8** Balen Keiheuvels, – **9** Lommel Maatheide, – **10** Lommel Molse Nete, – **11** Achel De Waag, – **12** Zolder Terlamen, – **13** Helchteren Sonnisse Heide, – **14** Rekem Hangveld, – **15** Tongeren Plinius, – **16** Lixhe Chemin des Meuniers.

the landscape, pushed by winds from the north (west). The shape of these dunes was asymmetrical, with a downwind-slope in the north and a slipface in the south, and this asymmetry remained when the dunes were fixed by the Late Glacial vegetation. This explains the alternation of interfluvia and depressions showing a regular pattern, with the top of the dunes very close to the depression on the north side and a much less steep and therefore wet and marshy slope towards the next dune to the south. This asymmetry is very visible at Lommel, but sediment layering following the slipface has also been observed in other sites.

During the Allerød interstadial, as well as in the early Holocene, the river network constituted the only defining landmark in the forested and relatively flat Campine landscape. It is therefore highly likely that human groups used the river networks to find and (re)visit their sources (springs), where they found fens such as were present at Lommel. The distribution of the Federmessergruppen sites in the Campine region (**Fig. 9**), preferentially situated along the Scheldt-Meuse interfluvium, strongly supports this idea. A newly discovered Federmessergruppen site at Tongeren Plinius, the first one to be excavated in the loessic area, seems to confirm this pattern even south of the Campine region (Dijkstra et al. 2006).

Conclusions

One of the type site locations of the Federmessergruppen, represented in various museums by tens of thousands of artefacts, and well-known in the archaeological literature, can now be placed in the framework of its geomorphological and palaeoecological contexts. It appears that the site complex of Lommel Maatheide was located on a large Late Glacial sand ridge on the northern edge of a contemporary shallow lake. This specific location repeatedly attracted the Final Palaeolithic residents, and is very typical for the Final Palaeolithic and Mesolithic sites in the Campine region (Van Gils / De Bie 2006; De Bie / Van Gils 2009). The current preservation of the artefact scatters is quite variable, with only some minor, well-preserved concentrations in a typical Usselo soil. Excavations of the more disturbed locations on top of the ridge, although these were affected by Younger Dryas deflation and Holocene podsolisation processes, have provided new insights into the depositional context of the finds recovered earlier.

In the fen depression, where the Allerød soil continues as a peat layer, the preservation of pollen, beetles and macro-botanical elements is excellent. First results of the palynological analysis show a vegetation evolution characteristic for the Allerød oscillation in northern Belgium and the southern Netherlands, with domination of the arboreal vegetation by *Betula* in the lower part of the peat deposit and *Pinus* in the upper part. However, some very characteristic species can also be found and the results are very promising for further interdisciplinary palaeoecological research.

If these analyses do indeed demonstrate that the environment displayed a high degree of biodiversity, they will help to explain why Final Palaeolithic hunter-gatherer societies, presumably guided by the river network, repeatedly selected locations such as Lommel Maatheide for occupation – irrespective of whatever further social or ritual meanings such sites may have had in their respective cultural traditions.

References

Bos 1998: H. Bos, Aspects of Lateglacial-Early Holocene vegetation development in Western Europe. Palynological and palaeobotanical investigations in Brabant (The Netherlands) and Hessen (Germany) (Utrecht 1998).

Creemers / Carolus 1989: G. Creemers / J. Carolus, Epipaleolithicum te Lommel-Blokwaters. Limburg 68, 195-200.

De Bie 2007: M. De Bie, La dynamique des burins dans les industries à Federmesser (aziliens): observations sur le site de Rekem. In: J.-P. Bracco / M. de Araujo Igreja (eds.), Burins préhistoriques: formes, fonctionnements, fonctions. ArchéoLogiques 2 (Luxembourg 2007) 277-296.

De Bie / Gullentops / Van Gils 2003: M. De Bie / F. Gullentops / M. Van Gils, Een laat-paleolithische concentratie in een Usselobodem op de Maatheide te Lommel. Notae Praehistoricae 23, 33-37.

De Bie / Van Gils 2005: M. De Bie / M. Van Gils, Federmessersites te Lommel-Maatheide. Opgravingscampagne 2005. Notae Praehistoricae 25, 109-112.

2006: M. De Bie / M. Van Gils, Les habitats des groupes à Federmesser (aziliens) dans le nord de la Belgique. Bulletin de la Société Préhistorique Française 103, 781-790.

2009: M. De Bie / M. Van Gils, Mesolithic settlement and land use in the Campine region (Belgium). In: S. McCartan / R. Schulting / G. Warren / P. Woodman (eds.), Mesolithic Horizons. Proceedings of the 7th International Conference on the Mesolithic in Europe, Belfast 2005 (Oxford 2009) 282-287.

Dijkstra et al. 2006: P. Dijkstra / M. Bink / M. De Bie / G. Vynckier / H. Van Rechem / T. Dyselinck, Laatpaleolithische vindplaatsen op het Plinius-terrein bij Tongeren (prov. Limburg). Notae Praehistoricae 26, 109-124.

Geerts 1984: F. Geerts, The Caris collection of Lommel. Notae Praehistoricae 4, 17-22.

Hamal-Nandrin / Servais / Louis 1935: J. Hamal-Nandrin / J. Servais / M. Louis, Nouvelle contribution à l'étude du préhistorique dans la Campine limbourgeoise (Belgique). Bulletin de la Société Préhistorique Française 32, 175-203.

Hoek 1997: W. Hoek, Palaeogeography of Lateglacial Vegetations. Aspects of Lateglacial and Early Holocene vegetation, abiotic landscape and climate in the Netherlands. Netherlands Geografical Studies 230 (Utrecht 1997).

Mullenders / Gullentops / Crevecoer 1958: W. Mullenders / F. Gullentops / E. Crevecoer, L'oscillation de Bölling à Lommel. Bulletin de la Société de Botanique de Belgique 90, 315-317.

Munaut 1967: A.-V. Munaut, Recherches paléo-écologiques en Basse et Moyenne Belgique. Acta Geographica Lovaniensia 6 (Leuven 1967).

Palmans 2006: T. Palmans, De laag van Usselo op de archeologische site »de Maatheide«. Unpublished report, University of Leuven.

Schwabedissen 1954: H. Schwabedissen, Die Federmesser-Gruppen des nordwesteuropäischen Flachlandes. Zur Ausbreitung des Spät-Magdalénien (Neumünster 1954).

Van Gils / De Bie 2005: M Van Gils / M. De Bie, Steentijdsites op de Maatheide te Lommel. Archeologische opgravingen 2004. Intern rapport VIOE (Brussel 2005).

2006: M. Van Gils / M. De Bie, Uitgestrekte Mesolithische sitecomplexen in de Kempen. Ravels Witgoor en Opglabbeek Ruiterskuilen-Turfven (boorcampagne 2002). Relicta. Archeologie, monumenten- en landschapsonderzoek in Vlaanderen 1, 11-28.

Verbruggen 1979: C. Verbruggen, Vegetational and palaeoecological history of the Lateglacial period in Sandy Flanders (Belgium). Acta Universitatis Ouluensis 82, 133-142.

Verheyleweghen 1956: J. Verheyleweghen, Le paléolithique final de culture périgordienne du gisement préhistorique de Lommel (Province de Limbourg-Belgique). Bulletin de la Société Royale Belge d'Anthropologie et de Préhistorique 67, 1-79.

Vermeersch 1975: P. M. Vermeersch, Haltplaats van het Tjongeriaan te Lommel-Werkplaatsen. Archeologie 2, 64-67.

Abstract

Human occupation in a Late Glacial landscape: The Federmessergruppen site complex at Lommel Maatheide (Belgium)

Three years of new fieldwork at the extensive Federmessergruppen site of Lommel Maatheide in northern Belgium provided excellent new insights into the location, extension, stratigraphy and preservation of this site complex, as well as on the geographical and palaeo-ecological context of the settlement. This paper discusses some of the main results. Archaeologically, the new excavations yielded abundant lithic materials, confirming the site's fame as a rich find spot of Final Palaeolithic artefacts and providing better a insight into the spatial boundaries of the lithic scatters and their exact position in the landscape. Some scatters were excellently preserved in a Late Glacial Usselo soil. The excavated artefacts also enrich the typological and technological picture obtained earlier. The first results of palaeoecological research on peat from a former shallow lake south of the occupation reveal a typical evolution of Late Glacial vegetation.

Key-words

Limburg (B), Lommel, Final Palaeolithic, Federmessergruppen, Usselo soil, Allerød, palaeoecology.

Acknowledgments

We thank the Lommel museum, the city of Lommel and Sibelco n. v. for supporting our research.

ERIK BRINCH PETERSEN

THE HUMAN SETTLEMENT OF SOUTHERN SCANDINAVIA 12500-8700 CAL BC

»Do you know the longing for new areas?
Do you know the longing for new people?«
(Quillarsuaq in Rasmussen 1905)

The present contribution deals with the cultural development of southern Scandinavia following the last deglaciation. The subject thus includes the Late Glacial as well as the Early Holocene or, in archaeological terms, the Late Palaeolithic and the Early Mesolithic. For better or for worse, the combination of the topics involved, deglaciation, land/sea relationship, floral and faunal dispersal as well as human immigration, has become a sort of textbook classic depicted as environmental changes followed by adaptive response by Early Man. Until now, most archaeological papers dealing with this period have concentrated on the chronological aspect of Late Glacial cultures, emphasising a successive replacement or even an *in situ* development of the various cultures. Unfortunately, the proposed linear development of successive human cultures or technocomplexes has led to a stalemate with no room for alternative views or for a dynamic interpretation. Given the present situation with its scarce, but nonetheless conflicting evidence, the time should now be ripe for discussing other alternatives.

First of all, there are too many problems, or rather a lack of good evidence, to agree with the simple scenario in which one culture gives rise to the next. Excavated sites remain rare, much of the evidence comes from surface collections and most excavated sites from the region contain only lithics with no faunal remains or bone tools. Moreover, pollen dates have been used very freely in the past, and, in particular, there has been much disagreement concerning the definition and identification of the Bølling period (De Klerk 2004). Even reliable radiocarbon dates are few and far between. Only the faunal succession now seems well established, being based upon direct radiocarbon dates of the species themselves, whereas the relative chronology of the human technologies is still based upon typological reasoning involving a strong use of supposed type fossils (Schild 1984). Finally, one is also confronted by a certain compulsion among some archaeologists to try to make evidence from their particular region appear as old as possible.

Placing this discussion into its local framework, the theme can perhaps be characterized in the following way. Many colleagues apparently believe that current information about the Final Palaeolithic of southern Scandinavia is very fragmentary and also lacking in essential data for topics such as regional distribution patterning. I, on the other hand, accept the available data, including the implication of its restricted distribution, more or less at face value and will argue from this point of view.

An important aspect left aside for present purposes is that of the use and abuse of the terms »cultures« or »technocomplexes«. I make use of these entities to define separate and distinct analytical units, but am also painfully aware that this is, for the time being, merely the best available substitute for what should have been circumscribed groups of human individuals (Gamble 1998).

All the following radiocarbon dates have been calibrated using the CalPal program (Weninger / Jöris / Danzeglocke 2007; Weninger / Jöris 2008). Calibrations are with two standard deviations as recommended by Pettitt et al. (2003) and are given as cal BC.

Background

The following information has contributed to the prospect of rethinking of the topic under consideration:

1) The GRIP-calibration of Late Glacial ^{14}C dates (Björck et al 1998; Jöris / Weninger 2002) as well as the new Greenland Ice Core Chronology 2005, GICC05 (Rasmussen et al. 2006)

2) Results of the AMS-dating of Early Man in Northern Europe after the Late Glacial Maximum (Housley et al. 1997; Housley / Gamble / Pettitt 2000; Jacobi 2004)

3) Radiocarbon dating of the South Scandinavian Late Glacial fauna (Aaris-Sørensen 1998; 2000; 2007; Aaris-Sørensen / Mühldorff / Brinch Petersen 2007; Larsson et al. 2002)

Of importance is also the recent fieldwork from southern Scandinavia and adjacent regions, where the excavation at Slotseng headed by J. Holm is one of the most important (Holm 1996; Holm / Christensen / Aaris-Sørensen 2002; Holm / Rieck 1992; Mortensen in prep).

Briefly, it takes seven steps and two to three thousand years for Early Man to settle in southern Scandinavia, whereas only two steps and a couple of hundred more years are needed for Mesolithic Man to expand over the rest of Scandinavia, both from the south (Bang-Andersen 2003; Bjerck 1995) and from the north (Bergman et al. 2004; Grydeland 2005; Kankaanpää / Rankama 2005). However, the maritime settling of the Baltic islands seems to need more than one step (Casati / Sørensen 2006; Kriiska 2003; Lindquist 1996).

In chronological order, the following Late Glacial cultures or industries are of interest: Hamburgian *sensu stricto*, Havelte Group, Federmessergruppen, Brommian, Ahrensburgian, Epi-Ahrensburgian/Long Blade Industry and, finally, the early Holocene Maglemosian. Given the well established distribution of the late Magdalenian from the Dutch province of Limburg, to the Middle Rhine, Thuringia and the Polish upland zone, there should be no prospect of finding such material so far to the north. The site of Gadenstedt (and possibly Schweskau) in Lower Saxony represent at present the Magdalenian site(s) closest to our region (Breest / Veil 1991; Veil / Veil 2004).

Problems

In order to distinguish pioneers from residentials Housley et al. (1997) have looked at topics such as site seasonality and size, the presence of dwelling structures, size of the faunal assemblage (and whether this was reindeer dominated or not), the presence or absence of art and, finally, occurrence of male *versus* female burials. Given the very nature of early sites from southern Scandinavia, most of these issues are simply not represented here, since the sites in question have now become embedded in the modern plough-zone, leaving only disturbed flint scatters (kshemenitsa after Schild 1989) to work with. In fact, not even a simple hearth has been preserved. However, what are preserved are the following data: the northernmost distribution of sites from the above-mentioned cultures, the size of the sites as well as information on their lithic technology and typology. In most cases, the exact date of a site can only be suggested on the comparison with the age of the few better-dated ones. This is indeed a meagre yield of information, but still one that merits discussion.

In dealing with open-air sites located on sandy ridges, the question of site integrity becomes paramount. This is especially true in the case of all transitional industries being used to bridge the chronological and/or geographical gap between two adjacent cultures. The present paper relies heavily on »proper« sites rather than on stray finds of alleged type fossils; as has by now been said so often: there is no such thing as a lithic type fossil!

Table 1 Site classification.

Site	no. of cores	no. of tools	Category
Ramsgaard II	< 25	< 25	small
Segebro	< 50	< 75	middle
Rundebakke	<100	< 150	large
Stoksbjerg Bro	<400	>1000	extremely large

A further critical problem is whether the present distribution of sites provides a fair representation of their past distribution. The very recent discovery of most of these Late Glacial cultures in Denmark perhaps indicates that many sites could have been overlooked in the past. Some authors have gone to the extreme of suggesting human occupation right up to the front of the ice cap (Noe-Nygaard / Knudsen / Houmark-Nielsen 2006), while Holm and Rieck (1992) have argued that the Havelte group occupied the entire ice-free area of southern Scandinavia. However, as will be seen in the following discussion, there is no evidence for such suggestions.

On the other hand, three major regional investigations, headed by T. Mathiassen (1937; 1948; 1959), all failed to detect any Palaeolithic evidence other than for the Brommian (Andersen / Sterum 1971). Furthermore, two smaller, but more intensive investigations of river catchments in Jutland, Vejle Å (Berthelsen 1944) and Varde Å (Christiansen / Skelmose 1963) came to the same result. Nevertheless, a lesson learned from the recent discoveries of Slotseng and Sølbjerg is the fact that some sites were apparently located high in the landscape, commanding a good view of the surrounding area. Such sites could have thus escaped detection, although in the case of Vejle Å the moraine landscape flanking the river valley was also investigated (Berthelsen 1944). The still restricted and southerly distribution of most of these new sites therefore seems to me to be an acceptable indication of overall past site distribution. On the other hand, the location of a genuine Ahrensburgian site, Dværgebakke, as far to the north as Lake Bølling in Jutland (Møbjerg / Rostholm 2006) could perhaps indicate that this present concept might soon be in need of revision!

Site Classification

»Postes de débitage« or »lithic workshops«, »hunting stands«, »settlements dominated by hunting«, and »settlements with a broad economic basis« have all been so classified by Fischer (1993), whereas Johansson (2002) has characterized a number of the same sites as »base camps«, »hunting sites« and »kill sites«. Other definitions, such as »observation stands« (Rensink 1992), could equally have been used, as could have »field camps«, »travelling camps« and »extraction sites« (Audouze 2006; Binford 1982), not to speak of »resting places« (Clausen 2005). This nomenclatural confusion merely underlines the fact that, without faunal elements, any functional characterisation of a lithic scatter remains problematic and this is exaggerated by the lack of accepted definitions. For our purpose, which aims first of all to distinguish pioneers from residentials, a simple hierarchical classification is preferred, accordingly characterizing a site according to the total number of tools and cores (Weniger 1987). With some interesting exceptions, the relationship between tools and cores seems to be linear. It is also suggested that a rich site could represent a residential population or an aggregation of people, whereas a small site could be a first scouting or hunting episode, as in the case of the Swiderian pioneers at Salaspils Lauskskola to the south of Riga (Eberhards / Zagorska 2002). The sites in question will therefore be divided into the four categories »small«, »middle«, »large« and »extremely large« (**Table 1**).

Fig. 1 A migrating family (Enooesweetok del.).

The background for this division is provided by the following sites. The first, small site is the only one being excavated among a larger number of small sites around Hollendskær in Northern Jutland (Nilsson 1989). It would be very interesting to investigate the relationship between the thirteen different lithic scatters represented here, which could be done by way of refitting. Although we normally define an aggregation camp as one with a large or even extremely large amount of material, if these thirteen scatters should be contemporaneous, this could then become the type site for a form of aggregation camp that so far has eluded identification (Aaris-Sørensen / Mühldorff / Brinch Petersen 2007).

Segebro from Scania (Salomonsson 1964) could represent a single, one family location, with remains of flint working as well as tool repair, apparently located inside an oval structure like the one from Langå (Madsen 2000). Rundebakke on Knudshoved Odde (Pedersen / Hansen 2006) is representative of a large inventory, but since the excavation has not yet reached the border of the site (sites?) it might even be larger. The example of an extremely large site is taken from my own excavation at Stoksbjerg Bro, Zealand (Pedersen / Brinch Petersen 2006), where refitting has demonstrated the presence of a single occupation. Furthermore, there is also a unique small knapping floor without any tools (Fischer 1991) and a lithic cache (Holm 1973).

Immigration models

The model for animal dispersal into the deglaciated area of southern Scandinavia is fairly simple, with pioneer species such as reindeer moving into an unoccupied area at the time when climate and vegetation became adequate for survival. Human immigration into southern Scandinavia can be seen in the same way, as that of a group of people coming into a virgin, but promising area adjacent to one already occupied (**Fig. 1**). Animals, as well as humans were moving northwards in a synchronized response to the withdrawal of the Scandinavian ice cap. On present evidence, reindeer and the first humans seem to arrive in southern Scandinavia at the same time, since the oldest date for both comes from the same archaeological site, Slotseng. This is certainly a coincidence, since reindeer ought to precede Early Man. We have the same contemporaneity of man and reindeer at Poggenwisch in the Ahrensburg Tunnel Valley. The two earliest industries, the Hamburgian and the Havelte group, being novelties on the northern tundra, must not only be considered as pioneers *per se*, but must also be regarded as reindeer-dependant and reindeer-followers (Burch 1972; 1991; Gordon 1990), since reindeer was the only available prey species on the tundra at the time.

Following the initial arrival of the first humans in southern Scandinavia around 12 500 or 12 300 cal BC, the question remains as to the nature of the subsequent settlement process. Is there a rapid transition from pioneers to residentials, as has often been suggested, with the replacement of one industry by the next following the *in situ* development of the residentials? Or is there a different situation, in which the first pioneers are succeeded, after the passage of time, by yet another group of pioneers which may or may not be descendants of the first group. This is the »pulsation« model originally suggested for the arctic (Dekin 1976) and is perhaps difficult to verify with our material. Nonetheless, given the apparent episodic nature of most of the successive human groups, it is a model that might be very appropriate.

Step-wise or leapfrogging immigration with patchy occurrence of outliers?

Even if we believe that the first human immigration into southern Scandinavia resembles the wave-of-advance model (Martin 1973), just like animal dispersion, the present distribution of sites across the landscape might also show a certain resemblance to the leapfrogging model (Anderson / Gillam 2000). Sometimes, hundreds of kilometres can separate a northern advance party from its nearest relative to the south, but, given the obvious demographic constraints of such behaviour (Moore / Moseley 2001), this is perhaps not a correct archaeological distribution. Another model sees the patchy occurrence of sites from the same culture as a way of coping with a harsh, but unfamiliar environment while trying to establish a more permanent occupation. Following the first occupation of a virgin location, sites of following cultures tend to appear at the same locations, with the Ahrensburg Tunnel Valley being, of course, the most interesting hot spot of them all on the northern plain. Also the strategic topography at sites such as Ahrenshöft (Clausen 1998), Alt-Duvenstedt (Kaiser / Clausen 2005), Slotseng (Holm 1996), Bølling Sø (Brinch Petersen 1967; Mathiassen 1937; Møbjerg / Rostholm 2006; Sørensen 2007), Sølbjerg (Petersen / Johansen 1996), Knudshoved Odde (Hansen / Pedersen 2006; Petersen 2001; Rasmussen 1972), and Porsmosen (Johansson 2003; Pedersen / Brinch Petersen 2006) have all drawn humans to successive occupations. The same can be seen at other open-air sites across the lowlands of Continental Europe.

Yet another model could be the »competition« model, in which a group of people from one technocomplex attempts to exploit the same area which is occupied by another group of people from a different technocomplex (Burch 2005). All these models are thus concerned with time and space, but where the first ones require succession over time, the last one presupposes contemporaneity between two or more industries. As a matter of fact, these models are not mutually exclusive, but could even be the different guises of one and the same human group during its northward expansion. Given the fact that, for southern Scandinavia, we simply do not know whether one industry was directly followed by another or whether there was a time gap or, the opposite case, an overlap of the successive technocomplexes, the stage remains open for various scenarios. Other models, such as the »beachhead« or the »string of pearls« variants (Anderson / Gillam 2000), are both concerned with the geographical organization of the advance of the pioneers. However, due to the loss of so much land area to the rising sea, this is not an easy aspect to identify, although two different »strings of pearls« have been proposed, with the first one running up through the middle part of Jutland while the second one crosses over from the South and reaches the present islands of eastern Denmark (Petersen / Johansen 1996).

Finally, the British Isles might serve as a parallel situation for southern Scandinavia regarding early immigration. Here, the process has been divided into three different stages. The first is the initial colonization, beginning around 12 500 cal BC, the second is the phase of consolidation, from ca. 11 000-9 000 cal BC, while the third phase was one of rapid expansion, between 9 000-7 000 cal BC (Tolan-Smith 2003). The suggested dates are interesting, but to me the designation and characterization of the phases resemble more a mercantile expansion, as in an Anglo-Indian mercantile company, rather than the movement of groups of prehistoric people. Moreover, in South Scandinavia the scenario is much more detailed, and the British model is only of limited use.

Fig. 2 Reindeer track across the tundra, western Greenland.

Pulls and Pushes

It has recently been suggested that use of southern Scandinavia as a Late Glacial calving ground by reindeer might have served to »pull« some of the first human groups into the North for the exploitation of a hitherto unexplored reindeer herd on the northernmost barren grounds (Aaris-Sørensen / Mühldorff / Brinch Petersen 2007).

Moreover, members of a group of dedicated reindeer-eaters, like the Chipewyan (Gordon 1990; Burch 1991), simply had to follow the reindeer during its migration to the north (**Fig. 2**). On the other hand, the continuing reduction in the size of Doggerland due to progressive marine transgression might certainly have been responsible for »pushing« people to resettle in the surrounding areas.

This northern area devoid of other humans would also have been a perfect area for seeking refuge for people pushed by social conflicts (Rowley 1985). That this was indeed possible is demonstrated by an arctic voyage into the (nearly) unknown by Quillarsuaq, an angakok (shaman) and murderer, and his followers during the 1850s (Mary-Rousselière 1980; 1991; 2002; Rasmussen 1905). Apparently, many a pioneer in the past might have also been a social outcast!

Certainly, there are many different models and scenarios to choose among! Unfortunately, so flimsy is the nature of our present data that it is perhaps possible to argue in favour of any of the discussed models at any given period during our time interval. It would therefore only take one new site with good faunal preservation and qualitative radiocarbon samples to change accepted concepts. Needless to say, I too am looking forward to that information, but in the meantime we all have to make do with the evidence we have so far.

Faunal Evidence

Eleven of the most important herbivore species are now well dated and six of these become locally extinct within the studied time period. The first two species, the saïga antelope (Aaris-Sørensen / Petersen / Henriksen 1999) and the mammoth (Berglund / Håkansson / Lagerlund 1976) represent a late faunal expansion from the European Mammoth Steppe, and they appear and then disappear before humans come into the area. The first appearance of reindeer, on the other hand, is associated with humans of the Havelte tradition (Aaris-Sørensen / Mühldorff / Brinch Petersen 2007). This, of course, is a coincidence, but do we here see an effect of pull and push between Late Palaeolithic man and Late Glacial reindeer? Reindeer is the only species present through all the Late Glacial stages, only to become extinct at the end of the Preboreal period. Reindeer is numerically also by far the best represented species (ibid.) and must, without any doubt, have been the most important prey during the Late Palaeolithic, regardless of the fact that it is also the most visible species, as both sexes leave their antlers behind every year when migrating to their winter quarters elsewhere. According to the present list of ^{14}C dates reindeer was the only game species on the tundra during two periods, the end of Meiendorf/Bølling and the second half of the Younger Dryas.

A recent paper (ibid.) has used the oldest radiocarbon date from Slotseng (AAR-906) to place the first arrival of reindeer immediately after 13 000 cal BC, which corresponds to the beginning of the Meiendorf/Bølling interstadial. However, and as shall also be argued later, pollen analysis has now shown that all the reindeer remains and flint implements were embedded here in the same sediment sequence, which dates to the *Hippophaë*-maximum of the late Bølling at approximately 12 300-12 200 cal BC (M. F. Mortensen personal information). The earliest reindeer should therefore be placed at around this date instead of immediately after 13 000 cal BC. This is one of the rare cases where pollen dates can take precedence over an AMS date. The oldest dates for reindeer in the Ahrensburg Tunnel Valley from Poggenwisch, Meiendorf and Stellmoor seem to be slightly older (Fischer / Tauber 1987), but again all these reindeer dates also come from archaeological sites thus emphasising the close relationship between reindeer and Early Man.

In Denmark the oldest direct date (K-6124: 11 770 ± 190 BP) for elk, *Alces alces*, is some three hundred years later than for the first reindeer. The specimen comes from Voms Mose and the date corresponds to 11 852-11 467 cal BC. However, there is actually one very early elk from Scania antedating the reindeer, at around 12 400 BP (Liljegren / Ekström 1996). No further details are given by the authors, but from a zoogeographical point of view such an early date for elk is either aberrant, or an indication of a much earlier arrival of reindeer in southern Scandinavia. The giant deer seems to arrive at the same time as the Danish elk. The elk is absent during the second half of Greenland Stadial 1 and giant deer becomes extinct at the same time (Aaris-Sørensen / Liljegren 2004). Horse is not very numerous and is also absent from the region at the same time as the elk (Aaris-Sørensen 2007; Larsson et al. 2002). Both elk and horse re-immigrate together at the beginning of the Preboreal period. However, horse disappears again, only to reappear much later at the end of the Atlantic period (Aaris-Sørensen 2007). Finally, it must be mentioned that horse is no longer to be included in the Late Glacial fauna from the site of Bromme (Degerbøl 1946), due to a medieval date obtained on the bone itself (Heinemeier / Rud 2000).

Bison (Aaris-Sørensen 2007) and aurochs (Ekström 1993; Aaris-Sørensen 1999) both have their first appearance at the very beginning of the Preboreal period, bison becoming extinct with the Boreal period, whereas the aurochs continues to be present. The last three species, red deer, roe deer and wild pig (Aaris-Sørensen 2007), all so characteristic for the Mesolithic, should have appeared right from the beginning of the Preboreal, however, due to the lack of southern Scandinavian early Mesolithic dwelling sites with faunal remains we have to look for indications of their early Preboreal appearance to Friesack (Gramsch 2001) and Potsdam-Schlaatz (Benecke 2004), both in Brandenburg, to Pinnberg in Schleswig-Holstein (Benecke

2004), to Bedburg-Königshoven in the Lower Rhineland (Street 1991; 1999) and, finally, to Star Carr in Yorkshire (Legge / Rowley-Conwy 1988). In short, the Preboreal fauna of southern Scandinavia resembles the Allerød fauna of the Central Rhineland, but with one important exception namely the presence of reindeer in the former.

Archaeological Evidence

13 000 cal BC is a time prior to the arrival of man in southern Scandinavia. It is, however, the time of Late Magdalenian expansion into areas like the Central Rhineland and the Thuringian Basin (Housley et al. 1997) and the Polish upland zone (Fiedorczuk / Schild 2002; Fiedorczuk et al. 2007). At this time, northern parts of countries such as Belgium (Charles 1996), the Netherlands (Stapert 2000), Germany (Terberger 2006a) and Poland (Schild 1984) are devoid of human groups, as is England (Barton et al. 2003; Jacobi 2004). This is the »availability phase« discussed by Zvelebil and Rowley-Conwy (1986) in terms of Neolithisation and, in our case, it means, that humans were just on the threshold of moving into our region.

Hamburgian *sensu stricto* 12 500-12 000 cal BC

The period between 12 500 and 12 000 cal BC corresponds to the continued occupation by the Final Magdalenian of the Central Rhineland, Thuringia and southern Poland. Final Magdalenian pioneering groups now enter the cave sites of Belgium (Charles 1996) and perhaps also the open-air sites further to the northeast (Rensink 2000). This period furthermore marks the first occupation by another group of pioneers, the Hamburgian, of areas of northern Germany, the northern Netherlands and Polish Silesia. In the case of the last region, it must be emphasized that this group forms a concentration of its own, some 400 km to the east of the other, classic Hamburgian sites (Burdukiewicz 1987; Burdukiewicz / Herman 2000; Kabacinski et al. 2002). The classic Hamburgian covers Schleswig-Holstein and Lüneburg, but also Bremerland and Friesland together with the northernmost Netherlands (Tromnau 1975; Stapert 2000).

According to some authors (Burdukiewicz / Schmider 2000) the Hamburgian originates from certain Late Magdalenian industries of the Paris basin, while other researchers, including Rust (1937; Grimm / Weber 2008) suggest an Eastern origin. The typology of the classic Hamburgian has been presented by Rust (1937; 1943; 1958b) and Tromnau (1975), while Hartz (1987) has described the lithic technology.

Furthermore, other authors have claimed a Hamburgian occupation of Brandenburg and of Mecklenburg-Vorpommern (Gramsch 2004; Terberger 1996; 2006a; Terberger / Lübke 2005), but this has been denied most vehemently by Cziesla (2001). For the present author, the demonstrable absence of the Hamburgian here can not simply be explained away as a research *lacuna*!

Hamburgian dates for Poggenwisch, Meiendorf and the Stellmoor lower horizon all come from the laboratory in Copenhagen (Fischer / Tauber 1987), while Ahrenshöft (lower level) provides a new AMS date (Clausen 2004). Apparently, the classic Hamburgian is distributed within the thirteenth millennium (**Table 2**), but more precision seems difficult for the time being. According to a recent examination by Grimm and Weber (2008) of all the radiocarbon dates for the Hamburgian and the Havelte, a timing for the initial Hamburgian in Schleswig-Holstein of around 12 500 cal BC looks reasonable, while 12 000 cal BC marks the youngest date for the Hamburgian. At Ahrenshöft LA 73, the upper level, a Havelte layer, also has a ^{14}C date, but the two dates are in reverse order (Clausen 1998). The dates from the three Ahrensburg Tunnel Valley sites have all been commented upon by Fischer and Tauber (1987). The two radiocar-

Site	Lab no.	BP	cal BC 1std.	References
Ahrenshöft LA 73	KIA-3833	12 130±60	12 083-11997	Clausen 2004
Stellmoor, lower	K-4328	12 180±130	12 259-11894	Fischer / Tauber 1987
Stellmoor, lower	K-4261	12 190±125	12 267-11906	Fischer / Tauber 1987
Poggenwisch	K-4331	12 240±115	12 396-11976	Fischer / Tauber 1987
Meiendorf	K-4329	12 360±110	12 653-12169	Fischer / Tauber 1987
Poggenwisch	K-4577	12 440±115	12 776-12256	Fischer / Tauber 1987
Poggenwisch	K-4332	12 570±115	12 975-12746	Fischer / Tauber 1987

Table 2 Hamburgian radiocarbon dates for Schleswig-Holstein, Germany.

bon dates from Stellmoor, lower horizon (Fischer / Tauber 1987) could indeed indicate a temporal overlap of the classic Hamburgian with the Havelte. Different internal chronologies for the Hamburgian have been suggested in the past (Rust 1937; Schwabedissen 1937; Tromnau 1975), but none seem to correspond with the spread of the present radiocarbon dates.

The Hamburgian, as well as the later Ahrensburgian, have both been characterized as »specialised reindeer hunters«. But, as has been emphasised by Costagmagno et al. (2006), one must distinguish between »obligate« and »deliberate« specialization. Here in the north, where reindeer is the single species represented for the time interval of the Hamburgian/Havelte, this is certainly an environmental constraint and must therefore be classified as an obligate specialization.

The following evidence from southern Scandinavian has to be discussed for the Hamburgian:

　　1) Hvejsel or Bjerlev, Jutland (Becker 1970; 1971).

　　2) (?) Femø, Zealand archipelago (Petersen / Johansen 1993).

　　3) (?) Holmegårds Mose, Zealand (Johansson 2003; Petersen / Johansen 1993).

　　4) (?) Mölleröd, Scania (Larsson 1991; 1994a; 1994b; 1996; 1999).

1) The stray find of a shouldered Hamburgian point was first discovered in a school collection, but later verified by the finder as having been picked up in a field next to the village of Hvejsel on Bjerlev Hede in Jutland. Being the only indication of a classic Hamburgian here, some 300 km to the north of the nearest Hamburgian site on the island of Sylt (Clausen *in litteris*), we must regard this piece as possible evidence for an initial immigration. Such a single find could indeed be an indication of a scouting event, but as the only (stray) find of this character from the region, we can never be sure of its integrity.

2-3) Neither of these two stray finds of alleged Hamburgian character reported from eastern Denmark should be so characterized and will therefore not be considered further in the following.

4) The site of Mölleröd, a combined surface collection and excavation in the interior of Scania, has produced some odd-looking tools of zinken-type together with tanged lithic points of mostly Bromme, but also of Ahrensburgian types. To consider this particular material as an indication of a Hamburgian occupation simply cannot be correct, despite repeated claims by the excavator and others (Andersson / Knarrström 1999). Furthermore, the first appearance of reindeer in Scania dates to later than 12 000 cal BC, the time of the end of the Hamburgian (Aaris-Sørensen / Mühldorff / Brinch Petersen 2007), thus leaving this alleged Hamburgian without food resources except, perhaps, for the early elk discussed above. From any point of view, Mölleröd is certainly an outlier.

In conclusion, on the evidence of the arrowhead from Hvejsel, one might possibly incorporate southern Jutland into the Hamburgian world, although I am still hesitant to do so due to the uncertain find circumstances. The rest of southern Scandinavia lies outside of the Hamburgian world and this also applies to Sca-

Site	Lab no.	BP	cal BC 1std.	References
Oldeholtwolde	GrN-11264	11 340±110	11 352-11166	Johansen / Stapert 2004
Oldeholtwolde	OxA-2559	11 470±110	11 474-11275	Johansen / Stapert 2004
Oldeholtwolde	GrN-13083	11 600±250	11 769-11296	Johansen / Stapert 2004
Oldeholtwolde	OxA-2561	11 680±120	11 721-11457	Johansen / Stapert 2004
Oldeholtwolde	OxA-2558	11 810±110	11 841-11587	Johansen / Stapert 2004
Ahrenshöft LA 58D	AAR-2784	12 030±60	12 006-11863	Clausen 2004
Ahrenshöft LA 73	KIA-3605	12 200±60	12 186-12036	Clausen 2004
Slotseng	AAR-8161	12 065±80	12 052-11877	Grimm / Weber 2008
Køge Bugt 1	AAR-1036	12 140±110	12 167-11909	Petersen / Johansen 1993
Slotseng	AAR-8158	12 165±55	12 150-12004	Grimm / Weber 2008
Slotseng	AAR-8157	12 299±41	12 199-11948	Grimm / Weber 2008
Slotseng	AAR-8164	12 190±50	12 167-12037	Grimm / Weber 2008
Slotseng	AAR-8163	12 205±65	12 196-12036	Grimm / Weber 2008
Slotseng	AAR-8162	12 220±100	12 280-11979	Grimm / Weber 2008
Slotseng	AAR-8160	12 240±50	12 212-12080	Grimm / Weber 2008
Slotseng	AAR-8165	12 290±75	12 391-12074	Grimm / Weber 2008
Slotseng	AAR-8159	12 410±70	12 625-12277	Grimm / Weber 2008
Slotseng	AAR-906	12 520±190	12 985-12430	Grimm / Weber 2008

Table 3 Havelte radiocarbon dates for northern Germany, the Netherlands and southern Scandinavia.

nia. However, with its northernmost location now on the present day Frisian island of Sylt, the classic Hamburgian is indeed moving northward.

Apart from the evidence of reindeer remains from Meiendorf and Stellmoor (lower horizon) pointing to their interception by humans during the fall migration (Bratlund 1990; Grønnow 1987) there is very little information about the rest of the year for either the reindeer or for the Hamburgians. Considering that these people were specialised reindeer hunters they would have needed to follow the herd to its wintering range, most likely somewhere in the Doggerland area, perhaps around the mouth of the palaeo-Elbe Fjord.

Havelte 12 300-12 000 cal BC

Only finds of the Havelte group, the other variety of the Hamburgian, are represented at present in Southern Denmark, as well as in Schleswig-Holstein and the northern Netherlands. They are not represented in the Ahrensburg Tunnel Valley, nor found south of the Elbe River (Tromnau 1975). In western Schleswig (Clausen 1998) and the northern Netherlands (Johansen / Stapert 2004; Stapert 2000) there is a spatial overlap with the classic Hamburgian. At Ahrenshöft, western Schleswig (Clausen 1998; Clausen / Hartz 1988; Hartz 1987), a concentration of sites is found around a former lake. At one of these sites, Ahrenshöft LA 73, a classic Hamburgian is stratified below a Havelte layer, but this is to date the only example of stratification between the two (Clausen 1998). There are radiocarbon dates for both layers, but as has been remarked above, the two dates are inverted relative to the stratigraphy.

Dates from the Dutch Havelte site of Oldeholtwolde have been discussed by Johansen and Stapert (2004), while Clausen (1998) has presented the two dates from Ahrenshöft (**Table 3**). Like many other researchers I find the dates from Oldeholtwolde to be too young compared with other Havelte dates and with the local stratigraphy (Clausen 1998; Hartz 1987; Grimm / Weber 2008).

In 1947 Bohmers first suggested a chronological bipartition of the Hamburgian, with the classic Hamburgian as Hamburgian I and the Havelte group as Hamburgian II, and this temporal division seems to have been taken for granted by most researchers (Terberger 2006a). However, according to available radiocarbon dates there is also a temporal overlap between the two and this chronological overlap might indicate that we are dealing with two more or less contemporary, but spatially different facies of the Hamburgian *sensu lato*. No internal chronology for the Havelte group has been suggested so far, although Holm and Rieck (1992) noticed stylistic differences between the two concentrations at Jels. Apart from the aberrantly young radiocarbon dates from Oldeholtwolde (Johansen / Stapert 2004), the Havelte sites seem to represent a short episode. Finally, the lower horizon (II) at Ahrenshöft LA 73 is considered by Clausen (1998) to exhibit some transitional traits between Hamburgian and Havelte.

Some years ago Tromnau (1975) defined on typological grounds a transitional group between the Hamburgian *sensu lato* and the Federmessergruppen, the Teltwisch group as represented by Teltwisch 1 and Deimern 42. However, most Havelte sites also contain a number of Federmesser points. From a purely typological point of view, Teltwisch and Havelte could therefore both represent a local transitional stage between the Hamburgian and the Federmessergruppen, although this is not substantiated by the present radiocarbon dates. Apart from the typology, which has been described in various monographs, Havelte technology has been dealt with by Hartz (1987) and by Madsen (1992).

The following sites from South Scandinavian can be mentioned:

1) Jels I and II, Jutland (Holm / Rieck 1992).
2) Slotseng A & C, Jutland (Holm 1993; 1996; Holm / Christensen / Aaris-Sørensen 2002; Holm / Rieck 1992).
3) Slotseng, »kettle-hole«, Jutland (Holm / Christensen / Aaris-Sørensen 2002; Mortensen in prep.).
4) Sølbjerg 2-3, Lolland (Petersen / Johansen 1993; 1996).
5) Krogsbølle, Lolland, pending excavation.
6) (?) »Off Solrød Strand«, Øresund (Petersen / Johansen 1993; 1996), also known as Køge Bugt 1 (Aaris-Sørensen / Mühldorff / Brinch Petersen 2007).

1-2) and 4-5) Most of these sites are without dating possibilities, except for that of typological comparison. The concentrations at Jels, Slotseng and Sølbjerg belong to the richest group of sites. According to Johansen (2000) most of the tools at Sølbjerg must have been imported to the site, as there were hardly any refits of tools to the cores. At present, Sølbjerg and its neighbour Krogsbølle, being some 150 km away from Jels and Slotseng, are the sites located furthest to the north-east. However, due to their richness, none of these sites can represent initial pioneers and we can therefore expect more sites to be found north of the line between Jels and Sølbjerg.

3) There are now ten individual AMS dates (**Table 3**) on reindeer antler or bone from the kettle hole adjacent to the lithic concentrations at Slotseng (Aaris-Sørensen / Mühldorff / Brinch Petersen 2007; Holm / Christensen / Aaris-Sørensen 2002). Apparently, two dates (AAR-8159, AAR-8157.1) have been wrongly quoted in Aaris-Sørensen / Mühldorff / Brinch Petersen (2007); the correct dates are quoted here following Grimm and Weber (2008).

Whether or not the Slotseng kettle hole results also date the two nearby Havelte concentrations A and C can be debated, since there are also two Federmessergruppen occupations (concentrations B and D) at the same site. However, as one of the reindeer bones has been penetrated by what (to me) appears to be a typical Havelte point (Holm / Christensen / Aaris-Sørensen 2002), I interpret these dates as relevant to the Havelte occupation. The palynological investigation (Mortensen in prep.) places all the bones and the antlers from the kettle-hole at the end of the Bølling period, corresponding to the *Hippophaë*-maximum. This age is also in accordance with the German dates, but not with the Dutch ones from Oldeholtwolde (Johansen / Stapert 2004).

6) The only other Danish 14C date comes from a submarine site in the Øresund, referred to as »Off Solrød Strand« or Køge Bugt 1. The reindeer remains were found together with some non-characteristic flint flakes, but one antler beam shows application of the groove-and-splinter technique for extracting antler blanks. This technique is typical for the Hamburgian, although it also characterizes the Federmessergruppen. The nearest Havelte sites are found on the present island of Lolland, at a distance of about 100 km. This could be a caveat, telling us that either the distribution of the Havelte group should be larger than the distribution of the lithic sites indicates, or perhaps this single 14C date is incorrect and needs confirmation. Unfortunately, with the exception of the kettle-hole at Slotseng and the Køge Bugt 1 worked reindeer antler, all Havelte finds are without associated faunal remains. Still, we can envisage at least two different scenarios for the culture, when it comes to the annual use of the region. In one situation, the Havelte hunters were spending the warm season in the north, hunting reindeer around their calving area (Aaris-Sørensen / Mühldorff / Brinch Petersen 2007), with the cold season spent in the northern Netherlands. Alternatively, and perhaps more likely, the Havelte sites known from the Netherlands, Germany and Denmark all represent the warm season and these people therefore needed to follow reindeer on their annual migration out into the Doggerland region (Anonymous 2007; Behre 2003; Coles 1998). In both cases, human groups could thus have been wintering to either side of the palaeo-Elbe fjord, where they could have added sealing, fishing and fowling to their subsistence strategy. For both scenarios we are in need of faunal evidence from other Havelte sites, but this is unfortunately missing.

Irrespective of the correctness of either the first or the second alternative, the Havelte site at Slotseng takes on the same role as a place for intercepting migrating reindeer during the late fall/early winter migration. With regard to seasonality at this site, there is no reason to suspect that more than one event is represented. The remains of at least ten reindeer have been identified and of these the antlers from nine bulls testify to a period in the late fall/early winter, while one female antler is of a cow which could have been hunted between October and mid-May (Aaris-Sørensen / Mühldorff / Brinch Petersen 2007). With all reindeer antlers showing a seasonal overlap there is no reason to suggest more than a single event at the Slotseng kettle hole. Whether the two adjacent Havelte flint concentrations testify to more than one event remains to be verified, but the contemporaneity of all three must not be excluded *a priori*.

In conclusion the southern parts of Jutland and of eastern Denmark have now been included in the human world, perhaps even for the first time. This particular group, the Havelte, stretches from the northern Netherlands, through north-western Germany and well into southern Denmark. According to the richness of these sites we must expect more northerly sites to be detected in the future. However, the question of whether it also reaches the present Øresund strait, as perhaps suggested by the material from »Off Solrød Strand«, will have to await further confirmation. Like the Hamburgian the Havelte group must also be characterized as reindeer dependent and reindeer followers (Burch 1991; Gordon 1990) and therefore also as a migrating summer people, reindeer being the only available big game subsistence base in southern Denmark. On the other hand, if these people did choose to winter in Southern Denmark, their only means of survival would be caches of dried reindeer meat and fish, a risky undertaking, and for this there is no evidence.

Federmessergruppen 12 000-10 800 cal BC

Sites of the Federmessergruppen tradition (Schwabedissen 1954) in northern France (Coudret / Fagnart 2006), northern Belgium (De Bie / Van Gils 2006), the northern Netherlands (Stapert 2000), along the Central Rhine (Street et al. 2006) and in Poland (Taute 1963) mark a general human expansion to the North. Federmessergruppen sites are also represented in Schleswig-Holstein (Clausen 1998; Rust 1958b; Schwa-

Site	Lab no.	BP	cal BC 1 std.	References
Bad Breisig	GrA-17493	10 940±60	10 925-10869	Baales et al. 2002
Rekem	OxA-942	11 350±150	11 411-11143	De Bie / Caspar 2000
Alt-Duvenstedt LA 120b	-	11 780±110	11 801-11551	Clausen 2004
Klein Nordende	KI-2124	12 035±110	12 055-11834	Bokelmann et al. 1983

Table 4   Federmessergruppen radiocarbon dates for Germany and Belgium.

bedissen 1954), Ditmarschen (Bokelman 1978), Brandenburg (Pasda 2002; Taute 1963) and Lower Silesia (Vollbrecht 2005). Sites in Mecklenburg and Vorpommern (Terberger 2006a) also show the northward expansion. In Central Poland the Federmessergruppen are also known as the Arch-Backed Piece (ABP) complexes (Schild 1984). The lithic technology has been described by Hartz (1987).

The former separation of the Federmessergruppen into different groups (Schwabedissen 1954) can no longer be maintained (Ikinger 1998), whereas the »pointe de Malaurie« has apparently become recognized as an important new type, assigning some Federmessergruppen industries of northern France a very late date (Fagnart / Coudret 2000). The same chronological position has also recently been demonstrated for similar lithic types in the Rhineland, where they are dated at the site of Bad Breisig to a period following the Laacher See eruption (10 940 ± 11 cal BC), but still within the Allerød pollen zone (Baales et al. 2002; Grimm 2004; Waldmann / Jöris / Baales 2001).

Radiocarbon dates for the Federmessergruppen industries have tended to be highly scattered (**Table 4**), but one of the more reliable results comes from the Belgian site of Rekem, where resin adhering to a curved backed point was dated (De Bie / Caspar 2000). Closer to our area are some very early dates from Reichwalde, which fall even before 12 000 cal BC (Vollbrecht 2005). The date from Klein Nordende (Bokelmann / Heinrich / Menke 1983) and one from Alt Duvenstedt LA 120b (Clausen 2004) are also both early. Of three ^{14}C dates from Bad Breisig only one corresponds with the Allerød context (Grimm 2004).

The evidence from South Scandinavian is as follows:

1) Slotseng B and D, Jutland (Holm 1993; 1996; Holm / Christensen / Aaris-Sørensen 2002).

2) Jelling, Jutland (Fischer 1990c).

3) Hasselø Tværvej, Falster (Petersen 2006).

4) Rundebakke, Knudshoved Odde, Zealand (Petersen 2001 and excavation by Sydsjællands Museum in 2004).

5) (?) Stoksbjerg Vest, concentration II, Zealand (Johansson 2002; 2003).

1) The two Slotseng Federmessergruppen concentrations are found at the same location as the two Havelte concentrations and they too seem to be rich in content. Apparently no trace of the two occupations was recovered from the kettle hole and they might also be contemporaneous. The distance to the nearest Federmessergruppen site in northern Germany, Alt-Duvenstedt, amounts to some 150 km as the crow flies.

2) Jelling marks a very small site, actually a lithic workshop without any tools, and therefore also open for discussion. The site is only 40 km north of Slotseng.

3) Hasselø Tværvej is a recent excavation producing both Federmessergruppen and Bromme material. Whether these two units originally constituted a single occupation, and hence a representative of the Tolk-Sprenge group of Taute (1968), or whether artificial mixing of the two different traditions has occurred, could not be established during excavation.

4) Rundebakke. This is the best representative of a Federmessergruppen site in eastern Denmark. Unfortunately, due to its location in sand it seems to have been largely destroyed, first by ploughing activity and

subsequently by surface collection of lithic artefacts. The main part of the Rundebakke material consists of a surface collection, whereas the 2004 excavation only yielded one or two flakes per square meter despite sampling of the area by some 55 x 1 m² test pits. The total of nearly fifty tools in all is dominated by burins, with many burin spalls. Some ten penknife points and a few scrapers, together with some cores also make up this small assemblage (Petersen 2001). Leaving aside Hasselø Tværvej, the distance to the next Scandinavian Federmessergruppen site, Slotseng in Jutland, is more than 300 km. In a southern direction the nearest site would be Endingen in Mecklenburg-Vorpommern (Terberger 2006a), again 160 km away.

5) According to the excavator (Johansson 2002; 2003) the Bromme site at Stoksbjerg Vest also contained a small Federmessergruppen component, in the shape of backed points, some double end scrapers and a few fan-shaped end scrapers on blades. Whether this can be regarded as the mixture of a uniquely Federmessergruppen site with a later Bromme material, or as an original assemblage showing a combination of Federmessergruppen and Bromme features (cf Tolk-Sprenge group: Taute 1968) remains unclear.

Unfortunately, Taute based his distinction of the Tolk-Sprenge group on surface collected material from Angeln in Schleswig and to date all sites of this group originate from surface collections and not from excavations (Bokelman 1978; Breest / Böhmer / Renner 1999). In one sense, the definition and application of this particular group seems logical, as an industry allegedly transitional not only in time, but also in space between the Federmessergruppen and the Brommian; nevertheless, there is no unqualified proof for this interpretation. The site of Dohnsen in Niedersachsen (ibid.) seems to be the most southerly situated site within this group.

Whether the Stoksbjerg Vest material represents one original assemblage or the result of mixing cannot be established by the information available, but a refitting program might solve some of the problems here, and the same problem and procedure might also apply to Hasselø Tværvej.

In conclusion the Federmessergruppen tradition is not particular well represented in southern Scandinavia. The nature of its occupation is therefore difficult to understand, but the »outpost« position of the easternmost site of Rundebakke could indicate a second pioneering push during the Late Glacial. If this push took place sometime between 12 000 and 11 500 cal BC then the Federmessergruppen would enter an apparently unoccupied area. In the case of contemporaneity with the Brommian, which is also possible, the appearance of the Federmessergruppen would necessarily imply an intrusion into an already occupied area. Its seasonal round also escapes us due to the limited evidence and the total lack of faunal remains, however, the sites in the Ahrensburg Tunnel Valley (unfortunately also without any faunal remains; Rust 1958a; Tromnau 1975) are suggestive of the interception of reindeer herds. Elsewhere, the Federmessergruppen are seen to be hunting a »Boreal« type fauna, but in the north there would still have been reindeer to predate. An irritating question still remains though - have we been overlooking sites of this typology?

Brommian 11 500-10 500 cal BC

With the Brommian we encounter the first residential period in southern Scandinavia. Sites are now located all over Denmark and Scania, and in Schleswig-Holstein as far as the Ahrensburg Tunnel Valley at the mixed site of Pinnberg (Rust 1958a). It also covers a major part of Mecklenburg-Vorpommern, judging by the numerous stray finds of large tanged points here, and perhaps even includes parts of Pomerania (Taute 1968; Terberger 1996; Szymczak 2002). Schild (1984) has characterized level 5a at Calowanie in Poland as Bromme-like. However, the presence of tanged points of Bromme type and style in the Masovian of Poland should not come as a surprise, since the preforms for Masovian points cannot be distinguished from typical Bromme points. Further to the east, in Lithuania, the so-called »Late Magdalenian« or Perstunian also bears a certain resemblance to the Brommian (Kozłowski 1975; Rimantené 1996; Szymczak 1999). Still furt-her east, Brommian or Bromme elements have been recognized by Zaliznyak (1995) in the Pripet catchment area and by Zhilin (2006) along the Upper Volga. Whether this eastern distribution has anything to do with the Brommian of southern Scandinavia remains to be clarified, but most authors interpret these eastern Bromme elements as a result of immigration from the northwest or as a partly younger phenomenon.

Turning to the west, some authors would now like to see the Federmessergruppen and the Brommian as two different seasonal facies of one and the same basic culture (Houtsma et al. 1996), or suggest that the Brommian would derive from one or other Federmessergruppen industry (Paddayya 1973). This idea would perhaps be in accordance with the interpretation of Taute's (1968) Tolk-Sprenge group as an earlier indus-try (Bokelmann 1979, Madsen 1983; Petersen 2006), a viewpoint which still needs to be verified. In the end, this is a question of how one lithic industry, or culture, is derived from another. In fact, the same ques-tion can be posed to any succession of Palaeolithic, Mesolithic or Palaeo-Inuit hunter-gatherers; very often the new culture seems to appear as a *deus ex machina*, with no obvious ancestor. The appearance of the Brommian could therefore alternatively mark a third pioneering event just as well as the first residential phase. Although very little faunal material is preserved at the Bromme sites, some authors have been of the opi-nion that these people favoured elk. However, given the list of radiocarbon dated reindeer, this species was certainly also present at the same time as elements of the »Boreal« fauna, some of which, such as elk, glut-ton, beaver, swan and pike, were represented at Bromme itself together with a single find of reindeer ant-ler (Degerbøl 1946). The lithic technology has been discussed by Hartz (1987) and by Madsen (1992). The following sites from south Scandinavian must be mentioned:

1) Feldingbjerg Bæk, Jutland (Jensen 2001).
2) Langå I, Jutland (Madsen 1983; 2000).
3) Løvenholm I-II, Jutland (Madsen 1983).
4) Hollandskær, Jutland (Nilsson 1989).
5) Nørre Lyngby, Jutland (Aaris-Sørensen 1995; Iversen 1942; Jessen / Nordmann 1915).
6) Bro 1-2-3, Fyn (Andersen 1973).
7) Ærø, Archipelago of Fyn (Holm 1973).
8) Skoven, Fejø, Archipelago of Zealand (Petersen 2001).
9) Knudshoved Odde, Zealand (Petersen 2001).
10) Stoksbjerg Bro, Zealand (Pedersen / Brinch Petersen 2006).
11) Stoksbjerg Vest, Zealand (Johansson 1996; 2002; 2003).
12) Fensmark, Zealand (Fischer 1996).
13) Trollesgave, Zealand (Fischer 1990a; 1990b; 1996).
14) Højgaard, Zealand.
15) Bonderup, Zealand (Becker 1971; Mathiassen 1959).
16) Bromme, Zealand (Iversen 1946; Fischer / Nielsen 1987; Mathiassen 1946).
17) Skovmosen, Gentofte, Zealand (Boye 2006).
18) Jørlunde Sø, Zealand (Petersen 2001).
19) Segebro, Scania (Salomonsson 1964).
20) Vångamossen, Scania (Anderson / Knarrrström 1999).
21) Mölleröd, Scania (Larsson 1991; 1994a; 1994b; 1996; 1999).

In addition, single finds of Bromme points are apparently distributed all over the region. With the presence of different types of sites, the Brommian must be regarded as a residential period in the eastern part of sou-thern Scandinavia. Whether its presence in northern Jutland (Nilsson 1989) and in Scania (Salomonsson 1964; Larsson 1996: Andersson / Knarrström 1999) represents further pioneering pushes is difficult to ans-

Fig. 3 Excavation at Stoksbjerg Bro, 1974.

wer, but Zealand remains the residential area since the richer sites such as Stoksbjerg (10-11) (**Figs. 3, 4**) and Bromme (12) have only been found here. It has also been discussed whether such rich sites should be considered rather as palimpsests of multiple occupations instead of a single occupation. Based on intra-site plots of various tool types Fischer and Nielsen (1987) have argued that the original site of Bromme must be divided up into different occupations; unfortunately there is no verification of this idea by refitting. The site of Stoksbjerg Vest has also been divided up into five different occupations, including the alleged Federmessergruppen occupation (Johansson 2003). However, apart from the latter, it is difficult to see more than two units at Stoksbjerg Vest, each with a tent-like structure and working areas at their front, and whether they represent a single or two occupational events remains unclear. Refitting of the lithic material has been

Site	Lab no.	BP	cal BC 1std.	References
Bromme	AAR-4539	10 720±90	10 891-10746	Heinemeier / Rud 2000
Fensmark	OxA-3614	10 810±120	10 957-10783	Fischer 1996
Trollesgave	K-2641	11 070±120	11 138-10952	Fischer 1996
Trollesgave	K-2509	11 100±160	11 185-10944	Fischer 1996

Table 5 Radiocarbon dates for Bromme sites, southern Scandinavia.

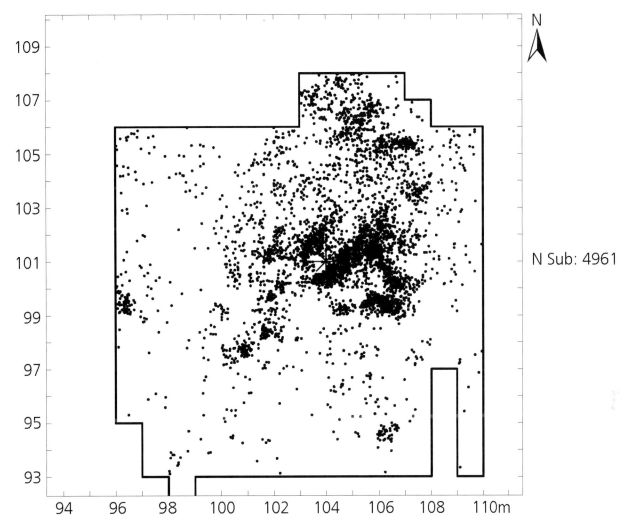

Fig. 4   Flint scatter from Stoksbjerg Bro, 1977.

attempted neither at Stoksbjerg Vest nor at Bromme. In contrast, the rich site of Stoksbjerg Bro (**Fig. 3. 4**) with its many refits indicates only one occupational phase (Pedersen / Brinch Petersen 2006).

Despite a fair number of Brommian sites there are only a few radiocarbon dates available and none of them are of particularly good quality (**Table 5**). The date from the Bromme site was produced on an unmarked elk rib (Heinemeier / Rud 2000). The others were all on bulk samples of charcoal (Fischer 1996) with an unsecured relationship to the lithic scatters. However, the four dates cluster around 11 000 cal BC, corresponding to the transition Allerød/Dryas III, and this would be more or less in accordance with the palynological indications from Bromme itself (Iversen 1946).

It has been argued by Andersen (1973) and subsequently Eriksen (2002) that the presence of frost-shattered flint cores at the site of Bro 1 should be an indication of a Younger Dryas date for this particular site. However, the same phenomenon has also been observed at Stoksbjerg Bro, where a *terminus ante quem* is provided by periglacial phenomena that affected the cultural horizon, which are most likely to be dated to the Younger Dryas. Similar frost damage on flint cores has also been observed at some Mesolithic sites; apparently some Palaeolithic and Mesolithic flint knappers worked cores that had been partially affected by frost before the knapping process occurred.

Site	Lab no.	BP	cal BC 1std.	References
Hässleberga	LuA-4492	11 300±140	11 360-11 113	Larsson et al. 2002
Hässleberga	Ua-3296	11 390±90	11 387-11 227	Larsson et al. 2002
Nørre Lyngby	AAR-1511	11 570±110	11 594-11 347	Aaris-Sørensen 1995

Table 6   Radiocarbon dates for (Brommian?) cut-marked bones.

Possibly Brommian?

Whether a number of radiocarbon dates on cut-marked bones (**Table 6**) are actually connected with Brommian occupation must be regarded as questionable, but they do fall within the Allerød period, and are even slightly earlier than the dates obtained from the sites themselves. Both dates from Hässleberga are on reindeer (Larsson et al. 2002), as is the one from Nørre Lyngby on a cut-marked rib (Aaris-Sørensen 1995). This find is from the same site as the well known arrow point and antler hammer, but is apparently not of the same age. These dates, or rather the lack of more dates, leave us with the problem of whether the Brommian covers the entire Allerød period or only the latter half, together with the earlier part of the Younger Dryas.

Additionally, a small number of reindeer antler harpoon heads has been found as stray finds in peat bogs, but until these have been radiocarbon dated we simply do not know their correct age (Johansen 2000). The same can no longer be said about so-called Nørre Lyngby hammers, since Clausen (2005) has recently scrutinized their spatial as well as their chronological distribution. The majority dates to the Younger Dryas, including the two southern Scandinavian finds from Mickelsmosse, Scania (Larsson 1996) and Arreskov, Fyn (Fischer 1996). A find from Klappholz in Schleswig-Holstein has an Allerød date and is about the same age as the reindeer rib from Nørre Lyngby. Whether the two Scandinavian hammers should be ascribed to the Brommian or to the Ahrensburgian remains problematic, however the present author is in favour of a Brommian origin, since the Ahrensburgian is still unknown from Scania.

Apparently, we cannot use this characteristic reindeer implement as a type fossil and, furthermore, even the original hammer from Nørre Lyngby has now been AMS-dated to the late Preboreal (**Table 7**) (Aaris-Sørensen / Mühldorff / Brinch Petersen 2007; Stensager 2004). Although this is the second youngest reindeer date from southern Scandinavia, the result must nevertheless be accepted, since this particular hammer also bears typically Maglemose ornamentation. The youngest date for a hammer, from Bara in Scania, must probably now also be accepted (*contra* Larsson 1996), given the young date for Nørre Lyngby (**Table 7**). In conclusion, we can only say that for as long as reindeer and reindeer hunters coexisted, the latter will have apparently fabricated such antler implements (Clausen 2005; Nordmann 1936).

As mentioned before, all sites, with the exception of a few from Zealand, are of small size. Most interesting of them all is Ærø (7), which has been presented and discussed by Holm (1973), who sees it as a kill site with the remains of at least 87 tanged points. For the present author, this collection of only lithic points represents a cache, in which some of the points show impact scars. Unfortunately, the points came from different private collections and a later excavation did not provide much information.

Despite the fact that the Brommian has been known for such a long time there is still a lack of information concerning both its general chronology and the seasonal round. Its internal chronology has been based either upon the presence of alleged Federmessergruppen types, representing an older phase (Petersen 2006), or on interpretation of seriation diagrams including burins (Fischer / Nielsen 1987; Johansson 1996; 2002;

Site	Lab no.	BP	cal BC 1std.	References
Bara	OxA-2793	9 090±90	8 451-8 232	Larsson 1996
Nørre Lyngby	AAR-8919	9 110±65	8 426-8 254	Stensager 2004
Arreskov	OxA-3173	10 600±100	10 849-10 452	Fischer 1996
Mickelsmosse	OxA-2971	10 980±110	11 071-10 902	Larsson 1996

Table 7   Radiocarbon dates for reindeer antler hammers from southern Scandinavia.

2003). But as we have demonstrated recently, the burin is a very versatile tool type, which is reworked all the time, whereby the use of such diagrams becomes futile (Pedersen / Brinch Petersen 2006).

In view of the few radiocarbon dates from Bromme sites, and also taking into account the contextually less certain ones, assigning the Brommian to between 11 500 cal BC and 10 500 cal BC seems reasonable for the time being. This is half a millennium later than the latest Hamburgian *sensu lato*, but is also an age range that could indicate a co-existence with the Federmessergruppen, given of course, that the Federmessergruppen tradition was indeed present here in the north during the same interval.

Regarding site distribution, several sites are located in the typically Mesolithic fashion along lakes and rivers, and especially around their inlets and outlets. A new type of site, the cache from Ærø (Holm 1973), adds a new dimension to a Late Glacial culture, as does the recognition of a special hunting area around Knudshoved Odde (Petersen 2001). Unfortunately, no specific Bromme site has been excavated here, but the area is littered with tanged points of a robust type rarely found at the dwelling sites (Petersen 2001). The southern part of the Bromme area, from the central and southern part of Jutland to Mecklenburg-Vorpommern also lacks excavations.

A stylistic approach is perhaps possible when trying to subdivide the Brommian into regional groupings. Just as the Ahrensburgian point and its derivatives are characterized by the different shaping of the tang - by normal, inverse or alternate retouch – so is the tanged point of Bromme type, although the distribution of such subtypes has not yet been mapped accordingly. It might also be interesting to investigate the absolute size of the points, since the contrast between Bromme and Ahrensburgian specimens at some sites of these traditions seems to be very fluid. Even a Hintersee point (Taute 1968) has been recognized in the material from Stoksbjerg Bro.

Contrasting and comparing Bromme and Ahrensburgian sites could also be very interesting, as it can indeed be difficult to distinguish among the two. They do not only share the reindeer antler axe, but from now on, other types such as sandstone arrow shaft polishers are also to be included in the Brommian repertoire (Jensen 2001).

Ahrensburgian 11 000-10 000 cal BC

This is a culture with a very wide distribution, stretching all the way from the Belgian Ardennes to the Oder River and even beyond (Arts 1988; Arts / Deeben 1981; Kobusiewicz 2002). According to the latter author (Kobusiewicz 2002, 119) there is general agreement that both the Ahrensburgian and the Swiderian are derived from the Brommian. However, I, for one, certainly disagree. If the Ahrensburgian is more or less contemporaneous with the Brommian, as is maintained by Clausen (1995; 1996; 1999) based on his own excavation at Alt Duvenstedt in Schleswig-Holstein, then the two should be seen as contemporaneous regional facies, which are very close to each other in a typological sense. Clausen claims an Allerød date

Site	Lab no.	BP	cal BC 1std.	References
Stellmoor	K-4580	9 810±100	9 286-9 266	Fischer / Tauber 1987
Stellmoor	K-4324	9 900±105	9 352-9 299	Fischer / Tauber 1987
Stellmoor	K-4323	9 930±100	9 364-9 321	Fischer / Tauber 1987
Stellmoor	K-4579	9 980±105	9 450-9 382	Fischer / Tauber 1987
Stellmoor	K-4581	9 990±105	9 646-9 389	Fischer / Tauber 1987
Stellmoor	K-4325	10 010±100	9 652-9 448	Fischer / Tauber 1987
Stellmoor	K-4578	10 100±100	9 808-9 697	Fischer / Tauber 1987
Stellmoor	K-4226	10 110±105	9 817-9 701	Fischer / Tauber 1987
Stellmoor	K-4326	10 240±105	10 095-10 032	Fischer / Tauber 1987
Melbeck	Hv-17306	10 515±95	10 690-10 449	
Alt Duvenstedt LA 121	AAR-2245.2	10 770±60	10 904-10 883	Clausen 1998
Alt Duvenstedt LA 121	AAR-2245.1	10 810±80	10 929-10 843	Clausen 1998

Table 8   Ahrensburgian and reindeer dates for Schleswig-Holstein, Germany.

for the Ahrensburgian industry at Alt Duvenstedt on pedological grounds, but the radiocarbon dates gives a slightly later age, at the beginning of the Younger Dryas (**Table 8**).

Nevertheless, with the dates for Duvenstedt LA 121 in Schleswig-Holstein lying around 10 900 to 10 800 cal BC (Clausen 1995; 1996; 1998), there are certainly grounds for suggesting a temporal overlap between the Brommian and the Ahrensburgian (**Table 8**). On the other hand, most other radiocarbon dates for the Ahrensburgian seem to cluster at the very end of the Younger Dryas (Baales 1996; Dewez 1974; Fischer / Tauber 1987). Whether all the dates from Stellmoor obtained upon reindeer remains are relevant for the Ahrensburgian remains problematic, since there are also some later dates on »Boreal« faunal elements apparently relating to unrecognized Mesolithic horizons at the same site (Bratlund 1996).

To begin with the evidence from Stellmoor (Bokelmann 1991a; Bratlund 1990; 1996; Grønnow 1987), it is still the annual migration behaviour of reindeer that is used to explain the Ahrensburgian settlement pattern. In accordance with Rust (1943), Bokelmann (1979) has argued for a transhumance between autumn and winter residence in the north and summer residence to the south of the Elbe River. The same idea has been forwarded most explicitly by Baales (1996; 2000), who sees herds of reindeer leaving their northern winter quarters in order to use different areas of the upland Mittelgebirge as calving grounds. These interpretations refer back to previous analyses of Danish reindeer material by Degerbøl / Krog (1959), who unfortunately stated that »Altogether, the large amount of shed antlers, and that of young animals and females, too, in Denmark indicates that at least many reindeer lived in this area even in winter«.

The same conclusion has apparently also been reached by Larsson et al. (2002), who claim winter hunting based upon the evidence from Hässlaberga. Unfortunately, they omit to provide information about the osteological evidence, which makes it difficult to accept the claim for a winter presence of the reindeer in Scania during the Younger Dryas. Most recently, it has been concluded on the same subject that »During the Younger Dryas and the Preboreal newborns (of reindeer) together with young calves and cows from May to June definitely testifies to southern Scandinavia as a calving ground« (Aaris-Sørensen / Mühldorff / Brinch Petersen 2007). This is quite the opposite interpretation, meaning that reindeer were here in the summer, but left the area during the fall or early winter. Apparently, they also passed through the Ahrensburg Tunnel Valley, as witnessed by the many remains from the Stellmoor upper horizon. A north-south oriented migration pattern for the south Scandinavian reindeer herd must therefore be abandoned. Instead, the trajectory from the north is replaced by an east-west directional focus, a pattern which could indeed have existed during the whole of the Late Glacial (Aaris-Sørensen / Mühldorff / Brinch Petersen 2007; Rust 1937). It must finally be borne in mind that it is simply not possible to give a qualified seasonal determination of the herd in question on the basis of a single stray find of reindeer antler; only with the help of an assemblage of several reindeer can the seasonal question be adequately approached.

The identification of a much more varied fauna at the Kartstein rock shelter in the Eifel (Baales 1996) and at Remouchamps in the Ardennes (Bouchud 1974; Gordon 1988) simply demonstrates that the further to the south the Ahrensburgian is present, the less it is forced to rely on reindeer only. We can discuss the following South Scandinavian evidence:

1) Hjarup Mose, Jutland (Andersen 1977).
2) Fiil Sø, Jutland (Becker 1971).
3) Dværgebakke, Jutland (Møbjerg / Rostholm 2006; Sørensen 2007).
4) Sølbjerg 1, Lolland (Petersen / Johansen 1993; 1996).
5) Ellebjerg, Lolland (excavation in 2006 by Sydsjællands Museum).
6) Eskebjerg, Knudshoved Odde, Zealand (Pedersen / Hansen 2006; Rasmussen 1972).
7) (?) Stoksbjerg Vest, Section I, Zealand (Johansson 1996; 2002; 2003).

Additionally, a fair number of stray and single finds of so-called Ahrensburgian points has been found all over southern Scandinavia (Andersson / Knarrström 1999), but whether these indeed represent the Ahrensburgian is quite another matter. Firstly, similar points have been identified in the Mesolithic Kongemose culture (Petersen 1977) and secondly, smaller tanged points, less than 5 cm in length (Taute 1968), often also appear in the Brommian. These single stray-finds will therefore not be taken as indicators of the Late Glacial Ahrensburgian and shall be left aside. Applying this criterion, it appears that there are no genuine Ahrensburgian sites from Scania, despite claims made for this (Andersson / Knarrström 1999).

The excavator of Stoksbjerg Vest (7) has referred Section I of the site to the Ahrensburgian (Johansson 2002; 2003) and this cultural designation, although erroneous, has also been followed by others (Eriksen 2002). Several authors (Fischer / Nielsen 1987; Johansson 1996; 2002; 2003; Petersen 2001) have described at great length the proportion of tanged points with or without a preserved bulbar end; the latter the result of using the Zwillingskerbrest (twin microburin) technique (Bohmers 1947; Taute 1968). However, this practise of snapping off the bulbar end of tanged points is not reserved for the Ahrensburgian alone, but can also be found within a Bromme context (Pedersen / Brinch Petersen 2006). At the present, therefore, the site (or sites) at Eskebjerg constitutes the easternmost occurrence in Denmark. However, Eskebjerg, as well as Ellebjerg, are both very rich in content so that we cannot regard them as evidence for pioneers. By contrast, Dværgebakke in central Jutland certainly has all the characteristics of a pioneering site, such as being situated far ahead of its neighbours and having only a small lithic assemblage. Unfortunately, this particular material is mixed with other lithic concentrations of Mesolithic age (Sørensen 2007).

There are no radiocarbon dates available for the Danish Ahrensburgian, so we cannot evaluate the possibility of a temporal overlap between the youngest Brommian and the oldest Ahrensburgian. There might in fact have been a pause in human occupation of southern Scandinavia between the Brommian and the Ahrensburgian, at the same time that elk and horse are absent from the region. The same gap seems also to be represented in the British Isles (Jacobi 2004), while the classic Ahrensburgian in the Netherlands moved away from the northern part of the region in order to settle further south during the cold interval of the Younger Dryas (Rensink 2000). Against this background Dværgebakken in Jutland (3) would represent a true pioneering site.

Having rejected the reindeer hammer as a typical Ahrensburgian artefact, there now remains only the »biserial harpoon, double barbed and with a stem of a circular section«, also known as Havel type 12B (Clark 1936; Kozłowski 1981). For Taute (1968) this too was an Ahrensburgian type, but recently two pie-

Site	Lab no.	BP	cal BC 1std.	References
Belloy-sur-Somme	OxA-426	9 720 ±130	-	Fagnart 1997
Sproughton	HAR-259	9 880 ±120	-	Wymer / Jacobi / Rose 1975; Wymer / Rose 1976
Belloy-sur-Somme	OxA-723	9 890 ±150	-	Fagnart 1997
Belloy-sur-Somme	OxA-722	10 110 ±130	-	Fagnart 1997
Uxbridge	OxA-1902	10 010 ±120	9 761-9 326	Lewis 1991
Belloy-sur-Somme	OxA-724	10 260 ±160	-	Fagnart 1997
Uxbridge	OxA-1788	10 270 ±100	10 396-9 869	Lewis 1991

Table 9   Radiocarbon dates for the Long Blade Industry from England and France.

ces from Bützsee in Brandenburg have been AMS dated, one to Younger Dryas and the other to within the early Preboreal (Cziesla / Pettitt 2003). So far, none of the Danish harpoons have been dated, but this particular type also seems to be closely associated with the presence of reindeer.

In conclusion, the Ahrensburgian occupation of southern Scandinavia can be seen in many ways. It is perhaps a new pioneering push that comes in at a very late date, the end of the Younger Dryas, and during this push extends far up into central Jutland. Its residential area occupies only the southern part of Denmark. Alternatively, it may represent repeated Ahrensburgian visits to an area already occupied by the Brommian.

Any such potential encounter, whether friendly or hostile, has unfortunately left no evidence still recognizable today. With no reliable radiocarbon dates it is indeed difficult to say much at all about the local Ahrensburgian. To date, there is no evidence for its continuation into the Preboreal from either southern Scandinavia or Schleswig-Holstein.

From the sites of Eskebjerg and Sølbjerg come single points of the so-called Chwalibogowice type (Taute 1968). The presence of this type might be a hint as to the ultimately eastern origin of the eastern Danish Ahrensburgian; however similar single finds have also been located in Lower Saxony (Gerken 2001; Taute 1968).

During the final part of the Younger Dryas reindeer seems to be the only surviving species, with a calving area in southern Scandinavia. Unfortunately, none of the Danish Ahrensburgian sites preserve faunal remains and we are perhaps forced to use the Hamburgian *sensu lato* as a model for this period as well. In both cases reindeer was the only game species present on the tundra. While it has been argued that reindeer migration routes across the prehistoric landscape could be reconstructed by aligning Late Palaeolithic sites of various ages (Petersen / Johansen 1993; 1996; Petersen 2006), without any faunal evidence such an idea becomes, of course, self fulfilling.

Epi-Ahrensburgian and the Long Blade Industry 10 000-9 500 cal BC

The final part of the Ahrensburgian was assigned by Taute (1968) to what he named the Diddersee-Lavesum group, which would be defined by the presence of many microliths and the absence of tanged points and should bridge the transition between Younger Dryas and the Early Preboreal. Neither this group, nor any of Taute's other Ahrensburgian groups has been confirmed by subsequent discoveries of further sites and none has been confirmed by radiocarbon dates. Gob (1988; 1991) was the first researcher after Taute to assign more assemblages to this group under his definition of the Epi-Ahrensburgian. Later, Johansen and Stapert (2000) assigned the Dutch sites of Oudehaske and Gramsbergen to this group and suggested

Site	Lab no.	BP	cal BC 1std.	References
Årup context 1	-	9 390 ±65	-	Nilsson / Hanlon 2006

Table 10   Radiocarbon date, *terminus ante quem*, for an Epi-Ahrensburgian context from Scania.

that many more sites ought to be included. Other sites are Waubach in the Netherlands (Arts 1984), Gahlen in the Rhineland (Richter 1981) and Höfer (Veil 1987) in Lower Saxony. The only radiocarbon date for this group is from Gramsbergen, but this seems to be too young (Lanting / Van der Plicht 1996).

At the same period there is also the so-called »Long Blade Industry« (LBI).For some researchers this represents a culture at the same hierarchical level as the Epi-Ahrensburgian or the Federmessergruppen (Bodu / Valentin 1991). For others, however, this is merely a technology which is employed when sites are situated next to a rich source of flint in which intensive flint knapping has taken place (Froom 2005) for the production of blades more than 10 cm in length using a soft hammer technique. The characteristic bruised blades have been interpreted by some workers as the result of preparing the surface of a chalk hammer stone (Bodu / Valentin 1991), whereas others see them as having been used to work wood and antler (Arts 1984; Barton 1998). This particular industry or technology is also known as the Belloisien or the »industrie à pieces machurées« and is found in particular around Somme River in north-eastern France (Fagnart 1997), in the Paris Basin (Bodu / Valentin 1991) as well as in eastern England (Barton 1998, Froom 2005). Horse seems to be the only species hunted (or preserved), both at at Belloy-sur-Somme and elsewhere.

According to Barton (1998) the LBI can be defined by: 1) Presence of blades more than 12 cm. long. 2) Presence of bruised blades. 3) Dominance of blade production. 4) High quality raw material is frequently available within a few hundred metres of the sites. 5) Blade cores with opposed platform types, and individual cores may display crested backing. 6) Use of soft hammer stones.

Due to the presence of long blades (Gross- and Riesenklingen) in the Ahrensburgian (Taute 1968) some authors have linked the later part of the Ahrensburgian with the Long Blade Industry, in particular in western Germany, where Jöris and Thissen (1995) described a lithic assemblage from the site of Übach-Palenberg on the German-Dutch border.

Three radiocarbon dates from Belloy-sur-Somme fall around 10 000 cal BC (**Table 9**) (Fagnart / Coudret 2000), with similar results from Uxbridge, while dates for Sproughton and the youngest from Belloy-sur-Somme are somewhat younger (Barton 1998).

Although several radiocarbon dates for reindeer from Stellmoor fall into the Preboreal (Fischer / Tauber 1986) there is no evidence for a survival of the Ahrensburgian into the early Preboreal period (Bratlund 1996). As a matter of fact, any one of the described Late Glacial industries could be reconstructed with material from the Stellmoor Hügel (Hill) surface collections (Taute 1968). Chronologically, only the Epi-Ahrensburgian of the Netherlands and western Germany can be placed at this time, perhaps with the addition of the Long Blade Industry, provided this can be interpreted as a tradition and not simply an expedient technology. In south Scandinavia the following sites are of relevance for this context:

   1) Nørregaard VI, Jutland (Sørensen / Sternke 2006).

   2) Bonderup, Zealand (Fischer 1978; 1982).

   3) Årup context 1, Scania (Nilsson / Hanlon 2006).

These three sites are, for the time being, the only ones from southern Scandinavia that can be considered transitional, the first one being related to the Long Blade Industry, while the other two belong to the Epi-Ahrensburgian. There are no direct radiocarbon dates from any of the three sites, but a radiocarbon sample from the layer above context 1 at Årup gives a terminus ante quem for this particular material (**Table 10**). The excavators favour a date at the end of the Late Glacial (Nilsson / Hanlon 2006), but the age of the assemblage might equally well be early Preboreal.

1) The tool component at Nørregård VI is much richer than is normally seen at LBI sites and includes blade end scrapers, numerous burins and burin spalls, microliths, showing use of the microburin technique, some bruised blades and flake- and core-axes with a couple of axe rejuvenation flakes. The first two mentioned tool categories, blade end scrapers and burins, clearly reflect a Palaeolithic mode, whereas the microliths, microburins and axe component are in the Mesolithic mode. This particular site has therefore tentatively been placed right on the boundary between Younger Dryas and the Preboreal, which is also in accordance with the radiocarbon dates from southern England and northern France. No evident structures were found, but a sort of a roundhouse/tent has been envisaged based on the intra-site distribution maps.

How to explain the presence of such an industry at one single site in central Jutland? If we are dealing with a cultural tradition with a distribution in easternmost England and north-eastern France, then a large stretch of Doggerland must also have been occupied by the same culture in order to explain its presence in Jutland. On the other hand, if the bruised blades are merely the result of a technology for the shaping or renewal of soft stone hammers or for working bone and wood, then Nørregaard VI becomes easier to understand, since some of the German Ahrensburgian sites also have what Taute (1968) referred to as Gross- and Riesenklingen, i.e. heavy and sturdy long blades, some of which even show characteristic bruising on the bulbar face. Nørregaard VI also differs from most other LBI sites not only in its sheer number of tools and typologically later »signature«, but also by the fact that it was not situated next to a rich flint occurrence.

2) The site of Bonderup (Åmosen Bog), excavated by Fischer in 1976, is much more difficult to deal with. The relationship with the Bromme site excavated nearby (Mathiassen 1959) remains unclear, as does the integrity of the material. Nevertheless, it has been suggested that this particular site could represent a »missing link« between the Final Palaeolithic and the Early Mesolithic with a date either at the end of the Younger Dryas, or at the beginning of the Preboreal (Fischer 1978; 1982).

3) Årup, context 1 is a very interesting and well-documented site. Due to its lithic technology and typology it can be regarded as Epi-Ahrensburgian. Most of the lithics have been made of the locally available Kristianstad flint, while some Senonian flint shows import of material from south-western Scania. There were no tanged points and the microliths are of simple lanceolate type. Following the reconstruction of the authors, Årup context I represents a very small site, perhaps the remains of a simple butchering situation, although no faunal remains were preserved.

With one single site, Nørregård VI, showing affinities with the LBI and the two others, Bonderup and Årup context 1, resembling the Epi-Ahrensburgiana, a new enigma has perhaps been added to the ones already present in the Late Glacial of southern Scandinavia. For some researchers, these industries appear to be very appropriate for the attempt to link the Late Glacial Ahrensburgian with the early Holocene Maglemosian (Barton 1998; Johansen / Stapert 2000; Sørensen / Sternke 2006). Perhaps the former Early Preboreal hiatus (Brinch Petersen 1973) will now be filled with this type of industry, although the relevant radiocarbon dating evidence still eludes us.

Early Maglemosian 9 700-8 700 cal BC

This Mesolithic culture is the last to be dealt with and, according to the available radiocarbon dates, could already be present from the very beginning of the Preboreal period (Hansen / Brinch Petersen / Aaris-Sørensen 2004). The Maglemosian, like the Ahrensburgian, has a very wide distribution, from Picardy in north-

Site	Lab no.	BP	cal BC 1 std.	References
Star Carr	OxA-2343	9 350 ±90	8 751-8 476	Dark et al. 2006
Star Carr	OxA-1154	9 500 ±120	9 128-8 642	Dark 1998
Star Carr	OxA-10808	9 505 ±609	9 119-8 732	Dark et al. 2006
Star Carr	OxA-10809	9 530 ±55	9 120-8 765	Dark et al. 2006
Star Carr	OxA-4578	9 570 ±90	9 151-8 832	Dark et al. 2006
Star Carr	OxA-4577	9 670 ±100	9 255-8 846	Dark et al. 2006
Star Carr	OxA-1176	9 700 ±160	9 295-8 831	Dark 1998

Table 11   Maglemose radiocarbon dates for Star Carr, England.

eastern France (excavation by T. Ducrocq at Warluis), over eastern England and Yorkshire, across the now drowned landscape of Doggerland, with Brown Bank as one point of reference (Louwe Kooijmans 1971) and perhaps Europoort as a second (Verhart 1988; 1990), into Denmark, Scania, northern Germany and north-western Poland (Bagniewski 2001).

Although it has been suggested that the lack of early Preboreal Mesolithic sites could be explained by a late survival of the Ahrensburgian (Hansen / Pedersen 2006), at the moment this does not seem to be the case. Only in Poland do we have such a late survival of the local Swiderian (Schild 1996), so for the time being, the Maglemosian seems to start with the beginning of the Preboreal period.

In »later« Ahrensburgian assemblages, such as the Diddersee-Lavesum group of Taute (1968) or the Epi-Ahrensburgian of Gob (1988; 1991) a number of microliths showing use of the microburin technique are present, not only as lanceolates but also as triangles. However, the same is also true of some sites of the LBI such as Nørregård IV (Sørensen / Sternke 2006) and the Kings Site, Mildenhall, Suffolk (Barton 1998). The very same microliths also form part of the Early Maglemosian, but here the triangular forms appear somewhat later than the simple points (Brinch Petersen 1973; Sørensen 2006). On an interpretation of the microliths as time-ordered types, one could perhaps argue that all three industries, the Final or Epi-Ahrensburgian, the LBI and the Early Maglemose, existed side by side on the dry landscape of the Doggerland at the beginning of the Preboreal, however this can be neither proved nor disproved.

The genesis of the early Maglemosian has recently been discussed by Gramsch (2004), who sees an influence from the south, from Federmessergruppen which had previously been displaced from the north by the cold of the Younger Dryas. He presents inter alia a typological development of barbed points and fish leisters from a late Magdalenian to an early Mesolithic context. Spindle-shaped bone points are also considered, as are fishhooks and even some pieces of art. In the case of the latter, only the barbed lines reflect a Maglemose identity, while a lozenge pattern is more likely a later characteristic. Cziesla (2004) sees a local development of Maglemose fishing gear from Late Palaeolithic types. The definition of the Epi-Ahrensburgian and its perceived distribution across Northern Europe from present day Belgium to Scania could present another good candidate. However, in view of the diversity of information (David 2006a; 2006b; Sørensen 2006; Toft 2006), we need to examine a broad range of sites and stray finds before anything definitive can be said.

Radiocarbon dates for Star Carr (**Table 11**) were all made on archaeological artefacts, both from the original excavation by Clark (1954; Dark et al. 2006) and from a more recent excavation in 1985 (Mellars / Dark 1998). They seem to fall into two different periods, the oldest being around 9 100 cal BC, while the younger ones are around 8 500 cal BC, in accordance with a stratigraphical sequence from the bog (Dark 1998; 2000). The Star Carr dates are therefore not particular old within the Preboreal period and neither are the dates for Thatcham V (Barton 1991, 240).

Site	Lab no.	BP	cal BC 1 std.	References
Friesack 4	Bln-1914	9 450±65	8 825-8 626	Görsdorf / Gramsch 2004
Friesack 4	Bln-2753	9 490±100	9 121-8 641	Görsdorf / Gramsch 2004
Friesack 4	Bln-2761	9 560±100	9 141-8 787	Görsdorf / Gramsch 2004
Friesack 4	Bln-2756	9 630±100	9 226-8 841	Görsdorf / Gramsch 2004
Friesack 4	Bln-3019	9 640±70	9 227-8851	Görsdorf Gramsch 2004
Friesack 4	Bln-3036	9 680±70	9 256-8 919	Görsdorf / Gramsch 2004
Friesack 4	Bln-2828	9 640±70	9 227-8 851	Görsdorf / Gramsch 2004
Friesack 4	Bln-3020	9 640±60	9 226-8 854	Görsdorf / Gramsch 2004
Friesack 4	Bln-3001	9 580±60	9 136-8 826	Görsdorf / Gramsch 2004
Friesack 4	Bln-3026	9 670±60	9 247-8 924	Görsdorf / Gramsch 2004

Table 12   Friesack, Brandenburg/Germany. Maglemose radiocarbon dates for phase I.

Maglemose radiocarbon dates from Friesack, phase I (Brandenburg/Germany)
Radiocarbon dates from Friesack 4, of which only the oldest horizon is quoted here (**Table 12**; Gramsch 2001; Görsdorf / Gramsch 2004), do not represent the oldest Maglemose site in Brandenburg, as the site of Friesack 27a in the same bog should be slightly earlier according to the palynological evidence (Gramsch 1991). Friesack 4 has been assigned to the middle of the Preboreal period (Gramsch 2001).

Of the several dates from Bedburg-Königshoven two results on plant material from the gyttja containing the archaeological layer show the best agreement with the palynologically established mid-Preboreal date of the site (**Table 13**; Street 1999). In recent discussion of the proper designation of this particular site Johansen and Stapert (2000) have suggested that it might be older than the Maglemosian and equivalent to the Epi-Ahrensburgian. Dates for Duvensee come from three different sites, but are all in good accordance with the other Preboreal dates (**Table 13**).

Probably the worst problem to be dealt with for this period is the plateau in the calibration curve between 10 000 and 9 600 cal BC (Baales et al. 2002; Cziesla / Pettitt 2003; Mellars 1990). This makes it difficult to pinpoint the exact end of the Ahrensburgian and the beginning of the Maglemosian, but most dwelling sites of the Maglemosian appear during the middle of the Preboreal, around 9 300 cal BC.

The presence of the Maglemosian over such a large area testifies to a certain dynamism, but from where and by whom? One could, of course, suggest that, since only the Ahrensburgian, the Epi-Ahrensburgian and the LBI have a comparable broad distribution, the amalgamation of these three entities could have led to a »Mesolithisation« of the lithic industry. Unfortunately, none of the spatial and/or chronological Ahrensburgian groups proposed by Taute (1968) has been confirmed by independent radiocarbon dates. The southern Scandinavian evidence is as follows:

1) Draved 604 S, 611 and 329 Jutland (Sobotta 1991).
2) Klosterlund, Jutland (Brinch Petersen 1967; Mathiassen 1937).
3) Flaadet, Langeland (Skaarup 1979).
4) Skottemarke, elk deposits, cultural horizon, Lolland (Fischer 1996; Møhl 1980; Sørensen 1980).
5) Lundby kettle-hole, Zealand (Hansen / Brinch Petersen / Aaris-Sørensen 2004).
6) Barmosen I, Zealand (Johansson 1990).
7) Favrbo, Zealand (Møhl 1980).
8) Vig, Zealand (Fischer 1996; Hartz / Winge 1906).
9) Øresø Mølle, Zealand, pending excavation.
10) Bjergby Enge, Zealand (Andersen 1981).

Site	Lab no.	BP	References
Duvensee 6	KI-1111	9 100±130	Bokelmann / Averdieck/ Wilkomm 1981
Duvensee 2	KI-1884.02	9 280±100	Bokelmann / Averdieck/ Wilkomm 1981
Duvensee 6	KI-1110	9 300±180	Bokelmann / Averdieck/ Wilkomm 1981
Duvensee 2	KI-1884.01	9 420±130	Bokelmann / Averdieck/ Wilkomm 1981
Duvensee 8	KI-1819	9 410±110	Bokelmann / Averdieck/ Wilkomm 1981
Duvensee 8	KI-1818	9 640±100	Bokelmann / Averdieck/ Wilkomm 1981
Bedburg-Königshoven	KN-3998	9 600±100	Street 1991
Bedburg-Königshoven	KN-3999	9 780±100	Street 1991

Table 13   Early Mesolithic dates for northern Germany.

11) Årup, context 2, Scania (Nilsson / Hanlon 2006).

12) Henninge Boställe, Scania (Althin 1954).

The distribution of the early Maglemose sites seems to cover the whole region of southern Scandinavia, with the earliest dwelling site at Årup in Scania, context 2 (11). From the Maglemosian onwards, a residential population should now have occupied southern Scandinavia.

Unfortunately, all of the presently known Preboreal dwelling sites, with the exception of Øresø Mølle, are without faunal remains and we therefore only have the deposited elk remains and the wounded aurochs from Vig to represent the actual fauna. However, a number of large game species, both old established and newly arrived ones, are to be expected in this context. The Preboreal could apparently have been a hunter's paradise. Excavation of the Preboreal site of Øresø Mølle on Zealand (9) with its well-preserved bone industry together with numerous faunal remains has therefore now become a desideratum.

Radiocarbon dates for south Scandinavian Preboreal Maglemose sites vary greatly in their quality (**Table 14**). Conventional dates from the Copenhagen laboratory are mostly made on bulk samples of charcoal, except for a number of dated animal remains. Only the dates on individual animal bones have a better resolution. Some of the dates younger than the Preboreal, such as the ones from Draved (Sobotta 1991), are clearly from larger sites with several find concentrations. Klosterlund must also have consisted of several concentrations, to which the present author did not pay much interest in 1967. Only the two oldest dates from Barmosen 1 (Johansson 1990) are used here (Fischer 1996). Dates for two fishing leisters from Skottemarke (Fischer 1996) neatly bracket the one from the deposit containing many elk remains (Møhl 1980), but whether they indeed formed part of the same deposit still remains a problem.

Viewing all the presently available ^{14}C dates might suggest that the early Mesolithic of southern Scandinavia could possibly span the entire Preboreal period and there would, accordingly, no longer be a gap at the beginning of this period (Brinch Petersen 1973; Hansen / Brinch Petersen / Aaris-Sørensen 2004). However, radiocarbon dates from the dwelling sites in England, Denmark, Sweden and Germany all suggest that the Maglemosian begins later within the Preboreal. The question therefore still remains as to what was going on at the beginning of the Preboreal. Dates from the elk deposits at Lundby (Hansen / Brinch Petersen / Aaris-Sørensen 2004) and for the wounded Vig bull (Fischer 1996), as well as dates from fishing leisters (Fischer 1996) all point to an earlier presence of the Maglemosian, provided of course, that these tool types are confined exclusively to the Maglemosian.

Apart from Barmosen I on Zealand (Johansson 1990) and Årup context 2 in Scania the remaining dated dwelling sites are all in Jutland. One other reason why the Preboreal period is not that visible must lie in the

Site	Lab no.	BP	cal BC 1std.	References	
Draved 611	K-790	8 990 ±140	8 330-7 876	Tauber 1967	**Table 14** Radiocarbon dates for the south Scandinavian (Preboreal) Maglemosian.
Draved 611	K-1139	9 250 ±180	8 726-8 285	Tauber 1967	
Draved 332	K-791	8 430 ±140	-	Tauber 1967	
Draved 332	K-1140	9 210 ±180	-	Tauber 1967	
Klosterlund	K-1315	8 920 ±140	8 276-7 841	Tauber 1971	
Klosterlund	K-1316	9 140 ±150	8 604-8 231	Tauber 1971	
Klosterlund	K-1452	9 200 ±140	8 604-8 285	Tauber 1971	
Klosterlund	K-1317	9 230 ±150	8 631-8 289	Tauber 1971	
Draved 604 S	K-1794	8 790 ±140	8 181-7 660	Tauber 1971	
Draved 604 S	K-1465	9 130 ±150	8 607-8 223	Tauber 1971	
Draved 604 S	K-1605	9 280 ±160	8 710-8 303	Tauber 1971	
Skottemarke	OaX-5528	9 310 ±90	-	Fischer 1996	
Barmosen I	K-1359	9 240 ±150	-	Tauber 1971	
Barmosen I	OaX-2248	9 370 ±90	8 772-8 487	Fischer 1996	
Draved 604 S	K-1466	9 390 ±120	9 109-8 463	Tauber 1971	
Skottemarke	K-2075	9 400 ±140	9 144-8 802	Møhl 1980	
Vig	OaX-3616	9 510 ±115	9 132-8 657	Fischer 1996	
Favrbo	K-2071	9 540 ±150	9 174-8 730	Møhl 1980	
Skottemarke	OaX-4864	9 570 ±100	-	Fischer 1996	
Favrbo	K-2070	9 610 ±130	9 211-8 833	Møhl 1980	
Årup, context 2	-	7 395 ±60	6 368-6 224	Nilsson / Hanlon 2006	
Årup, context 2	-	9 650 ±140	9 251-8 836	Nilsson / Hanlon 2006	
Lundby 3	AAR-5471	9 860 ±70	9 393-9 252	Hansen et al. 2004	
Lundby 2	AAR-5470	9 930 ±70	9 648-9 290	Hansen et al. 2004	
Lundby 1	AAR-5469	9 950 ±75	9 652-9 300	Hansen et al. 2004	

fact that during the Preboreal the water table was lower than during the better known Boreal period (Jørgensen 1963; Terberger 2006b). Due to the consequent lack of settlements with preserved faunal remains it becomes difficult to judge whether the Preboreal Maglemosian demonstrated the same seasonal round and settlement systems as have been demonstrated for later Boreal and early Atlantic sites (Andersen / Jørgensen / Richter 1982; Brinch Petersen 1973). Finally, it must be borne in mind that the Maglemosian, in covering so many different areas, does not necessarily have the same settlement pattern all over, and that each regional group could be different from the other.

In conclusion, the Preboreal of southern Scandinavia can be characterized as a strange period. Despite the variety and richness of the environment, informative dwelling sites are certainly missing from the area. Star Carr to the west (Clark 1954; 1972; Mellars / Dark 1998; Conneller / Schadla-Hall 2003), Bedburg-Königshoven (Street 1991; 1999) to the southwest, as well as Friesack and Duvensee to the south (Gramsch 2001; Bokelmann 1991b) all testify to the presence of rich and interesting sites. Nonetheless, quite a number of specimens of the early Mesolithic bone industry is known in our region, most of them stray finds recovered during peat cutting. These include elk-antler adzes, also known from Star Carr (Clark 1954) and Friesack (Pratsch 1994), although this form has its major concentration here in southern Scandinavia (Andersen 1976; Salomonsson 1962). Bodkins made of elk metacarpal bones known from Star Carr are also present here (Salomonsson 1962). The most abundant and important form of all seem to be fish leisters and these are represent by quite an array of different types (Clark 1936; Cziesla 1999; 2001; 2004; Cziesla /

Pettitt 2003; David 2006b; Gramsch 1990; Johansson 2006; Verhart 1988; 1990). At least fishing activities are well represented, as is the evidence for drives and communal hunting of elk, some remains of which were deliberately deposited (Hansen / Brinch Petersen / Aaris-Sørensen 2004). In short, while the Maglemosian of the Preboreal still seems to represent a nearly unknown period in southern Scandinavia, it is one which holds a lot of promise for future investigations.

Coming into southern Scandinavia

In the foregoing account I have tried to discuss the relevant evidence as fairly as possible, but a personal bias is perhaps unavoidable. First of all, neither the available series of radiocarbon dates nor the reliability of information for the various habitation sites are adequate for modern standards. It is also quite clear that more information is needed before this collection of problems can be solved. The following must therefore be considered as a personal voyage attempting to navigate between that perennial Scylla and Charybdis of archaeological studies, the »absence of evidence« or »evidence of absence« syndrome.

Details have been given about the first humans to arrive in the area of present day southern Scandinavia at the end of the last Glacial and at the beginning of the Holocene. This also represents an examination of the border between Renfrew's phase C, the »Final Pleistocene from ca. 15 000 BC and the retreat of the ice« and his phase D, the »Holocene from ca. 8 000 BC prior to the advent of the farming« discussed in his history of European population (Renfrew 2000). In the present case, however, only the small region of southern Scandinavia is being considered. This is one of the last areas of mainland Europe to be settled, but not the final one, as the north-eastern areas of the Baltic were occupied even later, as indeed were the other parts of Scandinavia, despite many claims for the opposite. However, this is certainly another story and better left for another day.

Recently Gamble et al. (2005) have also looked at Renfrew's population history, in particular phase B, »the retreat to the southern refugia during the Late Glacial Maximum of ca. 18 000-15 000 BC« and phase C, from the perspective of Western Europe. They claim to have been successful in using radiocarbon estimates treated as »dates-as-data« as an appropriate proxy for the study of population history at the sub-continental and regional scale. They have furthermore realized that the climate change provides no simple explanation for the major demic expansion that has been identified following 16 000 years ago. They finally claim that the links between genetic and archaeological data are extremely supportive of the study of regional population history, as shown by the timing of the demic expansion, as well as confirming its direction from southern refugia (Gamble et al. 2005).

Certainly, the present study is also about population history, but only about the Stone Age settling of southern Scandinavia. Unfortunately, there are not as many radiocarbon dates as one could wish for and, at the same time dating by pollen zones has been deliberately downplayed, although this used to be de rigeur in a south Scandinavian/north German context of this age (De Klerk 2004).

From the detailed discussion of the archaeological data it should be evident that it is now possible to argue for two opposite chronologies. On one hand there is a chronology based upon radiocarbon dates for lithic industries, on the other hand there is a chronology based upon lithic typological »evolution«, neither of which is confirmed by the other. In this case, which interpretation is to be favoured - an overlapping of different cultures, a straight linear development or something else in-between? There is also the problem of what is going on outside of the highlighted area of southern Scandinavia.

It is, indeed, difficult to imagine, that the relatively small area of southern Scandinavia could have been home to more than one culture at any time. And what about overlapping in time? Is this real or merely an effect of radiocarbon calibration with its problematic plateaux? As an example, if we assign one thousand years to the Brommian, should we not then expect to see some developments or at least some changes in the lithic inventory, but where are they? If overlapping is real, can we then explain it by adding the geographical factor, meaning that changes which originated in one place were then slowly transported across the landscape to other groups of people?

Immigrations and Adaptations

Southern Scandinavia seems to represent the very limit of European human occupation during the Final Palaeolithic/Late Glacial and, driven by the climatic oscillations, there are apparently advances as well as withdrawals. Following the deglaciation reindeer arrives first, together with *Homo sapiens*, followed somewhat later by elk, horse and giant deer. At the very end of the glaciation, during the cold Younger Dryas stadial, only reindeer seems to thrive here, while other animals were forced south or became regionally extinct, only to return, in some cases, at the beginning of the Holocene. Whether early humans did the same under pressure of the extreme cold of the younger Dryas is very difficult to judge by the present material. This might easily be the case, although the present resolution of the data tends to obscure the exact situation.

Such a series of ups and downs perhaps corresponds best with a pulsation model for population dispersal. At around 12 500 cal BC the Hamburgian *sensu stricto* is moving to the north, while the Havelte group takes a step further only a few centuries later. What happened to these two groups subsequently? Did they survive and change into the incoming Federmessergruppen or did they both disappear from the area, perhaps wiped out by famine, a fate so common to the arctic way of life?

Perhaps only a few centuries later, around 11 800 cal BC, the Federmessergruppen make a third push northwards, but do not advance far. Finally, in accord with the Allerød warming, the Brommian is able to advance even further north, into Jutland as well as Scania. The Brommian thus achieves the longest push towards the north, from a residential base on Zealand, but apparently to abandon the region towards the middle of the Younger Dryas. At the very end of the Younger Dryas, the Ahrensburgian makes a final push into the once more unsettled area.

In between all these repeated pushes, southern Scandinavia could have been periodically devoid of humans. I therefore view these initial landnams as a series of human undertakings, which only after two thousand years of trial and error finally succeed with the establishment of the Preboreal early Maglemosian, from which time southern Scandinavia remains populated by humans permanently and through the year.

In a final analysis, none of the »cultures« described above should be considered as either pioneers or residentials. Judging from the diversity of the sites involved, each group includes a residential core as well as a pioneering spearhead, but it is imperative that we should be able to distinguish between the two, especially when trying to investigate the earliest population history of the area. The definition of a pioneering site could therefore be the following; »A small site, the remains of a short stay, not much primary flint working, very few refits among the lithics, mostly only tool repairs and - in a perfect world - the import of some exogenous raw materials to show where the group of people came from«.

References

Aaris-Sørensen 1995: K. Aaris-Sørensen, Paleoecology of a Late Weichselian vertebrate fauna from Nørre Lyngby, Denmark. Boreas 24, 355-365.

1998: K. Aaris-Sørensen, Danmarks forhistoriske Dyreverden, 3rd ed. (Gyldendal 1998).

1999: K. Aaris-Sørensen, The Holocene History of the Scandinavian aurochs (*Bos primigenius* Bojanus, 1827). In: G.-C. Weniger (ed.), Archäologie und Biologie des Auerochsen. Wissenschaftliche Schriften des Neanderthal Museums 1 (Mettmann 1999) 49-57.

2000: K. Aaris-Sørensen, Development of the terrestrial mammal fauna in Fennoscandia after the last glaciation. In: P. Sandgren (ed.), Environmental changes in Fennoscandia during the Late Quaternary. LUNDQUA Report 37, 36-44.

2007: K. Aaris-Sørensen, Fra istid til nutid (Late and Postglacial mammals in Denmark). In: H. H. Baagøe / T. Secher (eds.), Dansk Pattedyratlas (København 2007), 312-321.

Aaris-Sørensen / Liljegren 2004: K. Aaris-Sørensen / R. Liljegren, Late Pleistocene remains of giant deer (Megaloceros giganteus Blumenbach) in Scandinavia: chronology and environment. Boreas 33, 61-73.

Aaris-Sørensen / Petersen / Henriksen 1999: K. Aaris-Sørensen / K. S. Petersen / M. B. Henriksen, Late Weichselian Record of Saiga (*Saiga tatarica* (L.)) from Denmark and its indications of Glacial History and Environment. Quartär 49-50, 87-94.

Aaris-Sørensen / Mühldorff / Brinch Petersen 2007: K. Aaris-Sørensen / R. Mühldorff / E. Brinch Petersen, The Scandinavian reindeer (*Rangifer tarandus*) after the last glacial maximum: Time, seasonality and human exploitation. Journal of Archaeological Science 34, 914-923.

Althin 1954: C. A. Althin, The Chronology of the Stone Age Settlement of Scania, Sweden. I. The Mesolithic Settlement. Acta Archaeologica Lundensia Series in 4°, 1 (Lund 1954).

Andersen 1981: K. Andersen, Bjergby Enge, en tidlig Maglemoseplads. Årbøger for nordisk Oldkyndighed og Historie 1980, 5-12.

Andersen / Jørgensen / Richter 1982: K. Andersen / S. Jørgensen / J. Richter, Maglemose hytterne ved Ulkestrup Lyng. Nordiske Fortidsminder Serie B in 4°, 7 (København 1982).

Andersen 1973: S. H. Andersen, Bro, en senglacial boplads på Fyn. Kuml 1972 (1973), 7-60.

1976: S. H. Andersen, En elgtakøkse fra Fovsåen. Nordslesvigske Museer 3, 9-12.

1977: S. H. Andersen, En boplads fra den ældre stenalder i Hjarup Mose. Nordslesvigske Museer 4, 18-27.

Andersen / Sterum 1971: S. H. Andersen / N. Sterum, Gudenåkulturen. Holstebro museums årsskrift 1970-71, 14-32.

Anderson / Gillam 2000: D. G. Anderson / J. C. Gillam, Paleoindian Colonization of the Americas: Implications from an Examination of Physiography, Demography, and Artifact Distribution. American Antiquity 65/1, 43-66.

Andersson / Knarrström 1999: M. Andersson / B. Knarrström, Senpaleolitikum i Scåne – en studie av materiell kultur och ekonomi hos Sveriges första fångstfolk. Riksantikvarieämbetet. Avdeling för arkeologiska undersökningar. Skrifter 26 (Lund 1999).

Anonymous 2007: Anonymous, Doggerland. Lost world of the Stone Age hunters. Current Archaeology 207, 12-19.

Arts 1984: N. Arts, Waubach: A Late Upper Palaeolithic/Mesolithic Lithic Raw Material Procurement Site in Limburg, The Netherlands. Helinium 24, 209-220.

1988: N. Arts, A survey of Final Palaeolithic archaeology in the Southern Netherlands. In: M. Otte (ed.): De la Loire à l'Oder. Les civilisations du Paléolithique final dans le nord-ouest européen. British Archaeological Reports (International Series) 444 (i) (Oxford 1988) 287-356.

Arts / Deeben 1981: N. Arts / J. Deeben, Prehistorische jagers en verzamelaars te Vessem: een model. Stichting Brabants Heem (Eindhoven 1981).

Audouze 2006: F. Audouze, Essai de modélisation du cycle annuel de nomadisation des Magdaléniens du Bassin de la Somme. Bulletin de la Société Préhistorique Française 104/4, 683-694.

Baales 1996: M. Baales, Umwelt und Jagdökonomie der Ahrensburger Rentierjäger im Mittelgebirge. Monographien des RGZM 38.

2000: M. Baales, L'archéologie du Paléolithique final en Rhénanie du centre et du nord (Allemagne). In: B. Valentin / P. Bodu / M. Christensen (eds.), L'Europe centrale et septentrionale au Tardiglaciaire: confrontation des modèles régionaux de peuplement. Actes de la table-ronde internationale de Nemours 1997. Mémoires du Musée de préhistoire d'Île-de-France 7 (Nemours 2000) 239-252.

Baales et al. 2002: M. Baales / O. Jöris / M. Street / F. Bittmann / B. Weninger / J. Wiethold, Impact of the Late Glacial Eruption of the Laacher See Volcano, Central Rhineland, Germany. Quaternary Research 58, 273-288.

Bagniewski 2001: Z. Bagniewski, Early Holocene Mesolithic groups in the territories of western Poland. Fontes Archaeologici Posnanienses 39, 75-94.

Bang-Andersen 2003: S. Bang-Andersen, Southwest Norway at the Pleistocene/Holocene Transition: Landscape Development, Colonization, Site types, Settlement Patterns. Norwegian Archaeological Review 36, 5-25.

Barton 1991: R. N. E. Barton, Technological Innovation and Continuity at the End of the Pleistocene in Britain. In: N. Barton / A. J. Roberts / D. A. Roe (eds.), The Late Glacial in north-west Europe: Human adaptation and environmental change at the end of the Pleistocene. Council for British Archaeology Research Report 77 (Oxford 1991) 234-245.

1998: R. N. E. Barton, Long Blade Technology and the Question of British Late Pleistocene / Early Holocene Lithic Assemblages. In: N. F. Ashton / F. Healy / P. Pettitt (eds.), Stone Age Archaeology. Essays in honour of John Wymer. Oxbow Monograph 102. Lithic Studies Society Occasional Paper 6, 158-164.

Barton et al. 2003: R. N. E. Barton / R. M. Jacobi / M. Street / D. Stapert, The late glacial reoccupation of the British Isles and the Creswellian. Journal of Quaternary Science 18, 1-13.

Becker 1970: C. J. Becker, Eine Kerbspitze der Hamburger Stufe aus Jütland. In: K. Gripp (ed.), Frühe Menschheit und Umwelt. Rust Festschrift. Fundamenta A/2, (Köln, Wien, Graz 1970) 362-364.

1971: C. J. Becker, Late Palaeolithic Finds from Denmark. Proceedings of the Prehistoric Society 37, 133-139.

Behre 2003: K.-E. Behre, Ein neue Meeresspiegelkurve für die südliche Nordsee. Transgressionen und Regressionen in den letzten 10.000 Jahren. Probleme der Küstenforschung im südlichen Nordseegebiet 28, 9-63.

Benecke 2004: N. Benecke, Faunal succession in the lowlands of northern Europe at the Pleistocene–Holocene transition. In: Th. Terberger / B. V. Eriksen (eds.), Hunters in a changing world. Environment and Archaeology of the Pleistocene - Holocene Transition (ca. 11 000-9 000 B.C.) in Northern Central Europe. Workshop of the U.I.S.P.P.-Commission XXXII at Greifswald, 2002. Internationale Archäologie, Arbeitsgemeinschaft, Symposium, Tagung, Kongress 5 (Rahden / Westfalen 2004) 43-52.

Berglund / Håkansson / Lagerlund 1976: B. E. Berglund / S. Håkansson / E. Lagerlund, Radiocarbon-dated mammoth (*Mammuthus primigenius* Blumenbach) finds in South Sweden. Boreas 5, 177-191.

Bergman et al. 2004: I. Bergman / A. Olofsson / G. Hörnberg / O. Zackrisson / E. Hellberg, Deglaciation and Colonization: Pioneer Settlements in Northern Fennoscandia. Journal of World Prehistory 18/2, 155-177.

Berthelsen 1944: W. Berthelsen, Stenalderbopladser i Sønderkær og Vejledalen. Bidrag til kendskabet til den Mesolitiske kulturperiode i Sydøstjylland. Einar Munksgaard (København 1944).

Binford 1982: L. R. Binford, The Archaeology of Place. Journal of Anthropology and Archaeology 45/1, 4-20.

Bjerck 1995: H. B. Bjerck, The North Sea Continent and the pioneer settlement of Norway. In: A. Fischer (ed.), Man and Sea in the Mesolithic. Oxbow Monograph 53 (Oxford 1995) 131-144.

Björck et al. 1998: S. Björck / M. J. C. Walker / L. C. Cwynar / S. Johnson / K.-L. Knudsen / J. J. Lowe / B. Wohlfarth / INTIMATE-group, An event stratigraphy for the Last Termination in the North Atlantic Region based on the Greenland ice-core record: a proposal by the INTIMATE group. Journal of Quaternary Science 13, 283-292.

Bodu / Valentin 1991: P. Bodu / B. Valentin, L'industrie à pièces mâchurées de Donnemarie-Dontilly (Seine-et-Marne, France): Un faciès tardiglaciaire inédit dans le Bassin Parisien. Préhistoire Européenne, 15-34.

Bohmers 1947: D. Bohmers, Jong-Palaeolithicum en Vroeg-Mesolithicum. In: H. E. Van Gelder, P. Glazema, G. A. Bontekoe, H. Halbertsma / W. Glasbergen (eds.), Een Kwart Eeuw Oudheidkundig Bodemonderzoek in Nederland. Gedenkboek A. E. Van Giffen (Meppel 1947) 129-201.

Bokelmann1978: K. Bokelmann, Ein Federmesserfundplatz bei Schalkholz, Kreis Dithmarschen. Offa 35, 36-54.

1979: K. Bokelmann, Rentierjäger am Gletscherrand in Schleswig-Holstein. Offa 36, 12-22.

1991a: K. Bokelmann, Some new thoughts on old data on humans and reindeer in the Ahrensburgian tunnel valley in Schleswig-Holstein, Germany. In: N. Barton / A. J. Roberts / D. A. Roe (eds.), The Late Glacial in north-west Europe: Human adaptation and environmental change at the end of the Pleistocene. Council for British Archaeology Research Report 77 (Oxford 1991) 72-81.

1991b: K. Bokelmann, Duvensee Wohnplatz 9. Ein präborealzeitlicher Lagerplatz in Schleswig-Holstein. Offa 48, 75-114.

Bokelmann / Averdieck / Wilkomm 1981: K. Bokelmann / F.-R. Averdieck / H. Wilkomm, Duvensee, Wohnplatz 8. Neue Aspekte zur Sammelwirtschaft im frühen Mesolithikum. Offa 38, 21-40.

Bokelmann / Heinrich / Menke 1983: K. Bokelmann / D. Heinrich / B. Menke, Fundplätze der Spätglazials am Hainholz-Esinger Moor, Kreis Pinneberg. Offa 40, 199-239.

Bouchud 1974: J. Bouchud, Étude de la faune ahrensburgienne de Remouchamps. Bulletin de la Societie Royale Belge d'Anthropologie et de Préhistoire 85, 118-127.

Boye 2006: L. D. Boye, Københavns Amt. Kulturhistorisk oversigt. Oldtiden indtil 1050 Københavns Amt & Kroppedal Museum (København 2006).

Bratlund 1990: B. Bratlund, Rentierjagd im Spätglazial. Eine Untersuchung der Jagdfrakturen an Rentierknochen von Meiendorf und Stellmoor, Kreis Stormarn. Offa 47, 7-34.

1996: B. Bratlund, Hunting Strategies in the Late Glacial of Northern Europe: A Survey of the Faunal Evidence. Journal of World Prehistory 10, 1-48.

Breest / Böhmer / Renner 1999: K. Breest / M. Böhmer / F. Renner, Ein spätpaläolithischer Oberflächenfundplatz mit Rücken- und Bromme (Lyngby)-Spitzen bei Dohnsen, Ldkr. Celle. Nachrichten aus Niedersachsens Urgeschichte 68, 3-18.

Breest / Veil 1991: K. Breest / S. Veil, The Late Upper Palaeolithic site of Schweskau, Ldkr. Lüchow-Dannenberg, Germany, and some comments on the relationship between the Magdalenian and Hamburgian. In: N. Barton / A. J. Roberts / D. A. Roe (eds.), The Late Glacial in north-west Europe: Human adaptation and environmental change at the end of the Pleistocene. Council for British Archaeology Research Report 77 (Oxford 1991) 82-99.

Brinch Petersen 1967: E. Brinch Petersen, Klosterlund-Sønder Hadsund-Bøllund. Les trois sites principaux du Maglémosien Ancien en Jutland. Essai de Typologie et de Chronologie. Acta Archaeologica 37, 77-185.

1973: E. Brinch Petersen, A Survey of the Late Palaeolithic and the Mesolithic of Denmark. In: S. K. Kozłowski (ed.), The Mesolithic in Europe (Warsaw 1973) 77-128.

Burch 1972: E. S. Burch jr., The caribou/wild reindeer as a human resource. American Antiquity 37, 339-368.

1991: E. S. Burch jr., Herd following reconsidered. Current Anthropology 32, 439-444.

2005: E. S. Burch jr., Alliance and Conflict. The World System of the Iñupiaq Eskimos (Lincoln, London 2005).

Burdukiewicz 1987: J. M. Burdukiewicz, Zum Forschungsstand der Hamburger Kultur. Jahrbuch des RGZM 34, 143-167.

Burdukiewicz / Herman 2000: J. M. Burdukiewicz / C. F. Herman, Recherches dans la partie orientale de l'aire d'extension hambourgienne: le nouveau site de Siedlnica 17 (Pologne). In: B. Valentin / P. Bodu / M. Christensen (eds.), L'Europe centrale et septentrionale au Tardiglaciaire: confrontation des modèles régionaux de peuplement. Actes de la table-ronde internationale de Nemours 1997. Mémoires du Musée de préhistoire d'Île-de-France 7. (Nemours 2000) 253-271.

Burdukiewicz / Schmider 2000: J. M. Burdukiewicz / B. Schmider, Analyse comparative des points à cran hambourgiennes du Bassin de l'Oder et des pointes à cran magdaléniennes du Bassin parisien. In: B. Valentin / P. Bodu / M. Christensen (eds.), L'Europe centrale et septentrionale au Tardiglaciaire: confrontation des modèles régionaux de peuplement. Actes de la table-ronde internationale de Nemours 1997. Mémoires du Musée de préhistoire d'Île-de-France 7 (Nemours 2000) 97-108.

Casati / Sørensen 2006: C. Casati / L. Sørensen, Bornholm i ældre stenalder. Status over kulturel udvikling og kontakter, Kuml 2006, 9-58.

Charles 1996: R. Charles, Back into the North: the radiocarbon evidence for human recolonization of the North-Western Ardennes after the Last Glacial Maximum. Proceedings of the Prehistoric Society 62, 1-17.

Christiansen / Skelmose 1963: C. H. Christiansen / K. Skelmose, Gudenåkulturen ved Varde Å, Kuml 1962 (1963) 144-156.

Clark 1936: J. G. D. Clark, The Mesolithic Settlement of Northern Europe. Cambridge University Press (Cambridge 1936).

1954: J. G. D. Clark, Excavations at Star Carr (Cambridge 1954).

1972: J. G. D. Clark, Star Carr. A Case Study in Bioarchaeology. Modular Publications 10 (Reading [MA] 1972).

Clausen 1995: I. Clausen, Alt Duvenstedt, Kreis Rendsburg-Eckenförde LA 121: Ein Ahrensburger Kulturvorkommen in allerødzeitlichen Boden. Archäologische Nachrichten aus Schleswig-Holstein 6 (Schleswig 1995) 103-126 .

1996: I. Clausen, Duvenstedt LA 121, Schleswig-Holstein. The occurrence of the Ahrensburgian Culture in soils of the Alleröd Interstadial. A preliminary Report. In: L. Larsson (ed.), The Earliest Settlement of Scandinavia and its relationship with neighbouring areas. Acta Archaeologica Lundensia Series in 8°, 24 (Stockholm 1996) 99-110.

1998: I. Clausen, Neue Untersuchungen an späteiszeitlichen Fundplätzen der Hamburger Kultur bei Ahrenshöft, Kreis Nordfriesland (ein Vorbericht). Archäologische Nachrichten aus Schleswig-Holstein 8, 1997 (Schleswig 1998) 8-49.

1999: I. Clausen, Alt Duvenstedt, Kr. Rendsburg-Eckernförde. Offa 53, 372-373.

2004: I. Clausen, The Reindeer antler axe of the Allerød period from Klappholz LA 63, Kreis Schleswig-Flenburg / Germany. Is it a relict of the Federmesser, Bromme or Ahrensburg culture? In: Th. Terberger / B. V. Eriksen (eds.), Hunters in a changing world. Environment and Archaeology of the Pleistocene - Holocene Transition (ca. 11 000-9 000 B.C.) in Northern Central Europe. Workshop of the U.I.S.P.P.-Commission XXXII at Greifswald, 2002. Internationale Archäologie, Arbeitsgemeinschaft, Symposium, Tagung, Kongress 5 (Rahden / Westfalen 2004) 141-161.

2005: I. Clausen, Das allerødzeitliche Rengeweihbeil aus Klappholz LA 63, Kreis Schleswig-Flensburg. Ein Relikt der Federmesser-, der Bromme- oder der Ahrensburger Kultur? Offa 59-60, 2002-2003 (2005) 15-39.

Clausen / Hartz 1988: I. Clausen, S. Hartz, Fundplätze des Spätglazials am Sorgetal bei Alt Duvenstedt, Kreis Rendsburg-Eckernförde. Offa 45, 17-41.

Coles 1998: B. J. Coles, Doggerland: a speculative survey. Proceedings of the Prehistoric Society 64, 45-81.

Conneller / Schadla-Hall 2005: C. Conneller / T. Schadla-Hall, Beyond Star Carr: The Vale of Pickering in the 10th Millennium BP. Proceedings of the Prehistoric Society 69, 85-105.

Costamagno et al. 2006: S. Costamagno / L. Meigne / B. Cédric / B. Vandermeersch / B. Maureille, Les Pradelles (Marillac-le-Franc, France): A Mousterian reindeer hunting camp? Journal of Anthropological Archaeology 25, 466-484.

Coudret / Fagnart 2006: P. Coudret / J.-P. Fagnart, Données préliminaires sur les habitats des groupes de la tradition à Federmesser du bassin de la Somme. Bulletin de la Société Préhistorique Française 103, 729-740.

Cziesla 1999: E. Cziesla, Zur Territorialität mesolithischer Gruppen in Nordostdeutschland. Ethnographisch-Archäologische Zeitschrift 40, 485-512.

2001: E. Cziesla, Zur Besiedlungsgeschichte von Berlin-Brandenburg: Die Anfänge. In: B. Gehlen / M. Heinen / A. Tillmann (eds.), Zeit- Räume. Gedenkschrift für Wolfgang Taute. Archäologische Berichte 14 (Bonn 2001) 381-396.

2004: E. Cziesla, Late Upper Palaeolithic and Mesolithic cultural continuity – or: bone and antler objects from the Havelland. In: Th. Terberger / B. V. Eriksen (eds.), Hunters in a changing world. Environment and Archaeology of the Pleistocene -

Holocene Transition (ca. 11 000-9 000 B.C.) in Northern Central Europe. Workshop of the U.I.S.P.P.-Commission XXXII at Greifswald, 2002. Internationale Archäologie, Arbeitsgemeinschaft, Symposium, Tagung, Kongress 5 (Rahden / Westfalen 2004) 165-182.

Cziesla / Pettitt 2003: E. Cziesla / P. Pettitt, AMS-^{14}C-Datierungen von spätpaläolithischen und mesolithischen Funden aus dem Bützsee (Brandenburg). Archäologisches Korrespondenzblatt 33, 21-38.

Dark 1998: P. Dark, Radiocarbon Dating of the Lake-edge Deposits. In: P. Mellars / P. Dark, Star Carr in context: new archaeological and palaeoecological investigations at the Early Mesolithic site of Star Carr, North Yorkshire. McDonald Institute Monographs (Cambridge 1998) 119-124.

2000: P. Dark, Revised »absolute« dating of the early Mesolithic site of Star Carr, North Yorkshire, in the light of changes in the early Holocene tree-ring Chronology. Antiquity 74, 304-307.

Dark et al. 2006: P. Dark / T. F. G. Higham / R. Jacobi / T. C. Lord, New Radiocarbon Accelerator Dates on Artefacts from the Early Mesolithic Site of Star Carr, North Yorkshire. Archaeometry 48/1, 185-200.

David 2006a: E. David, Technical behaviour in the Mesolithic (9th-8th millennium cal. BC): The contribution of the bone and antler industry from domestic and funerary contexts. In: L. Larsson / I. Zagorska (eds.), Back to the origin, New research in the Mesolithic-Neolithic Zvejnieki Cemetery and environment, Northern Latvia. Acta Archaeologica Lundensia Series in 8°, 52 (Stockholm 2006) 235-252.

2006b: E. David, Redskaber af ben og tak I tidlig Maglemosekultur – et teknologisk studie. In: B. V. Eriksen (ed.): Stenalderstudier. Tidligt mesolitiske jægere og samlere i Sydskandinavien. Jysk Arkæologisk Selskabs Skrifter 55 (Århus 2006) 77-99.

De Bie / Caspar 2000: M. De Bie / J.-P. Caspar, Rekem. A Federmesser Camp on the Meuse River Bank. Vol I-II. Instituut voor het Archeologisch Patrimonium (Leuven 2000).

De Bie / Van Gils 2006: M. De Bie / M. Van Gils, Les habitats des groupes à Federmesser (aziliens) dans le Nord de la Belgique. Bulletin de la Société Préhistorique Française 103/4, 781-790.

Degerbøl 1946: M. Degerbøl, II. Dyreknogler. In: T. Mathiassen, En senglacial boplads ved Bromme. Aarbøger for nordisk Oldkyndighed og Historie 1946, 136-142.

Degerbøl / Krog 1959: M. Degerbøl / H. Krog, The Reindeer (*Rangifer tarandus*) in Denmark. Biologiske Skrifter udgivet af Det Kongelige Danske Videnskabernes Selskab 10/4 (København 1959).

Dekin 1976: A. A. Dekin jr, Elliptical analysis. An heuristic technique for the analysis of artifact clusters. In: M. S. Maxwell (ed.), Eastern Arctic Prehistory: Paleoeskimo Problems. Memoirs of the Society for American Archaeology 31, 79-88.

De Klerk 2004: P. De Klerk, Confusing concepts in Lateglacial stratigraphy and geochronology: Origin, consequences, conclusions (with special emphasis on the type locality Bøllingsø). Review of Palaeobotany & Palynology 129, 265-298.

Dewez 1974: M. Dewez, Nouvelles recherches à la grotte de Remouchamps. Bullletin de la Société Royale Belge Anthropologique Préhistoire 85, 42-111.

Eberhards / Zagorska 2002: G. Eberhards / I. Zagorska, The environment and the earliest settlement of Latvia, East Baltic. In: B. V. Eriksen / B. Bratlund (eds.), Recent studies in the Final Palaeolithic of the European plain. Proceedings of a U.I.S.P.P. Symposium, Stockholm 1999. Jutland Archaeological Society Publications 39 (Århus 2002) 85-90.

Ekström 1993: J. Ekström, The Late Quaternary History of the Urus (*Bos primigenius* Bojanus 1827) in Sweden. Lundqua Thesis 29, 1-129.

Eriksen 2002: B. V. Eriksen, Reconsidering the geochronological framework of Lateglacial hunter-gatherer colonization of southern Scandinavia. In: B. V. Eriksen / B. Bratlund (eds.), Recent studies in the Final Palaeolithic of the European plain. Proceedings of a U.I.S.P.P. Symposium, Stockholm 1999. Jutland Archaeological Society Publications 39 (Århus 2002) 25-42.

Fagnart 1997: J.-P. Fagnart, La Fin Des Temps Glaciaires Dans le Nord De la France. Approches archéologiques et environnementale des occupations humaines du Tardiglaciaire. Mémoires de la Société Française 24.

Fagnart / Coudret 2000: J.-P. Fagnart / P. Coudret, Le Tardiglaciaire dans le Nord de la France. In: B. Valentin / P. Bodu / M. Christensen (eds.), L'Europe centrale et septentrionale au Tardiglaciaire: confrontation des modèles régionaux de peuplement. Actes de la table-ronde internationale de Nemours 1997. Mémoires du Musée de préhistoire d'Île-de-France 7 (Nemours 2000) 111-128.

Fiedorczuk et al. 2007: J. Fiedorczuk / B. Bratlund / E. Kolstrup / R. Schild, Late Magdalenian feminine flint plaquettes from Poland. Antiquity 81, 311, 97-105.

Fiedorczuk / Schild 2002: J. Fiedorczuk / R. Schild, Wilcyzyce – a new late Magdalenian site in Poland. In: B. V. Eriksen / B. Bratlund (eds.), Recent studies in the Final Palaeolithic of the European plain. Proceedings of a U.I.S.P.P. Symposium, Stockholm 1999. Jutland Archaeological Society Publications 39 (Århus 2002) 91-100.

Fischer 1978: A. Fischer, På sporet af overgangen mellem palæoliticum og mesolitikum i Sydskandinavien. Hikuin 4, 27-50.

1982: A. Fischer, Bonderup-bopladsen. Det manglende led mellem dansk palæolitikum og mesolitikum. Fortidsminder og bygningsbevaring. Antikvariske Studier 5, 87-100.

1990a: A. Fischer, A late palaeolithic »school« of flintknapping at Trollesgave, Denmark. Results from refitting. Acta Archaeologica 60, 33-49.

1990b: A. Fischer, On being a pupil of a flintknapper of 11.000 years ago. A preliminary analysis of settlement organization and flint technology based on conjoined flint artifacts from the Trollesgave site. In: E. Cziesla / S. Eickhoff / N. Arts / D. Winter (eds), The Big Puzzle. International symposium on refitting stone artifacts, Monrepos 1987. Studies in modern Archaeology 1 (Bonn 1990) 447-464.

1990c: A. Fischer, A Late Palaeolithic flint workshop at Egtved, East Jutland – a glimpse of the Federmesser culture in Denmark. Journal of Danish Archaeology 7, 1988 (1990) 7-23.

1991: A. Fischer, Pioneers in deglaciated landscapes: the expansion and adaptation of Late Palaeolithoc societies in Southern Scandinavia. In: N. Barton / A. J. Roberts / D. A. Roe (eds.), The Late Glacial in north-west Europe: Human adaptation and environmental change at the end of the Pleistocene. Council for British Archaeology Research Report 77 (Oxford 1991) 100-121.

1993: A. Fischer, The Late Palaeolithic. In: S. Hvass / B. Storgaard (eds.), Digging Into the Past. The Royal Society of Northern Antiquaries & Jutland Archaeological Society (Århus 1993) 51-56.

1996: A. Fischer, At the Border of human habitat. The late Palaeolithic and early Mesolithic in Scandinavia. In: L. Larsson (ed.), The earliest Settlement of Scandinavia and its relationship with Neighbouring Areas. Acta Archaeologica Lundensia, Series in 8⁰, 24 (Stockholm 1996) 157-176.

Fischer / Nielsen 1987: A. Fischer / F. O. S. Nielsen, Senistidens bopladser ved Bromme. Årbøger for Nordisk Oldkyndighed og Historie 1986 (1987), 5-42.

Fischer / Tauber 1987: A. Fischer / H. Tauber, New C-14 datings of Late Palaeolithic cultures from Northwestern Europe. Journal of Danish Archaeology 5, 1986 (1987) 7-13.

Froom 2005: R. Froom, Late Glacial Long Blade Sites in the Kennet Valley. Excavations and Fieldwork at Avington VI, Wawcott XII and Crown Acres. The British Museum Research Publication Nr. 153 (London 2005).

Gamble 1998: C. Gamble, Palaeolithic society and the release from proximity: a network approach to intimate relations. World Archaeology 29/3, 426-449.

Gamble et al. 2005: C. Gamble / W. Davies / P. Pettitt / L. Hazelwood / M. Richards, The Archaeological and Genetic Foundations of the European Population during the Late Glacial: Implications for »Agricultural Thinking«. Cambridge Archaeological Journal 15/2, 193-223.

Gerken 2001: K. Gerken, Studien zur jung- und spätpaläolithischen sowie mesolithischen Besiedlung im Gebiet zwischen Wümme und Oste. Archäologische Berichte des Landkreises Rotenburg (Wümme) 9 (Oldenburg 2001).

Gob 1988: A. Gob, L'Ahrensbourgien de Fonds-de-Fort et sa place dans le processus de Mésolithisation dans le nord-ouest de l'Europe. In: M. Otte (ed.), De la Loire à l'Oder. Les civilisations du Paléolithique final dans le nord- ouest européen. British Archaeological Research Reports (International Series) 444 (i) (Oxford 1988) 259-285.

1991: A. Gob, The early Postglacial occupation of the southern part of the North Sea Basin. In: N. Barton / A. J. Roberts / D. A. Roe (eds.), The Late Glacial in north-west Europe:

Human adaptation and environmental change at the end of the Pleistocene. Council for British Archaeology Research Report 77 (Oxford 1991) 227-233.

Gordon 1988: B. C. Gordon, Of men and reindeer herds in French Magdalenian prehistory. British Archaeological Re-search Reports (International Series) 390 (Oxford 1998).

1990: B. C. Gordon, More on Herd-Following Hypothesis. Current Anthropology 31/4, 399-400.

Görsdorf / Gramsch 2004: J. B. Görsdorf / B. Gramsch, Interpretations of ¹⁴C-datings of the Mesolithic Site Friesack, Germany. In: T. F. G. Higham / C. Bronk Ramsey / D. C. Owen (eds.), Radiocarbon and Archaeology: Proceedings of the 4th Symposium, Oxford 2002. Oxford School of Archaeology, Monograph 62 (Oxford 2004) 303-311.

Gramsch 1990: B. Gramsch, Die frühmesolithischen Knochernspitzen von Friesack, Kr. Nauen. Veröffentlichungen des Museums für Ur- und Frühgeschichte Potsdam 24, 7-26.

1991: B. Gramsch, Ausgrabungen auf einem weiteren frühmesolithischen Fundplatz bei Friesack, Kr. Nauen. Ausgrabungen und Funde 36, 51-56.

2001: B. Gramsch, Friesack: Letzte Jäger und Sammler in Brandenburg. Jahrbuch des RGZM 47, 51-96.

2004: B. Gramsch, From the Late Palaeolithic to the early Mesolithic in northeastern Germany. In: Th. Terberger / B. V. Eriksen (eds.), Hunters in a changing world. Environment and Archaeology of the Pleistocene - Holocene Transition (ca. 11 000-9 000 B.C.) in Northern Central Europe. Work-shop of the U.I.S.P.P.-Commission XXXII at Greifswald, 2002. Internationale Archäologie, Arbeitsgemeinschaft, Symposium, Tagung, Kongress 5 (Rahden / Westfalen 2004) 183-202.

Grimm 2004: S. Grimm, Ein spätallerödzeitlicher Fundplatz bei Bad Breisig. Kreis Ahrweiler. Berichte zur Archäologie an Mittelrhein und Mosel 9, 11-32.

Grimm / Weber 2008: S. Grimm, M.-J. Weber, The chronological framework of the Hamburgian in the light of old and new ¹⁴C dates. Quartär 55, 17-40.

Grydeland 2005: S. E. Grydeland, The Pioneers of Finnmark – from the earliest coastal settlements to the encounter with the inland people of Northern Finland. In: H. Knutsson (ed.), Pioneer settlements and colonization processes in the Barents region. Vuollerim Papers on Hunter-gatherer Archaeology 1 (Vuollerim 2005) 43-78.

Grønnow 1987: B. Grønnow, Meiendorf and Stellmoor Revisited. An Analysis of Late Palaeolithic Reindeer Exploitation. Acta Archaeologica 56, 131-166.

Hansen / Brinch Petersen / Aaris-Sørensen 2004: K. M. Hansen / E. Brinch Petersen / K. Aaris-Sørensen, Filling the gap: Early Preboreal Maglemose elk deposits at Lundby, Sjælland, Denmark. In: Th. Terberger / B. V. Eriksen (eds.), Hunters in a changing world. Environment and Archaeology of the Pleistocene - Holocene Transition (ca. 11 000-9 000 B.C.) in Northern Central Europe. Workshop of the U.I.S.P.P.-Commission XXXII at

Greifswald, 2002. Internationale Archäologie, Arbeitsgemeinschaft, Symposium, Tagung, Kongress 5 (Rahden / Westfalen 2004) 75-84.

Hansen / Pedersen 2006: K. M. Hansen / K. B. Pedersen, With or Without Bones. Late Palaeolithic Hunters in South Zealand. In: K. M. Hansen / K. B. Pedersen (eds.), Across the Western Baltic. Sydsjællands Museums Publikationer I (Vordingborg 2006) 93-110.

Hartz / Winge 1906: N. Hartz / H. Winge, Om Uroxen fra Vig, såret og dræbt med flintvåben. Aarbøger for nordisk Oldkyndighed og Historie 1906, 225-236.

Hartz 1987: S. Hartz, Neue spätpaläolithische Fundplätze bei Ahrenshöft, Kreis Nordfriesland. Offa 44, 5-52.

Heinemeier / Rud 2000: J. Heinemeier, N. Rud, AMS ^{14}C datings, Århus 1999. Arkæologiske udgravninger i Danmark 1999. Det Arkæologiske Nævn (København 2000) 296-313.

Holm 1973: J. Holm, Istidsjægere på Ærø. Fynske Minder 1972, 5-16.

1993: J. Holm, Settlements of the Hamburgian and Federmesser cultures at Slotseng, South Jutland. Journal of Danish Archaeology 10, 7-19.

1996: J. Holm, The earliest settlement of Denmark. In: L. Larsson (ed.), The Earliest Settlement of Scandinavia and its relationship with neighbouring areas. Acta Archaeologica Lundensia Series in 8°, 24 (Stockholm 1996) 43-60.

Holm / Christensen / Aaris-Sørensen 2002: J. Holm / C. Christensen / K. Aaris-Sørensen, Istidsjægere i Sønderjylland. Nationalmuseet Nyt 94, 10-13.

Holm / Rieck 1992: J. Holm / F. Rieck, Istidsjægere ved Jelssøerne. Hamburgkulturen i Danmark. Skrifter fra Museumsrådet for Sønderjyllands Amt 5 (Haderslev 1992).

Housley / Gamble / Pettitt 2000: R. A. Housley / C. S. Gamble / P. Pettitt, Reply to Blockley, Donahue & Pollard. Antiquity 74, 119-121.

Housley et al. 1997: R. A. Housley / C. S. Gamble / M. Street / P. Pettitt, Radiocarbon evidence for the Late Glacial human recolonisation of Northern Europe. Proceedings of the Prehistoric Society 63, 25-54.

Houtsma et al. 1996: P. Houtsma / E. Kramer / R. R. Newell / J. L. Smit, The Late Palaeolithic Habitation of Haule V: From Excavation Report to the Reconstruction of Federmesser Settlement Patterns and Land-Use (Assen 1996).

Ikinger 1998: E.-M. Ikinger, Der endeiszeitliche Rückenspitzen-Kreis Mitteleuropas. GeoArchaeoRhein 1 (Münster 1998).

Iversen 1942: J. Iversen, En pollenanalytisk tidsfæstelse af ferskvandslagene ved Nørre Lyngby. Meddelelser fra Danmarks Geologiske Forening 10/2, 130-151.

1946: J. Iversen, Geologisk Datering af en Senglacial Boplads ved Bromme. Aarbøger for Nordisk Oldkyndighed og Historie 1946, 198-231.

Jacobi 2004: R. Jacobi, The Late Upper Palaeolithic Lithic Collection from Gough's Cave, Cheddar, Somerset and Human Use of the cave. Proceedings of the Prehistoric Society 70, 1-92.

Jensen 2001: A. N. Jensen, Ældste Stenalder. Jægerstenalder. In: G. Gormsen / I. Kjær Kristensen / N. Mortensen / J. Simonsen (eds.), Skive kommunes historie fra oldtid til 1880 (Skive 2001) 11-14.

Jessen / Nordmann 1915: A. Jessen, V. Nordmann, Ferskvandslagene ved Nørre Lyngby. D. G. U. 2. Række 29.

Johansen 2000: L. Johansen, The Late Palaeolithic in Denmark. In: B. Valentin / P. Bodu / M. Christensen (eds.), L'Europe centrale et septentrionale au Tardiglaciaire: confrontation des modèles régionaux de peuplement. Actes de la table-ronde internationale de Nemours 1997. Mémoires du Musée de préhistoire d'Île-de-France 7 (Nemours 2000) 197-215.

Johansen / Stapert 2000: L. Johansen / D. Stapert, Two »Epi-Ahrensburgian« Sites in the Northern Netherlands: Oudehaske (Friesland) and Gramsbergen (Overijssel). Palaeohistoria 39-40, 1997-1998 (2000) 1-87.

2004: L. Johansen / D. Stapert, Oldeholtwolde. A Hamburgian family encampment around a hearth. A. A (Lisse 2004).

Johansson 1990: A. D. Johansson, Barmosegruppen. Præboreale bopladsfund i Sydsjælland (Århus 1990).

1996: A. D. Johansson, Stoksbjerg Vest and Knudshoved Odde. A Base Camp and Kill Sites from the Bromme Culture in South Zealand, Denmark. In: L. Larsson (ed.), The Earliest Settlement of Scandinavia and its relationship with neighbouring areas. Acta Archaeologica Lundensia Series in 8°, 24 (Stockholm 1996) 89-98.

2002: A. D. Johansson, Late Palaeolithic settlement in South Zealand, eastern Denmark. In: B. V. Eriksen / B. Bratlund (eds.), Recent studies in the Final Palaeolithic of the European plain. Proceedings of a U.I.S.P.P. Symposium, Stockholm 1999. Jutland Archaeological Society Publications 39 (Århus 2002) 61-74.

2003: A. D. Johansson, Stoksbjerg Vest. Et senpalæolitisk Fundkompleks ved Porsmose, Sydsjælland. Fra Bromme- til Ahrensburgkultur i Norden. Nordiske Fortidsminder, Serie C 3 (København 2003).

2006: A. D. Johansson, Maglemosekulturens fiskepladser i Køng Mose og Barmose, Sydsjælland. In: B. V. Eriksen (ed.), Stenalderstudier. Tidligt mesolitiske jægere og samlere i Sydskandinavien. Jysk Arkæologisk Selskabs Skrifter 55 (Århus 2006) 119-134.

Jørgensen 1963: S. Jørgensen, Early Postglacial in Aamosen. Geological and Pollen-Analytical Investigations of Maglemosian Settlements in the West-Zealand Bog Aamosen, vol I and II. Danmarks Geologiske Undersøgelse II række 87 (København 1963).

Jöris / Thissen 1995: O. Jöris / J. Thissen, Übach-Palenberg. In: W. Schirmer (ed.), INQUA 1995. Quaternary field trips in Central Europe 2 (München 1995) 957-961.

Jöris / Weninger 2002: O. Jöris / B. Weninger, ^{14}C-Alterskalibration und die absolute Chronologie des Spätglazials. Archäologisches Korrespondenzblatt 30, 461-471.

Kabacinski et al. 2002: J. Kabacinski / R. Schild / B. Bratlund / L. Kubiak-Martens / K. Tobolski / K. van der Borg / A. Pazdur, The Lateglacial sequence at the Hamburgian site at Mirkowice: stratigraphy and geochronology. In: B. V. Eriksen / B. Bratlund (eds.), Recent studies in the Final Palaeolithic of the European plain. Proceedings of a U.I.S.P.P. Symposium, Stockholm 1999. Jutland Archaeological Society Publications 39 (Århus 2002) 109-116.

Kaiser / Clausen 2005: K. Kaiser / I. Clausen, Palaeopedology and Stratigraphy of the Late Palaeolithic Alt Duvenstedt Site, Schleswig-Holstein (Northwest Germany). Archäologisches Korrespondenzblatt 35, 447-466.

Kankaanpää / Rankama 2005: J. Kankaanpää / T. Rankama, Early Mesolithic pioneers on Northern Finnish Lapland. In: H. Knutsson (ed.), Pioneer settlements and colonization processes in the Barents region. Vuollerim Papers on Hunter-gatherer Archaeology 1 (Vuollerim 2005) 109-161.

Kobusiewicz 2002: M. Kobusiewicz, Ahrensburgian and Swiderian: two different modes of adaptation? In: B. V. Eriksen / B. Bratlund (eds.), Recent studies in the Final Palaeolithic of the European plain. Proceedings of a U.I.S.P.P. Symposium, Stockholm 1999. Jutland Archaeological Society Publications 39 (Århus 2002) 117-122.

Kozłowski 1975: S. K. Kozłowski, Quelques remarques sur le Brommien. Acta Archaeologica 46, 134-142.

1981: S. K. Kozłowski, Single-barbed Havel type harpoons in the European Lowland. In: J. K. Kozłowski / S. K. Kozłowski (eds.): Préhistoire De La Grande Plaine De L'Europe. Archaeologia Interregionalis. Universitas Varsoviensis et Universitas Jagellonica (Kraków, Warszawa 1981) 77-88.

Kriiska 2003: A. Kriiska, Colonisation of the west Estonian archipelago. In: L. Larsson / H. Kindgren / K. Knutsson / D. Loeffler / A. Åkerlund (eds.), Mesolithic on the Move (Oxford 2003) 20-28.

Lanting / Van der Plicht 1996: J. N. Lanting / J. Van der Plicht, De ^{14}C-chronologie van de Nederlandse pre- en protohistorie. I: Laat Paleolithicum. Palaeohistoria 37-38, 1995-1996 (1996) 71-125.

Larsson 1991: L. Larsson, The Late Palaeolithic in southern Sweden: Investigation into a marginal area. In: N. Barton / A. J. Roberts / D. A. Roe (eds.), The Late Glacial in north-west Europe: Human adaptation and environmental change at the end of the Pleistocene. Council for British Archaeology Research Report 77 (Oxford 1991) 122-127.

1994a: L. Larsson, Neue Siedlungsfunde der Späteiszeit im südlichen Schweden. Archäologisches Korrespondenzblatt 23, 275-283.

1994b: L. Larsson, The Earliest Settlement in Southern Sweden. Late Palaeolithic Remains at Finjasjön, in the North of Scania. Current Swedish Archaeology 2, 159-177.

1996: L. Larsson, The Colonization of South Sweden During the Deglaciation. In: L. Larsson (ed.), The Earliest Settlement of Scandinavia and its relationship with neighbouring areas. Acta Archaeologica Lundensia Series in 8°, 24 (Stockholm 1996) 141-155.

1999: L. Larsson, Perspectives on the colonization of the Scandinavian Peninsula. In: M. Kobusiewicz / J. Kozłowski (eds.), Post-pleniglacial Re-colonization of the Great European Lowland. Folia Quaternaria 70 (Kraków 1999) 175-196.

Larsson et al. 2002: L. Larsson / R. Liljegren / O. Magnell / J. Ekström, Archaeo-faunal aspects of bog finds from Hässleberga, southern Scania, Sweden. In: B. V. Eriksen / B. Bratlund (eds.), Recent studies in the Final Palaeolithic of the European plain. Proceedings of a U.I.S.P.P. Symposium, Stockholm 1999. Jutland Archaeological Society Publications 39 (Århus 2002) 61-74.

Legge / Rowley-Conwy 1988: A. J. Legge / P. Rowley-Conwy, Star Carr Revisited: a Re-analysis of the Large Mammals (London 1988).

Lewis 1991: J. Lewis, A Late Glacial and early Postglacial site at three Ways Wharf, Uxbridge, London: interim report. In:N. Barton / A. J. Roberts / D. A. Roe (eds.), The Late Glacial in north-west Europe: Human adaptation and environmental change at the end of the Pleistocene. Council for British Archaeology Research Report 77 (Oxford 1991) 246-255.

Liljegren / Ekström 1996: R. Liljegren / J. Ekström, The Terrestrial Late Glacial Fauna in South Sweden. In: L. Larsson (ed.), The Earliest Settlement of Scandinavia and its relationship with neighbouring areas. Acta Archaeologica Lundensia Series in 8°, 24 (Stockholm 1996) 135-140.

Lindquist 1996: C. Lindquist, Gotländska stenåldersstudier, I. De äldsta säljägarna på Gotland. Benbiten 9/3, 8-13.

Louwe Kooijmans 1971: L. P. Louwe Kooijmans, Mesolithic Bone and Antler Implements from the North Sea and from the Netherlands. Bericht van de Rijksdienst voor het Oudheidkundig Bodemonderzoek 20-21, 1970-1971 (1971) 27-73.

Madsen 1983: B. Madsen, New Evidence of Late Palaeolithic Settlement in East Jutland. Journal of Danish Archaeology 2, 12-31.

1992: B. Madsen, Hamburgkulturens flintteknologi i Jels. In: J. Holm / F. Rieck, Istidsjægere ved Jelssøerne. Hamburgkulturen i Danmark. Skrifter fra Museumsrådet for Sønderjyllands Amt Haderslev 5, 93-132.

2000: B. Madsen, Elgjægere ved Gudenåen. In: S. Hvass / Det Arkæologiske Nævn (eds.), Vor Skjulte kulturarv. Arkæologien under overfladen. Til Hendes Majestæt Dronning Margrethe II, 16. April 2000, 18-19.

Martin 1973: P. S. Martin, The discovery of America. Science 179, 969-974.

Mary-Roussellière 1980: G. Mary-Roussellière, Qitdlarssuaq: l'histoire d'une migration polaire (Winnipeg 1980).

1991: G. Mary-Roussellière, Qitdlarssuaq – the story of a Polar Migration (Winnipeg 1991).

2002: G. Mary-Roussellière, Qillarssuaq. Nunat issittut inuisa ingerlaarnerannik oqaluttuaq. Beretningen om en arktisk folkevandring. Bericht über eine arktische Völkerwanderrung (Nuuk 2002).

Mathiassen 1937: Th. Mathiassen, Gudenaa-Kulturen. En Mesolitisk Indlandsbebyggelse i Jutland. Aarbøger for Nordisk Oldkyndighed og Historie 1937, 1-181.

1946: Th. Mathiassen, En senglacial boplads ved Bromme. Aarbøger for nordisk Oldkyndighed og Historie 1946, 121-197.

1948: Th. Mathiassen, Studier over Vestjyllands Oldtidsbebyggelse. Nationalmuseets Skrifter, Arkæologisk-Historisk Række II (København 1948).

1959: Th. Mathiassen, Nordvestsjællands Oldtidsbebyggelse. Nationalmuseets Skrifter, Arkæologisk-Historisk Række VII (København 1959).

Mellars 1990: P. Mellars, A major »plateau« in the radiocarbon time-scale at ca. 9 650 BP: the evidence from Star Carr (North Yorkshire). Antiquity 64, 836-841.

Mellars / Dark 1998: P. Mellars / P. Dark, Star Carr in context: new archaeological and palaeoecological investigations at the Early Mesolithic site of Star Carr, North Yorkshire. McDonald Institute Monographs (Cambridge 1998).

Moore / Moseley 2001: J. H. Moore / M. E. Moseley, How Many Frogs Does It Take To Leap Around the Americas? Comments on Anderson and Gillam. American Antiquity 66.3, 526-529.

Mortensen in prep.: M. F. Mortensen, Palynological Investigations at Slotseng.

Møbjerg / Rostholm 2006: T. Møbjerg / H. Rostholm, Foreløbige resultater af de arkæologiske undersøgelser ved Bølling Sø. In: B. V. Eriksen (ed.), Stenalderstudier. Tidligt mesolitiske jægere og samlere I Sydskandinavien. Jysk Arkæologisk Selskabs Skrifter 55 (Århus 2006) 147-159.

Møhl 1980: U. Møhl, Elsdyrskeletterne fra Skottemarke og Favrbo. Skik og brug ved Borealtidens jagter. Aarbøger for Nordisk Oldkyndighed og Historie 1978 (1980) 11-28.

Nilsson / Hanlon 2006: B. Nilsson / C. Hanlon, Life and Work during 5.000 Years. In: P. Karsten / B. Nilsson (eds.), In the Wake of a Woman. National Heritage Board, Sweden 63 Rigsantikvarieämbetet (Lund 2006) 57-172.

Nilsson 1989: T. Nilsson, Senglacial bosættelse i Vendsyssel. Kuml 1987 (1989) 47-75.

Noe-Nygaard / Knudsen / Houmark-Nielsen 2006: N. Noe-Nygaard / K. L. Knudsen / M. Houmark-Nielsen, Fra Istid til og med Jægerstenalderen. In: K. Sand-Jensen (ed.), Naturen i Danmark (København 2006) 303-332.

Nordmann 1936: V. Nordmann, Menneskets Indvandring til Norden. Danmarks Geologiske Undersøgelse III, 27.

Paddayya 1973: K. Paddayya, A Federmesser site with tanged points at Norgervaart, Province of Drenthe (Netherlands). Palaeohistoria 15, 167-213.

Pasda 2002: C. Pasda, A short note on man in the Allerød/Younger Dryas environment of Lower Lusatia (Brandenburg, Germany). In: B. V. Eriksen / B. Bratlund (eds.), Recent studies in the Final Palaeolithic of the European plain. Proceedings of a U.I.S.P.P. Symposium, Stockholm 1999. Jutland Archaeological Society Publications 39 (Århus 2002) 123-128.

Pedersen / Brinch Petersen 2006: K. B. Pedersen / E. Brinch Petersen, Variability in the late Palaeolithic: the example of Stoksbjerg Bro, Zealand, Denmark. In: K. M. Hansen / K. B. Pedersen (eds.), Across the Western Baltic. Sydsjællands Museums Publikationer I (Vordingborg 2006) 75-92.

Pedersen / Hansen 2006: K. B. Pedersen / K. M. Hansen, With or without bones. Late Palaeolithic Finds in Southern Denmark. In: K. M. Hansen / K. B. Pedersen (eds.), Across the Western Baltic. Sydsjællands Museums Publikationer I (Vordingborg 2006) 93-110.

Petersen 2001: B. F. Petersen, Senpalæolitiske opsamlingsfund fra Sydsjælland, Fejø og Nordsjælland – et bidrag til udforskningen af de senglaciale kulturer i Danmark. Kulturhistoriske studier, Sydsjællands Museum 2001, 7-64.

Petersen 1977: P. V. Petersen, Vedbæk Boldbaner – endnu en gang. Søllerødbogen 1977, 131-170.

2006: P. V. Petersen, White flint and hilltops – Late Palaeolithic hunters finds in southern Scandinavia. In: K. M. Hansen / K. B. Pedersen (eds.), Across the Western Baltic. Sydsjællands Museums Publikationer I (Vordingborg 2006) 57-74.

Petersen / Johansen 1993: P. V. Petersen / L. Johansen 1993. Sølbjerg I – An Ahrensburgian site on a reindeer migration route through eastern Denmark. Journal of Danish Archaeology 10, 1991 (1993) 20-37.

1996: P. V. Petersen / L. Johansen, Tracking Late Glacial Reindeer Hunters in Eastern Denmark. In: L. Larsson (ed.), The Earliest Settlement of Scandinavia and its relationship with neighbouring areas. Acta Archaeologica Lundensia Series in 8°, 24 (Stockholm 1996) 75-88.

Pettitt et al. 2003: P. B. Pettitt / W. Davies / C. S. Gamble / M. B. Richards, Palaeolithic radiocarbon chronology: quantifying our confidence beyond two half- lives. Journal of Archaeological Science 30, 1685-1693.

Pratsch 1994: S. Pratsch, Die Geweihartefakte des mesolithisch-neolithischen Fundplatzes von Friesack 4, Kr. Havelland. Formenkundlich-chronologische und technologische Untersuchungen. Veröffentlichungen des Brandenburgischen Landesmuseums für Ur- und Frühgeschichte 28, 7-98.

Rasmussen 1905: J. Rasmussen, En folkevandring. Det Norske Geografiske Selskabs Aarbog 16, 42-54.

1972: J. Rasmussen, Æskebjerg – en rensdyrjægerboplads på Knudshoved Odde. Historisk Samfund for Præstø Amt, Årbog 1969-1970 (1972) 201-214.

Rasmussen et al. 2006: S. O. Rasmussen / K. K. Andersen / A. M. Svensson / J. P. Steffensen / B. M. Vinther / H. B. Clausen / M.-L. Siggaard-Andersen / S. J. Johnsen / L. B. Larsen / D. Dahl-Jensen / M. Biggler / R. Röthlisberger / H. Fischer / K. Goto-Azuma / M. E. Hansson / U. Ruth, A new Greenland ice core chronology for the last glacial termination. Journal of Geophysical Research 111, D06102, doi: 10.1029/2005JD 006079.

Renfrew 2000: C. Renfrew, At the edge of knowability: towards a prehistory of languages. Cambridge Archaeological Journal 10/1, 7-34.

Rensink 1992: E. Rensink, Eyserheide: A Late Magdalenian site on the fringe of the northern loessbelt. Archäologisches Korrespondenzblatt 22, 315-327.

2000: E. Rensink, Upper and Late Palaeolithic finds from the loess area of southern Netherlands. In: B. Valentin / P. Bodu / M. Christensen (eds.), L'Europe centrale et septentrionale au Tardiglaciaire: confrontation des modèles régionaux de peuplement. Actes de la table-ronde internationale de Nemours 1997. Mémoires du Musée de préhistoire d'Île-de-France 7 (Nemours 2000) 163-174.

Richter 1981: J. Richter, Der spätpaläolithischen Fundplatz bei Gahlen, Ldkr. Dinslaken. Archäologisches Korrespondenzblatt 11, 181-187.

Rimantené 1996: R. Rimantené, Akmens amzius Lietuvoje. Ziburo Zleidykla (Vilnius 1996).

Rowley 1985: S. Rowley, Population Movements in the Canadian Arctic. Études/Inuit/Studies 9/1, 3-21.

Rust 1937: A. Rust, Das altsteinzeitliche Rentierjagerlager Meiendorf (Neumünster 1937).

1943: A. Rust, Die Alt- und mittelsteinzeitlichen Funde von Stellmoor (Neumünster 1943).

1958a: A. Rust, Die Funde vom Pinnberg. Offa-Bücher 14 (Neumünster 1958).

1958b: A. Rust, Die jungpaläolithischen Zeltanlagen von Ahrensburg. Offa-Bücher 15 (Neumünster 1958).

Salomonsson 1962: B. Salomonsson, Some early Mesolithic Artefacts from Scania, Sweden. Meddelanden från Lunds universitets historiska museum 1961 (Lund 1962) 5-26.

1964: B. Salomonsson, Découverte d'une habitation du Tardiglaciaire à Segebro, Scanie, Suede. Acta Archaeologica 35, 1-28.

Schild 1984: R. Schild, Terminal Paleolithic of the North European Plain: a review of lost chances, potentials, and hopes. Advances in World Archaeology 3, 193-274.

1989: R. Schild, The formation of homogeneous occupation units (»Ksemenitsas«) in open air sandy sites and its significance for the interpretation of Mesolithic flint assemblages. In: C. Bonsall (ed.), The Mesolithic in Europe (Edinburgh 1989) 89-98.

1996: R. Schild, Radiochronology of the Early Mesolithic in Poland. In: L. Larsson (ed.), The Earliest Settlement of Scandinavia and its relationship with neighbouring areas. Acta Archaeologica Lundensia Series in 8°, 24 (Stockholm 1996) 285-295.

Schwabedissen 1937: H. Schwabedissen, Die Hamburger Stufe im nordwestlichen Deutschland. Offa 2, 1-30.

1954: H. Schwabedissen, Die Federmesser-Gruppen des nordwesteuropäischen Flachlandes. Zur Ausbreitung des Spät-Magdalénien. Offa-Bücher 9 (Neumünster 1954).

Skaarup 1979: J. Skaarup, Flaadet. En tidlig maglemoseboplads på Langeland. Meddelelser fra Langelands Museum (Rudkøbing 1979).

Sobotta 1991: J. Sobotta, Frühmesolithische Wohnplätze aus Draved Moor, Dänemark. Archäologisches Korrespondenzblatt 21, 457-467.

Stapert 2000: D. Stapert, The Late Palaeolithic in the Northern Netherlands. In: B. Valentin / P. Bodu / M. Christensen (eds.), L'Europe centrale et septentrionale au Tardiglaciaire: confrontation des modèles régionaux de peuplement. Actes de la table-ronde internationale de Nemours 1997. Mémoires du Musée de préhistoire d'Île-de-France 7 (Nemours 2000) 175-195.

Stensager 2004: A. O. Stensager, Nyt Lys på gammelt fund. Vendsyssel Nu og Da 2004, 38-43.

Street 1991: M. Street, Bedburg-Königshoven: A Pre-Boreal Mesolithic site in the Lower Rhineland (Germany). In: N. Barton / A. J. Roberts / D. A. Roe (eds.), The Late Glacial in north-west Europe: Human adaptation and environmental change at the end of the Pleistocene. Council for British Archaeology Research Report 77 (Oxford 1991) 256-270.

1999: M. Street, Remains of Aurochs (*Bos primigenius*) from the Early Mesolithic site Bedburg-Königshoven (Rhineland, Germany). In: G.-C. Weniger (ed.), Archäologie und Biologie des Auerochsen. Wissenschaftliche Schriften des Neanderthal Museums 1 (Mettmann 1999) 173-194.

Street et al. 2006: M. Street / F. Gelhausen / S. Grimm / F. Moseler / L. Niven / M. Sensburg / E. Turner / S. Wenzel / O. Jöris, L'occupation du bassin Neuwied (Rhénanie centrale, Allemagne) par les Magdaléniens et les groupes à Federmesser (aziliens). Bulletin de la Société préhistorique française 103/4, 753-780.

Sørensen 1980: I. Sørensen, Datering af elsdyrknoglerne fra Skottemarke og Favrbo. Aarbøger for Nordisk Oldkyndighed og Historie 1978 (1980) 33-44.

Sørensen 2006: M. Sørensen, Teknologiske traditioner i Maglemosekulturen. En diakron analyse af Maglemosekulturens flækkeindustri. In: B. V. Eriksen (ed.), Stenalderstudier. Tidligt mesolitiske jægere og samlere i Sydskandinavien. Jysk Arkæologisk Selskabs Skrifter 55 (Århus 2006) 19-76.

2007: M. Sørensen, Teknologi, typologi og traditioner på Dværgebakke I (HEM 2981), Bølling Sø. Unpublished report, Herning Museum.

Sørensen / Sternke 2006: M. Sørensen / F. Sternke, Nørregård VI – Lateglacial hunters in transition. In: K. M. Hansen / K. B. Pedersen (eds.), Across the Western Baltic. Sydsjællands Museums Publikationer I (Vordingborg 2006) 85-111.

Szymczak 1999: K. Szymczak, Late Palaeolithic cultural units with tanged points in north eastern Poland. In: S. Kozłowski / J. Gruba / L. L. Zaliznyak (eds.), Tanged points cultures in Europe. Colloquium Lublin 1993. Lubelskie Materiały Archeologiczne 13 (Lublin 1999) 93-101.

2002: K. Szymczak, Recherches Récentes sur le Swidérien dans le Nord de la Pologne et des Régions avoisinantes. L'Anthropologie 100/1, 132-155.

Tauber 1967: H. Tauber, Kulstof-14 Dateringer af Arkæologiske Prøver II. Aarbøger for Nordisk Oldkyndighed og Historie 1966 (1967) 102-130.

1971: H. Tauber, Danske Kulstof-14 Dateringer af Arkæologiske Prøver III. Aarbøger for Nordisk Oldkyndighed og Historie 1970 (1971) 120-142.

Taute 1963: W. Taute, Funde der spätpaläolithischen »Federmesser-Gruppen« aus dem Raum zwischen mittlerer Elbe und Weichsel. Berliner Jahrbuch für Vor- und Frühgeschichte 3, 62-111.

1968: W. Taute, Die Stielspitzen-Gruppen im Nördlichen Mitteleuropa. Ein Beitrag zur Kenntnis der späten Altsteinzeit. Fundamenta A5 (Köln, Graz 1968).

Terberger 1996: Th. Terberger, The Early Settlement of Northeast Germany (Mecklenburg-Vorpommern). In: L. Larsson (ed.), The Earliest Settlement of Scandinavia and its relationship with neighbouring areas. Acta Archaeologica Lundensia Series in 8°, 24 (Stockholm 1996) 111-122.

2006a: Th. Terberger, From the first humans to the Mesolithic hunters in the northern German lowlands – current results and trends. In: K. M. Hansen / K. B. Pedersen (eds.), Across the Western Baltic. Sydsjællands Museums Publikationer I (Vordingborg 2006), 23-56.

2006b: Th. Terberger, The Mesolithic Hunter-Fischer-Gatherers on the Northern Germain Plain. In: K. M. Hansen / K. B. Pedersen (eds.), Across the Western Baltic. Sydsjællands Museums Publikationer I (Vordingborg 2006), 111-184.

Terberger / Lübke 2005: Th. Terberger / H. Lübke, Hamburger Kultur in Mecklenburg-Vorpommern? Bodendenkmalpflege in Mecklenburg-Vorpommern 52, Jahrbuch 2004 (2005) 15-34.

Toft 2006: P. A. Toft, Hvor går grænsen? Et studium af sociale territorier og ornamentik i Maglemosekulturen. In: B. V. Eriksen, Stenalderstudier. Tidligt mesolitiske jægere og samlere i Sydskandinavien. Jysk Arkæologisk Selskabs Skrifter 55 (Århus 2006) 101-118.

Tolan-Smith 2003: C. Tolan-Smith, Colonisation – Event or Process. In: L. Larsson / H. Kindgren / K. Knutsson / D. Loeffler / A. Åkerlund (eds.), Mesolithic on the Move (Oxford 2003) 52-56.

Tromnau 1975: G. Tromnau, Neue Ausgrabungen im Ahrensburger Tunneltal. Ein Beitrag zur Erforschung des Jungpaläolithikums im nordwesteuropäischen Flachland. Offa-Bücher 33 (Neumünster 1975).

Veil 1987: S. Veil, Ein Fundplatz der Stielspitzen-Gruppen ohne Stielspitzen bei Höfer, Ldkr. Celle. Ein Beispiel Funktionaler Variabilität paläolithischer Steinartefaktinventare. Archäologisches Korrespondenzblatt 17, 311-322.

Veil / Veil 2004: B. Veil / S. Veil, Vor 15.000 Jahren – Das Lager der Eiszeitjäger auf dem Gradeberg bei Gadenstedt, Ldkr. Peine. In: M. Fansa / F. Both / H. Haßmann (eds.), Archäologie / Land / Niedersachsen. 25 Jahre Denkmalschutzgesetz - 400.000 Jahre Geschichte. Wissenschaftliche Begleitschrift zur Sonderausstellung (Oldenburg, Hannover, Braunschweig) (Bad Langensalza 2004) 299-303.

Verhart 1988: L. B. M. Verhart, Mesolithic barbed points and other implements from Europoort, The Netherlands. Oudheidkundige Meddelingen uit het Rijksmuseum van Oudheden te Leiden 68, 145-194.

1990: L. B. M. Verhart, Stone Age Bone and Antler Points as Indicators for »Social Territories« in the European Mesolithic. In: P. M. Vermeersch / P. Van Peer (eds.), Contributions to the Mesolithic in Europe. Papers Presented at the Fourth International Symposium »The Mesolithic in Europe« in Leuven 1990 (Leuven 1990) 139-152.

Vollbrecht 2005: J. Vollbrecht, Spätpaläolithische Besiedlungsspuren aus Reichwalde. Veröffentlichungen des Landesamtes für Archäologie mit Landesmuseum für Vorgeschichte 46 (Dresden 2005).

Waldmann / Jöris / Baales 2001: G. Waldmann / O. Jöris / M. Baales, Nach der Flut. Ein spätallerødzeitlicher Rückenspitzen-Fundplatz bei Bad Breisig. Archäologisches Korrespondenzblatt 31, 173-184.

Weniger 1987: G.-C. Weniger, Magdalenian Settlement Pattern and Subsistence in Central Europe. In: O. Soffer (ed.), The Pleistocene Old World: Regional Perspectives (New York 1987), 201-215.

Weninger / Jöris / Danzeglocke 2007: B. Weninger / O. Jöris / U. Danzeglocke, CalPal-2007. Cologne Radiocarbon Calibration & Palaeoclimate Research Package. http://www.calpal.de.

Weninger / Jöris 2008: B. Weninger / O. Jöris, A ^{14}C age calibration curve for the last 60 ka: the Greenland-Hulu U/Th timescale and its impact on understanding the Middle to Upper Paleolithic transition in Western Eurasia. Journal of Human Evolution 55, 772-781.

Wymer / Jacobi / Rose 1975: J. J. Wymer / R. M. Jacobi / J. Rose, Late Devensian and Early Flandrian Barbed Points from Sproughton, Suffolk. Proceedings of the Prehistoric Society 41, 235-241.

Wymer / Rose 1976: J. J. Wymer / J. Rose, A long blade industry from Sproughton, Suffolk and the date of the buried channel deposits at Sproughton. Suffolk County Planning Dept. Report 3, 1-15.

Zaliznyak 1995: L. L. Zaliznyak, The Swidrian Reindeer-Hunters of Eastern Europe. Beiträge zur Ur- und Frühgeschichte Mitteleuropas 5 (Wilkau-Hasslau 1995).

Zhilin 2006: M. G. Zhilin, The terminal Palaeolithic – early Mesolithic of the Upper Volga and colonization of the northwest of Eastern Europe. In: H. Knutsson (ed.), Pioneer settlements and colonization processes in the Barents region. Vuollerim Papers on Hunter-gatherer Archaeology 1 (Vuollerim 2006), 163-180.

Zvelebil / Rowley-Conwy 1986: M. Zvelebil / P. Rowley-Conwy, Foragers and farmers in Atlantic Europe. In: M. Zvelebil (ed.), Hunters in Transition (Cambridge 1986), 67-93.

Abstract

The human settlement of southern Scandinavia 12 500-8 700 cal BC

The paper reviews the evidence for the dispersal of human populations in southern Scandinavia during the Last Glacial period and examines the model of 'pioneer' and 'residential' phases of occupation. It is suggested that following deglaciation reindeer arrived first, together with Homo sapiens, followed somewhat later by elk, horse and giant deer. At the very end of the glaciation, during the cold Younger Dryas stadial, only reindeer seems to have thrived in this area, with other species forced south or becoming regionally extinct, only to return, in some cases, at the beginning of the Holocene. It is unclear whether human settlement followed a similar pattern under pressure of the extremely cold Younger Dryas. The four main Late Glacial »cultures« are described in terms of successive 'pulses' of human activity and it is concluded that none of them can be considered as exclusively pioneer or residential, the diversity of the sites involved suggesting that each group includes a residential core as well as a pioneering spearhead. It is argued that a clear distinction needs to be made between these categories and a formula for doing this is proposed. The settlement of Late Glacial southern Scandinavia is contrasted with the later establishment of the Preboreal early Maglemosian, from which time the region remains permanently inhabited by humans remaining throughout the year.

Key-words

Hamburgian, Havelte, Brommian, Federmessergruppen, Ahrensburgian, resettlement

LARS LARSSON

AFTER THE COLD: MAMMAL FINDS, HUNTING AND CULTURAL AFFINITIES DURING THE PREBOREAL

In some former studies the transition from the Late Palaeolithic to the Early Mesolithic has been presented as a quite abrupt change from a society mainly based upon reindeer hunting to one hunting a new boreal fauna. The question is whether this indeed matches the information we have today about the period. The transition from the Late Pleistocene to the Holocene is reasonably well dated to 10 200 BP. This transition has also provided some kind of basis for the cultural transition between the Late Palaeolithic and the Mesolithic. The first real questioning of the contemporaneity between the climatic and cultural changes was inspired by dates presented from the north-western German site of Stellmoor, viewed as the eponymous site for the Ahrensburg culture, which provided a result close to 10 000 BP (Fischer / Tauber 1987). In contrast, the earliest well dated sites with a »typical« Mesolithic material culture are dated to about 9 600 BP (Dark 1998; Gramsch 2002). Other sites with artefacts attributed to the earliest Mesolithic give dates from 9 500 to 9 100 BP (Fischer 1996).

Even if there are some problems with the calibration of the radiocarbon scale during the period in question (Baales / Jöris / Weninger 2002; Cziesla / Pettitt 2003) this is probably not the only reason for the *lacuna* between the latest Late Palaeolithic and the earliest Mesolithic.

The find context of faunal remains

We need to be aware that finds from the Late Pleistocene and Early Holocene may cause great problems with regard to how representative they are for describing the cultural as well as environmental situation.

A number of direct radiocarbon dates on different mammal finds from southernmost Sweden yield reasonably good information for the appearance and existence of some animals during the period in question (Liljegren / Ekström 1996; Larsson et al. 2002). Skeletal parts of reindeer, especially antlers, have been found in a number of wetland contexts during drainage and peat cutting (Liljegren 1975) and more than forty finds have been dated (Liljegren / Ekström 1996) (**Fig. 1**).

The majority of the dates are correlated to what should be regarded as the first half of the Preboreal. The situation is the same in Denmark (Aaris-Sørensen / Mühldorff / Brinch Petersen 2007) and in the eastern Baltic region (Ukkonen et al. 2006). However, this does not indicate unreservedly that reindeer was more numerous during the early Preboreal than earlier. Drainage, and especially peat cutting, might not have extended to the lowermost layers of bogs. The vegetation around small lakes might have increased in the early Holocene and therefore attracted animals to the lakeshores for longer periods than before, including the time of shedding the antlers. Infilling by organic material had already started in the early Preboreal and more animals might therefore have become mired in the mud and died.

The numerous finds of reindeer in bogs are in most cases mainly antlers and skulls, due to fact that these skeletal parts were easily recognised as exotic. One needs to be aware that skulls with antlers have been easier to recognize and retrieve than shed crania and that winter bulls and early summer cows are therefore probably underrepresented (Aaris-Sørensen / Mühldorff / Brinch Petersen 2007, Fig. 5).

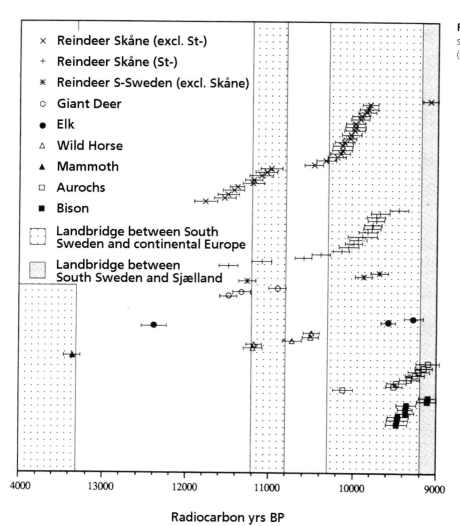

× Reindeer Skåne (excl. St-)
+ Reindeer Skåne (St-)
∗ Reindeer S-Sweden (excl. Skåne)
○ Giant Deer
● Elk
△ Wild Horse
▲ Mammoth
□ Aurochs
■ Bison
▢ Landbridge between South Sweden and continental Europe
▨ Landbridge between South Sweden and Sjælland

4000   13000   12000   11000   10000   9000

Radiocarbon yrs BP

Fig. 1 Radiocarbon dated terrestrial mammals from South Sweden (from Liljegren / Ekström 1996).

These several aspects might have contributed to an increased number of finds which are dated to the latest part of the Pleistocene and the earliest part of the Holocene, so there are arguments to suggest that the reindeer population need not have been larger after the Younger Dryas than before.

In a small number of kettle holes at Hässleberga, south-western Scania (**Fig. 2**), several antlers and skeletal parts of reindeers were found, together with remains identified as horse, elk, arctic fox and mountain hare (Larsson et al. 2002). That so many species were detected is completely dependent on the way the remains were found. The kettle holes were emptied of their filling and the entire organic material was examined for bones and antlers. This is the only case in southern Sweden where the complete filling has been carefully examined for finds. We must therefore recognize that the finds at Hässleberga so far form the only collection in which all bones and antlers were retrieved regardless of size or shape.

The reason the number of finds from wild horse is otherwise so small is therefore that the bones are not easy to identify. If, for example, any skulls were found during digging they would have been familiar to local rural people and might therefore be regarded as recently buried remains of domestic animals, perhaps because of natural death. Finds of wild horse should therefore be heavily underrepresented in faunal collections.

The museum stores of southernmost Sweden contain a number of elk remains. Unfortunately these finds have not been dated with the same intensity as those of reindeer. In southern Sweden elk appear during a

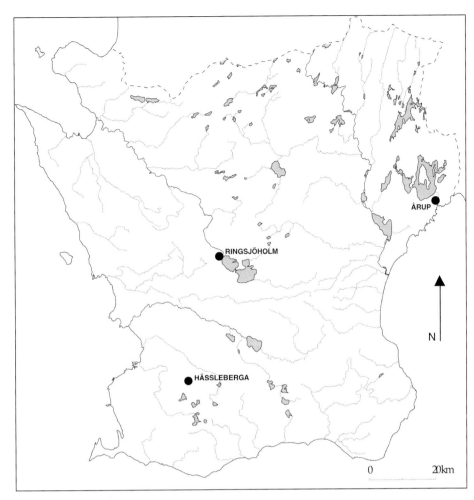

Fig. 2 Scania; the southernmost part of Sweden with the sites mentioned in the text.

rather early part of the Allerød and a small number of dates also show their presence during the Younger Dryas and Preboreal (Liljegren / Ekström 1996; Larsson et al. 2002). Just like horse, elk might be underrepresented with regard to their appearance during the later part of the deglaciation. Horse and elk might therefore have been of greater importance as human prey during the time in question than the number of finds indicates.

The importance of small lakes

Most of the finds of reindeer were made in south-western Scania, in an undulating landscape with small bogs in between hills. The Hässleberga sites are in a typical setting within this landscape. Cut marks on several reindeer bones at the Hässleberga sites demonstrate the presence of human involvement in the accumulation of skeletal parts in a number of kettle holes (Larsson et al. 2002). Cut marks on antlers and skull parts from other localities indicate that human intervention was also a factor in the accumulation of reindeer finds in other bogs.

During the Younger Dryas there are indications of hunting taking place on the ice or by chasing animals into the water (Larsson et al. 2002) and this kind of hunting might have continued and even increased

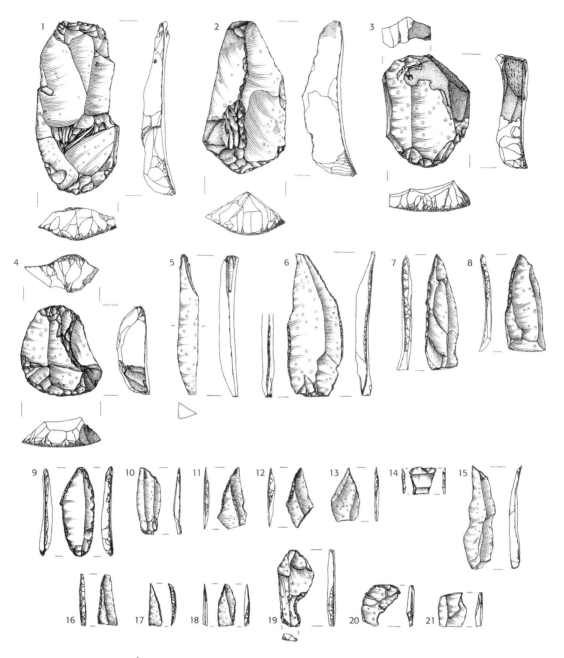

Fig. 3 Artefacts from the Årup settlement in the north-western part of Scania. – 1-4 scrapers, – 5 burin spall, – 6 blade knife, – 7-13 microliths – 14 transverse arrowhead, – 15-18 awls. After Nilsson / Hanlon 2006.

during the early Preboreal. A number of sites related to the Ahrensburgian culture are situated on the highest spot in the landscape, but close to valleys where streams or a row of small lakes or ponds were situated (Petersen 2006). Prey animals, in this case reindeer, would have been easy to hunt using the natural setting as a barrier.

Finds of elk remains close to the shore of the kettle hole at Lundby on Zealand (Hansen / Pedersen 2006), dated to the Pleistocene / Holocene transition, or remains from Skottemark dated to the Preboreal (Fischer 1996), might indicate that the use of small lakes or ponds as traps was of special importance not only for reindeer but also for elk during the period in question. However, the small lakes suitable for the pursuit and trapping of large animals already became in-filled and overgrown during the early Holocene. That particular hunting strategy therefore disappeared. The fact that these small lakes were already being filled by organic litter during an early stage of the Holocene made them extremely dangerous for animals to cross, which might also have been a factor making these wetland locations especially attractive for human hunters.

While we do not know whether the intentional deposition of elk remains at Lundby represents a common phenomenon or not, the finds at Skottemark and Vig (Fischer 1996) indicate that they might be rather frequent. Farmers digging the deposits might easily ignore this kind of find situation, since they look like »just another heap of bones«. They might also be destroyed by deep ploughing and totally disintegrated by even a small sinking of the water table.

The same type of deposition is indicated at the Ringsjöholm site in the bog Rönneholms Mosse, central Scania (Sjöström 1998) (**Fig. 2**). A spit of sand aligned partly parallel to the former lakeshore formed the foundation for a Late Boreal – Early Atlantic settlement. The spit was found to cover a layer of calcareous gyttja that formed, according to studies in other parts of the bog, during the Preboreal. An assemblage of three elk long bones with clear evidence of cut marks was found in this layer.

The fauna and hunting

Reindeer is now well dated in southern Scandinavia from the Allerød until well into the Preboreal (Liljegren / Ekström 1996; Aaris-Sørensen / Mühldorff / Brinch Petersen 2007). According to the accepted description of the earliest prehistory of southern Scandinavia, the deglaciation landscape was occupied by large herds of reindeer, without other mammals of importance for the human settlers. However, this picture might require several reservations. The number of sites with preserved osteological remains is in fact very small. One of them is the eponymous site of Bromme on central Zealand (Mathiassen 1946), where bones of elk turned out to represent the only big game (Degerbøl 1946). Two finds were identified as reindeer, but these are both parts of antlers which might simply have been gathered during hunting expeditions. At the Trollesgave site, also belonging to the Bromme culture, small pieces of bones have equally been identified as elk (Aaris-Sørensen 1989). In the generally presented view of the members of the Bromme culture, they are regarded as an elk-hunting people.

Horse is represented at the Hässleberga kettle holes by adult as well as juvenile individuals. These horses may well have fallen prey to the same hunting technique used for reindeer, namely winter hunting on ice. From what we know of the only surviving wild horse, the Przewalski horse, herds consist of small family units with a dominant stallion (Benecke 1994, 292; West 1996). Other male individuals live alone or in bachelor groups. The area used by the family groups is rather limited, with seasonal migration taking place from open terrain occupied during the summer to protected valleys during the winter. These migrations do not seem to have covered any great distance.

Judging by their present behaviour, reindeer as well as elk can adapt to rather different environments, ranging from forested regions to open tundra. In modern studies reindeer undergo marked changes in population size, in some instances with decreases by as much as 90 % (Grønnow / Meldgaard / Berglund Nielsen 1983).

The presence of shed and unshed finds of bulls and cows indicates a higher presence of reindeer during winter in the Younger Dryas but their presence during most of the year during the Preboreal (Aaris-Sørensen / Mühldorff / Brinch Petersen 2007). The presence of newborn, as well as young calves, shows that southern Scandinavia was a calving ground during the Younger Dryas and the Preboreal (Aaris-Sørensen / Mühldorff / Brinch Petersen 2007). During this period of the year migration of reindeer herds would have been of only limited extent. At the time under consideration, climatic changes of the magnitude known during the late deglaciation, in combination with the disappearance and appearance of land bridges across the present-day Öresund (Björck 1996), might have rendered the reindeer population very unstable and thereby an unpredictable prey for humans.

On the evidence of their modern behaviour, elk move within the same region during a yearly cycle. Horse and elk are more stable resources than reindeer, which was probably an important, but seasonal resource. Horse and elk should be much more reliable species for hunting, being augmented by a surplus from the mass killing of migrating herds of reindeer.

The importance of fishing and hunting of marine mammals during the latest deglaciation is a subject of ongoing debate (Kindgren 1996; Fischer 1996). With a small number of exceptions (Nilsson 1989), the sites in southern Scandinavia were located in inland environments. Due to interaction between isostasy and eustasy, the only coastal area in western Scandinavia with a preserved shoreline is found on the Swedish west coast and in southern Norway (Fischer 1996; Kindgren 1996). Several sites dating to the latest part of the Younger Dryas or the early Preboreal were situated at the shoreline or on islands in the archipelago. Although no sites preserve osteological material, the location of the site makes a role for them in fishing and hunting of marine mammals a most plausible suggestion.

The Årup site

A site of special importance in the discussion of material culture and the location of settlement is Årup in north-eastern Scania (**Fig. 2**). The site is located beside a short and narrow river connecting a large lake with the Baltic Sea. Due to the sea level changes the area was located more than 20 km from the Yoldia Lake but only a few kilometres away from the sea during the Preboreal (Lagerås / Yassin / Svensson 2006). The discovery of the earliest settlement phase at Årup provides an excellent example of the very typical circumstances under which such older levels are recognized. An area close to the river became of interest due to the identification of later prehistoric settlement remains during road building. Below these small concentrations of settlement, excavation uncovered further remains from the Mesolithic. During excavation of a trench in order to document stratigraphy down to the underlying clay several worked flints were detected more than 1.5 m beneath ground level (Nilsson / Hanlon 2006). Without this interest in documenting the stratigraphy, the earliest settlement would never have been found. One may think of other similar locations where the search for settlement remains might have ended at a much shallower level.

The existence of thin understorey vegetation during the Preboreal facilitated the formation of a thick colluvium of sand above the lowest archaeological level, so that while no samples for radiocarbon dating were available within the occupation level itself, a radiocarbon sample from this overlying layer produced a date of 9 390 ± 65 BP.

When the thick sand layer was removed a U-shaped concentration of flints was documented over a length of about five metres. The flint material contains indications both of an Ahrensburgian cultural tradition, such as opposed platform single-faced cores, as well as early Mesolithic types of microliths (**Fig. 3**).

The finds have some similarities to the material culture of the Myrvatn group from southwest Norway, dated to 9 600-9 400 BP and regarded as the earliest Mesolithic phase in Norway (Bang-Andersen 1990; 2003). These settlers have been interpreted as reindeer hunters, not based on finds of reindeer remains, since there is no organic preservation, but because the sites are located close to the present migration routes of reindeer. Structures marked by tent rings of stones (Bang-Andersen 2003) could very well have been associated with the distribution of flints at Årup. It might seem rather far-fetched to compare southernmost Scania with south-western Norway, separated by some 600 km. However, sites even more distant along the north European Atlantic coast show great similarities during a somewhat earlier stage regarded as equivalent to the Ahrensburgian culture (Fischer 1996).

Besides the oldest Årup concentration of flints, three other early Mesolithic settlement sites of similar size were found, all situated close to the bed of the river. Both the earliest settlement and the younger ones are interpreted as special-purpose camps, in this case for butchering. Their location must have been at a place strategic for hunting both migrating herds and individual prey. In situations such as that at Årup no major environmental changes occurred, which meant that the same hunting method and choice of settlement location could survive through a much longer part of the Holocene.

The Late Palaeolithic / Early Mesolithic transition

The finds from Lundby present a real challenge for the definition of the Mesolithic (Hansen / Brinch Petersen / Aaris-Sørensen 2004; Hansen / Pedersen 2006). The three finds of intentional deposition of elk bones dated from 9 950-9 860 BP, one of them in combination with an elk antler adze, are argued to represent clearly the earliest evidence for Mesolithic and Maglemose occupation.

The finds from Lundby seem to be somewhat difficult to associate with a typical Mesolithic flint industry. The elk antler adze is well known from early Mesolithic sites such as Star Carr (Clark 1954) and Friesack (Pratsch 1994); in Scandinavia it is known from stray finds (Andersen 1976; 1977). At Friesack the form appears in the middle and late Preboreal layers (Pratsch 1994). That the time of existence of this axe type was the Preboreal is indicated by the direct dating of three specimens from southernmost Sweden, providing results between 9 600 ± 65 BP (LuS-6535) and 9 170 ± 60 BP (LuS-6534) (Larsson 2007). However, even if the form is certainly in an early Mesolithic context, it could very well have been invented in the context of an otherwise Late Palaeolithic assemblage. As long as the organic material from the Preboreal is very rare we do not really know what is typically Late Palaeolithic or Early Mesolithic. For example, in northern Germany a »typical Mesolithic« bone leister-point has been dated to the late Younger Dryas (Cziesla 2004). Another tool exemplifying this problem is the large uniserially barbed harpoon, which is described as a typical Late Palaeolithic type (Cziesla 1999). However, a couple of radiometric dates indicate that this form existed in southernmost Sweden into the Boreal (Larsson 1996). As long as the organic tool finds are so few and often found outside dating contexts, the presence of an elk antler adze alone cannot be claimed as proof of a Mesolithic material culture and even less of a relationship to the Maglemosian.

Another argument for suggesting that a typically Mesolithic material culture can be assigned to the beginning of the Preboreal is the statement that the earliest sequence of the settlement at Friesack dates to that stage (Hansen / Brinch-Petersen / Aaris-Sørensen 2004). However, according to the excavator of the site, the dates from Friesack 4 do not relate to the early Preboreal but to the middle part of the Preboreal (Gramsch 2002) and are therefore contemporaneous with other sites with a typical Mesolithic material culture such as Star Carr. Even if we need to take into account the plateaux of the calibration curve during the Preboreal, there is no indication that the earliest settlement sites presenting typically Mesolithic material culture should be dated to the earliest part of the Preboreal.

By contrast, there are strong indications for the continued existence of the Ahrensburgian culture into the earliest part of the Preboreal although, unfortunately, we do not know how far into the Preboreal the typical Late Palaeolithic lithic industry survived. In addition, tools such as elk antler adzes, harpoons and leisterpoints and probably several other types were used or invented at this time. During the early Preboreal, hunting strategies involving the main herd animals such as reindeer and horse were complemented by the addition of more localized species such as elk and aurochs.

Due to influences from the south, new inventions were introduced into the lithic technology. The Myrvatn group in the north and the co-called epi-Ahrensburgian sites and the long-blade tradition in the continental south represent examples of these changes, which started during an early but not the earliest part of the Preboreal (Johansen / Stapert 2000; Sørensen / Sternke 2004; Terberger 2004). In the middle part of the Preboreal these changes resulted in a lithic material culture in combination with an assortment of bone and antler tools that we regard together as the typical early Mesolithic. We thus have to expect that radical changes attributed to new groups are more probably due to an input of new ideas based upon a flow of contacts.

Conclusion

The dates from Stellmoor provide very good indications for considering a continuation of the Ahrensburgian culture into the earliest part of the Preboreal. By contrast, the earliest typical Mesolithic settlements date to the middle part of the Preboreal. In southern Scandinavia the combination of arctic and boreal faunal elements is something we must expect from the Allerød until at least the first half of the Preboreal. During the late deglaciation, with the probable exception of the coldest part of the Younger Dryas, the elk might have been more important than the reindeer.

As suggested by the earliest proof for coastal settlement, fishing and the hunting of marine mammals would have been a more sustainable economy than reindeer hunting. In southernmost Scandinavia we still lack the evidence for coastal settlement as the area was later submerged. Movements along a south-north axis by the small human groups based on the migration of reindeer – »they followed the reindeer« – may have been exaggerated. However, human migrations from the coasts to inland locations should be more plausible. During a later part of the Preboreal, a mixture of Late Palaeolithic traditions adopted new influences from the south. By about 9 500 BP this combination had become the material culture that we accept as the typical early Mesolithic.

References

Aaris-Sørensen 1989: K. Aaris-Sørensen, Danmarks forhistoriske dyreverden. Fra istid til vikingetid (Køpenhavn 1989).

Aaris-Sørensen / Mühldorff / Brinch Petersen 2007: K. Aaris-Sørensen/ R. Mühldorff / E. Brinch Petersen, The Scandinavian reindeer (Rangifer tarandus L.) after the last glacial maximum; time seasonality and human exploitation. Journal of Archaeological Science 34, 914-923.

Andersen 1976: S. H. Andersen, En elgtakøkse fra Fovåen. Nordslesviske Museer 3, 9-12.

1977: S. H. Andersen, En Elgtakøkse fra Vædebro. Museumsforeningen for Skanderborg og omegn 10, 1-3.

Baales / Jöris / Weninger 2002: M. Baales / O. Jöris / B. Weninger, Comments on the Kartstein dates. In: C. Bronk Ramsey / T. F. G. Higham / D. C. Owen / A. W. G. Pike / R. E. M. Hedges, Radiocarbon dates from the Oxford AMS System. Archaeometry Datelist 31. Archaometry 44, 31.

Bang-Andersen 1990: S. Bang-Andersen, The Myrvatn Group, a Preboreal Find-Complex in Southwest Norway. In: P. M. Vermeerch / P. van Peer (eds.), Contribution to the Mesolithic in Europe. Papers presented at the fourth international symposium »The Mesolitic in Europe«, Leuven 1990 (Leuven 1990) 215-237.

2003: S. Bang-Andersen, Encircling the living space of Early

Postglacial reindeer hunters in the interior of southern Norway. In: L. Larsson / H. Kindgren / K. Knutsson / D. Loeffler / A. Åkerlund (eds.), Mesolithic on the Move. Papers presented at the Sixth International Conference on the Mesolithic in Europe, Stockholm 2000 (Oxford 2003) 193-204.

Benecke 1994: N. Benecke, Der Mensch und seine Haustiere. Die Geschichte einer jahrtausendealten Beziehung (Stuttgart 1994).

Björck 1996: S. Björck, Late Weichselian / Early Preboreal Development of the Örsund Strait; a Key area for northerly Mammal Immigration. In: L. Larsson (ed.), The Earliest Settlement of Scandinavia and its relationship with neighbouring areas. Acta Archaeologica Lundensia Series in 8°, 24 (Stockholm 1996) 123-134.

Clark 1954. J. G. D. Clark, Excavation at Star Carr. An early Mesolithic site at Seamer, near Scarborough, Yorkshire (Cambridge 1954).

Cziesla 1999: E. Cziesla, Der erste Neufund nach 70 Jahren: eine einreihige Widerhakenspitze aus dem Bützsee, Ldkr. Ostprignitz-Ruppin. Archäologie in Berlin und Brandenburg 1998 (1999) 38-39.

2004: E. Cziesla, Late Palaeolithic and Mesolithic cultural continuity – or: bone and antler objects from the Havelland. In: Th. Terberger / B. V. Eriksen (eds.), Hunters in a changing world. Environment and Archaeology of the Pleistocene - Holocene Transition (ca. 11 000-9 000 B.C.) in Northern Central Europe. Workshop of the U.I.S.P.P.-Commission XXXII at Greifswald, 2002. Internationale Archäologie, Arbeitsgemeinschaft, Symposium, Tagung, Kongress 5 (Rahden / Westfalen 2004) 165-182.

Cziesla / Pettitt 2003: E. Cziesla / P. B. Pettitt, AMS-^{14}C–Datierungen von spätpaläolithischen und mesolithischen Funden aus dem Bützsee (Brandenburg). Archäologisches Korrespondenzblatt 33, 21-38.

Dark 1998: P. Dark, Radiocarbon Dating of the Lake-edge Deposits. In: P. Mellars / P. Dark (eds.), Star Carr in context (Cambridge 1998) 119-124.

Degerbøl 1946: M. Degerbøl, Dyreknogler. In: T. Mathiassen, En senglacial Boplads ved Bromme. Aarbøger for nordisk oldkyndighed og historie 1946, 136-142.

Fischer 1996: A. Fischer, At the Border of Human Habitat. The Late Palaeolithic and Early Mesolithic in Scandinavia. In: L. Larsson (ed.), The Earliest Settlement of Scandinavia and its relationship with neighbouring areas. Acta Archaeologica Lundensia Series in 8°, 24 (Stockholm 1996) 157-176.

Fischer / Tauber 1987: A. Fischer / H. Tauber, New C-14 Datings of the Late Palaeolithic Cultures from Northwestern Europe. Journal of Danish Archaeology 5, 1986 (1987), 7-13.

Gramsch 2002: B. Gramsch, Friesack: letzte Jäger und Sammler in Brandenburg. Jahrbuch des RGZM 47, 2000 (2002) 51-96.

Grønnow / Meldgaard / Berglund Nielsen 1983: B. Grønnow / M. Meldgaard / J. Berglund Nielsen: Aasivissuit – The Great Summer Camp. Archaeological, ethnological and zoo-archaeological studies of a caribou-hunting site in West Greenland. Meddelelser om Grønland. Man and Society 5. (Copenhagen 1983).

Hansen / Pedersen 2006: K. M. Hansen / K. B. Pedersen, With or Without Bones – Late Palaeolithic Hunters in South Zealand. 93-110. In: K. M. Hansen / K. B. Pedersen (eds.), Across the western Baltic. Proceeding from the archaeological conference in Vordingborg. Sydsjællands Museum Publikationer I (Vordingborg 2006) 93-110.

Hansen / Brinch Petersen / Aaris-Sørensen 2004: K. M. Hansen / E. Brinch Petersen / K. Aaris-Sørensen, Filling the gap: Early Preboreal Maglemose elk deposits at Lundby, Sjælland, Denmark. In: Th. Terberger / B. V. Eriksen (eds.), Hunters in a changing world. Environment and Archaeology of the Pleistocene - Holocene Transition (ca. 11 000-9 000 B.C.) in Northern Central Europe. Workshop of the U.I.S.P.P.-Commission XXXII at Greifswald, 2002. Internationale Archäologie, Arbeitsgemeinschaft, Symposium, Tagung, Kongress 5 (Rahden / Westfalen 2004) 75-84.

Johansen / Stapert 2000: L. Johansen / D. Stapert, Two 'Epi-Ahrensburgian' sites in the northern Netherlands: Oudehaske (Friesland) and Gramsbergen (Overussel). Palaeohistoria 39-40, 1-87.

Kindgren 1996: H. Kindgren, Reindeer or seals? Some Late Palaeolithic sites in central Bohuslän. In: L. Larsson (ed.), The Earliest Settlement of Scandinavia and its relationship with neighbouring areas. Acta Archaeologica Lundensia Series in 8°, 24 (Stockholm 1996) 191-205.

Lagerås / Yassin / Svensson 2006: P. Lagerås / S. Yassin / N.-O. Svensson, Past vegetation, topography, and shore displacement. In: P. Karsten / B. Nilsson (eds), In the wake of a woman. Stone Age pioneering of north-eastern Scania, Sweden, 10 000-5 000 BC. The Årup Settlement. Riksantikvarieämbetet UV Syd Skrifter 63 (Malmö 2006) 21-56.

Larsson 1996. L. Larsson, The Colonization of Southern Sweden During the Deglaciation. In: L. Larsson (ed.), The Earliest Settlement of Scandinavia and its relationship with neighbouring areas. Acta Archaeologica Lundensia Series in 8°, 24 (Stockholm 1996) 141-155.

2007: L. Larsson, För mer än 10,000 år sedan. Våra Härader 2007, 3-8.

Larsson et al. 2002: L. Larsson / R. Liljegren / O. Magnell / J. Ekström, Archaeo-faunal aspects of bog finds from Hässleberga, Southern Scania, Sweden. In: B. V. Eriksen / B. Bratlund (eds.), Recent studies in the Final Palaeolithic of the European plain. Proceedings of a U.I.S.P.P. Symposium, Stockholm 1999. Jutland Archaeological Society Publications 39 (Århus 2002) 61-74.

Liljegren 1975: R. Liljegren, Subfossila vertebratfynd från Skåne. University of Lund. Department of Quaternary Geology Report 8 (Lund 1975).

Liljegren / Ekström 1996: R. Liljegren / J. Ekström, The Terrestrial Late Glacial Fauna in South Sweden. In: L. Larsson (ed.), The

Earliest Settlement of Scandinavia and its relationship with neighbouring areas. Acta Archaeologica Lundensia Series in 8°, 24 (Stockholm 1996) 135-139.

Mathiassen 1946: T. Mathiassen, En senglacial Boplads ved Bromme. Aarbøger for Nordisk Oldkyndighed og Historie 1946, 121-197.

Nilsson 1989: T. Nilsson, Senglacial bosættelse i Vendsyssel. Kuml 1987-1989 (1989) 47-75.

Nilsson / Hanlon 2006: B. Nilsson / C. Hanlon, Life and work during 5 000 years. In: P. Karsten / B. Nilsson (eds.), In the wake of a woman. Stone Age pioneering of north-eastern Scania, Sweden, 10 000-5 000 BC. The Årup Settlement. Riksantikvarieämbetet UV Syd Skrifter 63 (Malmö 2006) 57-178.

Pratsch 1994: S. Pratsch, Die Geweihartefakte des mesolithisch-neolithischen Fundplatzes von Friesack 4, Kr. Havelland. Veröffentlichungen des Brandenburgischen Landesmuseums für Ur- und Frühgeschichte 28, 7-98.

Petersen 2006: P. V. Petersen, White Flint and Hilltops – Late Palaeolithic Finds in Southern Denmark. In: K. M. Hansen / K. B. Pedersen (eds.), Across the western Baltic. Proceeding from the archaeological conference in Vordingborg. Sydsjællands Museum Publikationer I (Vordingborg 2006) 57-74.

Sjöström 1998. A. Sjöström, Ringsjöholm. A Boreal–Early Atlantic Settlement in Central Scania, Sweden. Lund Archaeological Review 1997 (1998) 5-20.

Sørensen / Sternke 2004: M. Sørensen / F. Sternke, Nørregård VI – Lateglacial hunters in transition. In: Th. Terberger / B. V. Eriksen (eds.), Hunters in a changing world. Environment and Archaeology of the Pleistocene - Holocene Transition (ca. 11 000-9 000 B.C.) in Northern Central Europe. Workshop of the U.I.S.P.P.-Commission XXXII at Greifswald, 2002. Internationale Archäologie, Arbeitsgemeinschaft, Symposium, Tagung, Kongress 5 (Rahden / Westfalen 2004) 85-111.

Terberger 2004: T. Terberger, The Younger Dryas – Preboreal transition in northern Germany – facts and concepts in discussion. In: Th. Terberger / B. V. Eriksen (eds.), Hunters in a changing world. Environment and Archaeology of the Pleistocene - Holocene Transition (ca. 11 000-9 000 B.C.) in Northern Central Europe. Workshop of the U.I.S.P.P.-Commission XXXII at Greifswald, 2002. Internationale Archäologie, Arbeitsgemeinschaft, Symposium, Tagung, Kongress 5 (Rahden / Westfalen 2004) 203-222.

Ukkonen et al. 2006: P. Ukkonen / L. Lõugas / I. Zagorska / L. Lukesevica / E. Lukesevics / L. Daugnora / H. Junger, History of the reindeer (Rangifer tarandus) in the eastern Baltic region and its implications for the origin and immigration routes of the recent northern European wild reindeer population. Boreas 35, 222-230.

West 1996: D. West, Horse hunting, processing, and transport in the middle Danube. In: J. Svoboda (ed.), Paleolithic in the Middle Danube Region. Festschrift B. Klíma, Av CR v Brno 5 (Brno 1996) 208-245.

Abstract

After the cold: Mammal finds, hunting and cultural affinities during the Preboreal

The transition from Late Pleistocene to Holocene has been seen as somewhat of a source for the cultural transition between the Late Palaeolithic and the Mesolithic. The question is whether this matches the information we have today about the period. The finds and how representative they are, together with the dating of reindeer, horse and elk in southern Sweden are presented and discussed. The importance of small wetland localities for hunting, especially during the Preboreal, is demonstrated. New finds from settlement sites as well as deposits in bogs contribute to a discussion of the cultural affinity.

Key-words

Late Palaeolithic, Mesolithic, hunting, Preboreal

PRZEMYSŁAW BOBROWSKI

THE EXPLOITATION OF LOCAL SOURCES OF FLINT ON THE POLISH PLAIN DURING THE FINAL PALAEOLITHIC

The aim of this paper is to discuss the exploitation of flint raw materials by Final Palaeolithic communities of the Polish Plain. Here, I do not refer to the exploitation of natural quarries of Jurassic flint (e. g. the source of »chocolate« flint) which, although generally associated with the Plain (Schild 2000), lie beyond its spatial borders.

The Polish Plain is situated on the border of two physical-geographical provinces, namely the Central European Plain and East European Plain (**Fig. 1**), however the whole territory shares topographic features such as seashore and lakes. To the south, the Polish Plain is enclosed by the Sudeten tectonic foreland and the belt of southern Poland uplands (Kondracki 1965/1981; 2000; Galon 1972).

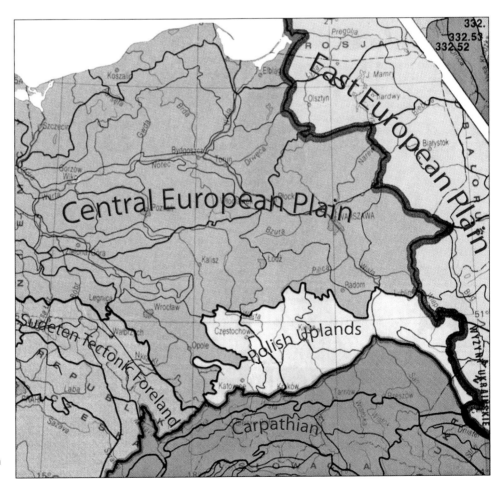

Fig. 1 The Polish Plain (after Kondracki 2000).

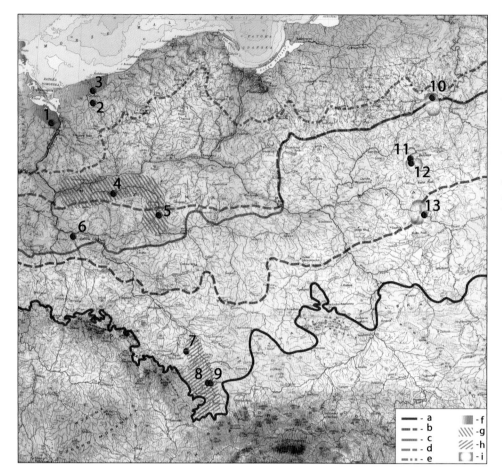

Fig. 2 Location of workshop sites on the Polish Plain.
Key: – **1-13** workshops (see Table 1), – **a** Odra Glaciation (maximum of the Riss), – **b** Warta Glaciation, – **c** Leszno Stadial of the Vistulian, – **d** Poznań Stadial of the Vistulian – **e** Pomeranian Stadial of the Vistulian, – **f**, **i** concentrations of glacial rafts with Cretaceous flint, – **g**, **h** rich occurrences of erratic flint.

Review of earlier studies

The issue of flint raw material exploitation has been the subject of research by Polish archaeologists for almost 100 years, due mainly to the efforts of Stefan Krukowski (1920; 1922). The discovery of natural beds of »banded« and »chocolate« flint, as well as prehistoric mines (including the now well known Final Palaeolithic »chocolate« flint mines), enabled Krukowski to distinguish so called »home« and »mining« subfacies within Late Palaeolithic Swiderian Culture. The latter was characterized by workshop sites founded on the territory where raw material beds occurred (Krukowski 1939/1948). Later, detailed studies dealing with mining, preparation and distribution of raw material during the Final Palaeolithic in a wider Central European perspective were conducted by B. Ginter (1974; 1984) and R. Schild (1976; 1980; Schild / Królik / Tomaszewski 1997), whose work still remains of fundamental significance. These studies were conducted at a larger scale and on the basis of material originating from natural flint beds located on the northern slopes of the Holy Cross Mountains and southern Poland uplands.

The question of exploitation of local sources on the European Plain has also been studied in detail by several other authors (Kobusiewicz 1961; 1967; 1989; 1997; 1999; Galiński 1987; 2000; 2001; Sulgostowska 1989; Szymczak 1992). In analysing erratic flints originating from Stone Age sites of north-western Poland, as well as their location, M. Kobusiewicz was the first to draw attention to the similarity of some of the »mine-type workshops« These were particularly well known in the region of southern Poland adjacent to the Plain (Kobusiewicz 1961; 1967; 1989). He also noticed that where erratic flint was abundant these sites formed concentrations sometimes dozens of kilometres across which he termed »flint raw material basins«

P. Bobrowski - The exploitation of local sources of flint on the Polish Plain during the Final Palaeolithic

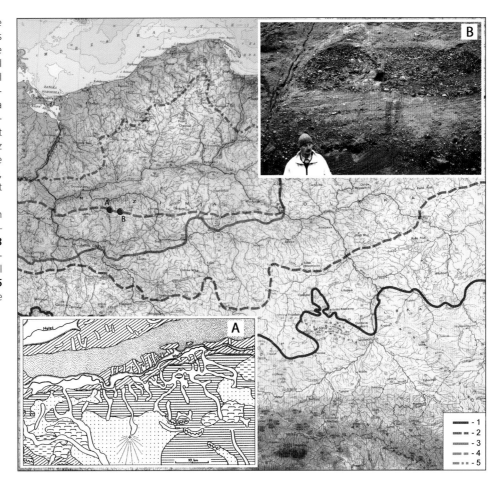

Fig. 3 Location of Lewice (**A**) and Łężce (**B**), sites exemplifying accumulative formations in the marginal zone of the Poznań Stadial of the Vistulian. – **A** Geomorphology of the area with secondary concentrations of erratic flint at Lewice (after Kobusiewicz 1997), – **B** an ablative frontal moraine in Łężce, with injected gravel clast containing flint.
Key: – **1** Odra Glaciation (maximum of the Riss), – **2** Warta Glaciation, – **3** Leszno Stadial of the Vistulian, – **4** Poznań Stadial of the Vistulian, – **5** Pomeranian Stadial of the Vistulian.

and interpreted as provisioning areas for prehistoric inhabitants (Kobusiewicz 1999). Further examinations of the flint inventories of Palaeolithic and later sites in the Polish region of the European Plain have enabled us to register several dozen further similar sites (workshops) where local raw material was exploited, prepared and distributed. The majority of these workshops date to the Final Palaeolithic.

Raw materials and their sources

Following Krukowski, it is still commonly believed that the main source of flint raw material on the Polish Plain was in the form of erratics, haphazardly distributed across the surface and usually of poor quality. It was felt that communities inhabiting this territory must have supplemented any shortages of raw material by importing flint from natural quarries in the South (Krukowski 1939/1948; Kobusiewicz 1997). I would like to discuss briefly the potential resources of raw material available on the Plain.

Across the Plain almost all *in situ* flint beds of Jurassic and Cretaceous origin are covered by a thick mantle of Quaternary sediments, usually several metres thick but exceeding 100-200 m in some places. A few quarries with primary silica rocks of pre-Quaternary types are occasionally exposed in Western Pomerania, Kujavia and Central Poland (Czekalska 1957; Wilczyński 1961; Wyrwicka 1987), however, there is no evidence that flint originating from these sources, expecially in Pomerania, was exploited by prehistoric communities. The only accessible sources of flint raw material were glacial rafts and other secondary occurrences of flint erratics in Quaternary formations. Glacial sedimentary rafts are constituted of fragments of rocks, most

no. on Fig. 2	Workshops	Poor surface collections with workshop-like features	References
1	Tanowo 3		Galiński – pers. comm.
2	Kocierz 3	Kocierz 1, 2, 4, 5, 6; Smolęcin 1, 2; Taczały 1; Lubieszewo 2; Budziszewcze 2, 3; Barkowo 3; Baszewice 3, 5; Skowrony 3	Czarnecki 1970; 1971; Kobusiewicz 1997; 1999; Galiński 2000
3	Rotnowo 18		Galiński – pers. comm.
4	Radgoszcz 15	Radgoszcz 3, 9, 17, 19, 26, 13; Mokrzec 13	Płonka 1997; 1999
5	Poznań Starołęka 1	Luboń-Lasek1b, 3, 13 Luboń 1b, »wydma nad Wartą« Wiórek 2	Bartkowski 1961 Kobusiewicz 1961;1967; 1989; 1997; 1999
6	Strumienno 1b		Brodzikowski 1988; 1989 Burdukiewicz 1988a;1988b; 1989
7	Sowin 7		Furmanek /Molenda / Rapiński 2001; Furmanek 2005
8	Kornice 5	Piotrowice Wielkie 15, 16	Kozłowski 1964
9	Kornice 8		Kozłowski 1964
10	Wołkusz 5		Szymczak 1992
11	Płonka Kozły 1		Gieysztor- Szymczak 1983b
12	Płonka Strumianka 2		Gieysztor- Szymczak 1981; 1982; 1983a; Szymczak 1992
13	Mielnik 2		Szmit 1929; Szymczak 1992

Table 1 Workshops and poor surface collections with workshop features located on the Polish Plain.

commonly of Cretaceous origin, from the glacier bed, which despite being detached and dislocated preserve their lithological features (Marks 1992). The flint obtained from them is often of good quality and macroscopically similar. It is possible to distinguish two basic zones where rafts occur. The first is in Western Pomerania in the area of the Stettin seashore (Sulimirski 1960; Balcer 1983), the other lies in the Podlasie lowland of north-eastern Poland (**Fig. 2**). Within the latter area three significant concentrations have been distinguished, in the vicinity of Dabrowa Białostocka, Białystok as well as Mielnik and Kornica (Szmit 1929; Rühle1961; Wyrwicka 1987; Szymczak 1992). The Cretaceous flint occurring in this territory is described as »north-eastern« (Cyrek 1983; Szymczak 1992). The flint coming directly from this bed is characterized by a thick, barely abraded cortex. It is more or less black in colour and devoid of carbonate inclusions and occurs in relatively large nodules (Szmit 1929). It has good knapping qualities.

Erratic flint, however, constitutes the most common raw material type on the Plain, including mainly Cretaceous but also Jurassic rock types (Balcer 1983; Ginter et al. 2002). A shared feature is their extreme variability. Undoubtedly, the main source of erratic flint came from Cretaceous beds in the area of the southern Baltic and its rim, but it is also obvious that the degradation of sediments containing such rocks also occurred on the central European Plain (Galon 1972; Kondracki 1965/1981; Śliwończuk 1987; Marks

| **P. Bobrowski** - The exploitation of local sources of flint on the Polish Plain during the Final Palaeolithic

1992). The origin and distribution of secondary assemblages of erratics, including flint, are closely connected with erosive processes, transportation and accumulation activities of Pleistocene glaciers. Glacial sediments including boulders, gravels and sands were deposited on the Plain during the Oder and Warta (Riss /
Saale) and Vistulian glaciations (Śliwończuk 1987). However, the distribution of flint erratics is by no means
uniform. They occur over the whole area of the Plain in the form of fine clasts, dispersed mainly during the
Oder glaciation (Saale maximum), when the continental glacier covered the northern slopes of the
Sudetenland and crossed the Moravian Gate.

The most significant assemblages of erratics generally resulted from the accumulation of material from the
melted frontal moraines and glacial outflow waters. Glacial clay, coarse boulders and gravel material were
deposited in such zones, while finer material was carried further away from the glacier. The secondary concentration of raw material may have also have occurred as a result of the outwash of boulder clay, usually
in the lower parts of the moraine column, forming residual deposits of moraine cobble stones (Książkiewicz
1957; 1968; Galon 1972; Marks 1992).

Specific regions with an enormous concentration of boulder-gravels with flint are the Toruń-Eberswald marginal valley in the Central Warta Valley and also the direct hinterland of the marginal zone of the Poznań
Stadial advance of the last glaciation (Fig. 2). Kobusiewicz identified the region of Lewice in the vicinity of
Miedzychód (Kobusiewicz 1997) as one such concentration. This site is located in the proximal part of a
sander apron, where the coarsest, most highly sorted erratic material was deposited (Fig. 3A). We now
know of considerably more examples of this kind in the marginal zone of the Poznań Stadial advance. One
example is a minor ablative frontal moraine in Łężce, also near Miedzychód, where the so called »gravel-
boulder-stone piston« (intruded clast) with flint may be seen in cross-section (Fig. 3B). This feature is located in the most proximal part of the glacio-marginal fan (Liszkowski / Radaszewski 1999). The usually high
concentration of these erratics in western Poland during the Vistulian Poznań Stadial is due to the active
recession of the glacier front and not to its sub-aerial decomposition, as is the case, for instance, in the eastern part of the Polish Plain. Accumulative formations were thus created under conditions of dynamic
balance and gradual recession of the continental glacier front (Kozarski 1995).

Glacio-fluvial beds of flint erratics in the region of the Silesian-Moravian border, situated in the direct hinterland of the marginal zone of the maximum continental glacier advance of the Oder glaciation, are believed
to have a similar origin (Fig. 3). The evident enrichment of glacio-fluvial formations by high quality flint in
the area furthest from the natural beds of Cretaceous rocks in the southern Baltic could perhaps be accoun-
ted for by erosion as well as due to transport by the continental glacier.

Workshops: Raw material sources

The exploitation of flint raw materials in the Stone Age is closely identified with particular types of archaeological sites. These are not only the localities of raw material procurement (mines, quarrying extraction),
but also places where the material was prepared and elaborated and even made into ready-to-use tools.
Ginter distinguished three types of workshops: »mine-type«, »adjacent-to-mine type« and »beyond-mine
type« workshops. He based these ideas on his analysis of flint material from Tanged Point Technocomplex
sites, which used Jurassic flint from the uplands of Poland. This classification was also founded on three
essential criteria: relationship with settlement locations, distance from sources of exploited raw material,
and the kind of products made at the workshop sites (Ginter 1974; Ginter / Kozłowski 1975). In addition,
the various types of workshop sites were classified according to their specific inventory with regard to function, the locality of the site and the aims of production. Observed differences were based on the presen-

ce/absence of particular categories of artefacts, mainly the by-products of the different early stages of preparation, primary waste flakes and blades, core pre-forms etc., but also on the presence of so-called mining tools, which are consistently present in flint inventories of workshops in areas where raw materials were exploited. They are often simply enlarged examples of domestic tools (Krukowski 1939/48; Ginter 1974; Ginter / Kozłowski 1975). A second category of classification involved the comparative numbers of particular products within the general inventory structure.

Using similar approaches, I have recorded 13 workshops on the Polish Plain connected with the exploitation and initial elaboration of local flint. These sites are located in four zones. Firstly, in Western Pomerania: Tanowo 3, Kocierz 3 and Rotnowo 18. Secondly, in the territory that can be generally described as Greater Poland, Lubuskie Province: Poznan-Starołęka 1, Radgoszcz 15 and Strumienno 15. Thirdly, the Silesian Lowland in the Upper Oder basin: Sowin 7, Kornice 5 and Kornice 8. Fourthly, in the eastern region of the Polish Plain in the Northern Podlasie Lowland, Wołkusz 5, Płonka Kozły 1, Płonka Strumianka 2 and Mielnik 2 (**Table 1**; **Fig. 2**). The sites consist of single workshops or, more rarely, workshop complexes such as at Wołkusz. The majority of these sites were investigated by conventional archaeological excavation. The only exceptions are the sites of Kornice and Mielnik at which the relatively rich flint assemblages originate from surface collections made in the first half of the 20th century. Apart from these 13 sites, a few dozen other sites with poor flint inventories were registered from the regions with conspicuous workshop features, all of them relatively close to the previously identified sites (cf. **Table. 1**).

The above-mentioned sites are located in areas particularly abundant in flint raw material, usually of good quality. At Kocierz the exploited raw material most probably derives from rafted Cretaceous sediment deposited in a ground moraine, subsequently washed by waters flowing from the receding glacier to the Pomeranian Marginal Valley and uncovered by the strongly meandering river Rega. The sites at Tanowo and Rotnowo are both located at the edge of moraine plateaux dissected by glacial tunnels along which water flows today. Here, the secondary accumulations of erratic flint spread from the base of the morainic plateau and form gravel beds containing nodules up to 1 m in diameter. These might have originally been forms of intruded fluvio-glacial clasts, but they seem more probably to have been created as a result of erosional and slope processes, with the erratic flint washing out and forming rubble at the foot of the slope. A similar phenomenon can be observed in the Dobiegniewo Lake District (Bagniewski 1999).

At the site of Poznań-Starołęka the exploited flint is found in secondary accumulations on Terrace VII of the Warta. This residue of the moraine plateau was eroded and transported by melt waters to the south of Poznań during the Poznań Stadial, as well as by meandering of the Warta (Bartkowski 1961; Kobusiewicz 1961; 1997; 1999). On the other hand, flint raw material at Radgoszcz close to Miedzychód is derived from flint deposits on Terraces II and III of the Warta and is a result of the moraine plateau being eroded by the meandering river (Płonka 1997). The origin of flint occurrences in the vicinity of the site in Strumienno (**Fig. 2, 6**; cf. **Table 1**), where the Warsaw-Berlin Marginal Valley, as well as the Oder and Bóbr Valleys dissect the moraine uplands (Brodzikowski 1988; 1989).

The flint used in Kornice, Silesia, was deposited in fluvio-glacial formations washed out by waters receding from the Oder Marginal Valley and intensely dissected by water from its tributaries. Fluvio-glacial formations of the moraine plateau at Sowino provided abundant good quality flint raw material.

All the sites in north-eastern Poland are located in zones where concentrations of rafts with Cretaceous flint occur. At the Wołkusz workshops this was supplemented by high quality erratic flints from nearby Cretaceous flint bearing sources. Such secondary accumulations were most probably deposited in moraine formations (the same in which rafts occurred), then eroded during the Poznań Stadial of the last glaciation by meltwater of the receding continental glacier that drained into the Biebrza Marginal Valley. Direct proof of raw material exploitation comes from pits found at Tanowo adjacent to gravel beds containing erratics (Galiński 2001).

Fig. 4 Examples of cores and pre-cores. – **1**, **2** Radgoszcz 15 (after Płonka 1997). – **3**, **4** Kocierz 3 (after Galiński 2000). – **5** Wołkusz 5 (after Szymczak 1992).

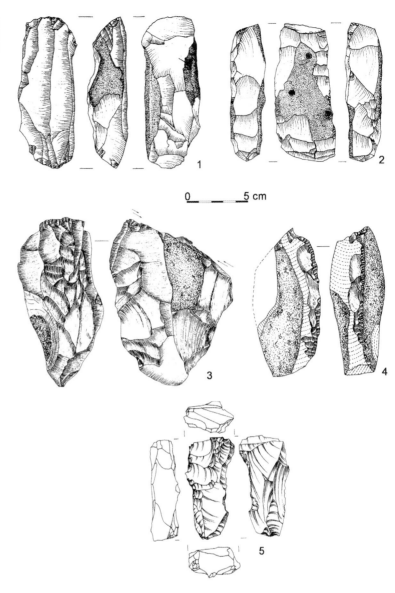

0 _____ 5 cm

Workshops: Flint assemblages and analysis

A brief description of the flint inventories from the above-mentioned sites shows that the total proportion of cores and retouched tools rarely exceeds 2 %. Slightly higher percentages of tools (4-7 %) are recorded from the workshop complexes at Płonka Kozły and Płonka Strumianka. On the other hand, the inflated occurrences of cores and tools at the sites of Mielnik (10 % and 16 % respectively) and Poznań-Staroleka (5 % and 1.7 %) can be explained by the recovery methods employed, since no small artefacts were recorded by the excavations.

The majority of assemblages are characterized by the presence of relatively high numbers of unprepared nodules of raw material, pre-cores and large cores in the primary stages of preparation (**Fig. 4**). However, a predominant feature in all cases is the substantial representation in the debitage of by-products of core preparation and elements of initial reduction, including primary (cortical) flakes, blades and chips as well as undefined (shatter) waste plus debitage from repairing cores. The flint artefacts are usually of relatively

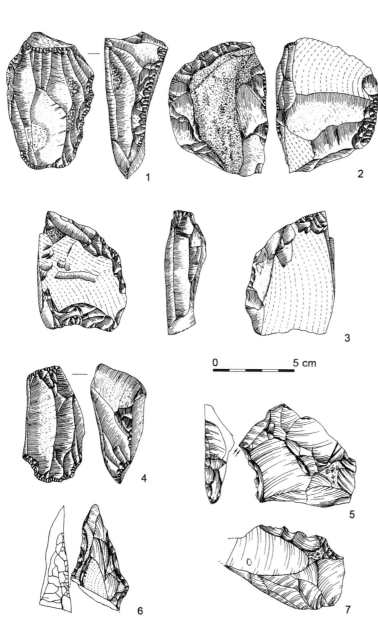

Fig. 5 Samples of »mine-type« tools: – **1-4** Kocierz 3 (after Galiński 2000), – **5-7** Strumienno 1b (after Burdukiewicz 1988a).

large size. The main aim of production at the majority of these workshops was undoubtedly the manufacture of blades. It seems likely that in some instances the blades were intended to be taken away for use elsewhere.

The typological structure of the tool kits is diverse but almost everywhere typically »domestic« forms of tools, such as end-scrapers, burins, truncated pieces, micro- truncated pieces, and tanged points predominate. The majority of the tools were made on low quality blanks (thick blades, cortical and core preparation flakes) and were not the main purpose of production. On certain sites another group of common tools comprises notches and denticulates, as well as simple retouched flakes and blades. Typical »mine-type« tools are recovered at nearly all workshop sites (**Figs. 5**.6), while in a few cases stone artefacts specifically related to production have been noted, such as hammerstones, retouchers and sandstone supports for working flint (**Fig. 6**, 4-6).

Fig. 6 Samples of »mine-type« tools and stone tools connected with flint production. – **1-3** Radgoszcz 15 (after Płonka 1999), – **4** Poznań Starołęka 1 (after Kobusiewicz 1961), – **5-6** Radgoszcz 15 (after Płonka 1999).

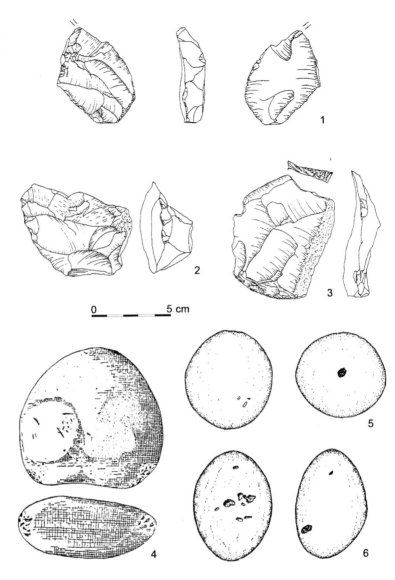

0 _____ 5 cm

Chronological framework

Major uncertainty still surrounds the age and origin of these sites. Some, like Sowino in Silesia, are thought to be of Magdalenian or possibly even much earlier Gravettian age (Furmanek 2005). However, others like Kornice are believed to be Final Palaeolithic and are assigned to the Tarnowa industry, thus forming part of the (Arch) Backed Blade technocomplex (Kozłowski 1964). Overall, it seems likely that the workshops were first developed by Magdalenian populations spreading into the southern part of Poland (including presumably Silesia) and, to a lesser extent, by later communities of the (Arch) Backed Blade technocomplex. This probable explanation accords with J. K. Kozłowski's view that the Magdalenian in the region exhibits an advanced technology of core preparation and blade production which would have been impossible without sources of good quality raw material. On this interpretation, raw materials would have been exploited by Magdalenian populations occupying sites in the Moravian Karstic region from the Meiendorf-Bølling period onwards (Kozłowski 2004).

Nonetheless, based on typological and technological variables recorded in the assemblages it can be observed that the majority of the above-mentioned workshops in Greater Poland, Pomerania and north-eastern Poland are characterized by a blade technology made from opposed platform cores of Masovian type and were connected with more recent activity of the Tanged Point Technocomplex.

For the Swiderian culture, raw material analyses of inventories from all of Poland enabled us to define zones of lithic provision and to identify four separate raw material provinces: a central province with a dominance of »chocolate« flint, a south-western province with Jurassic flint, a north-eastern province predominantly made up of Cretaceous flint and a western province with Baltic erratic flint (Szymczak 1992; Kozłowski 2004). Accordingly, the workshops in the regions of Silesia, Greater Poland, Pomerania and north-eastern Poland exploited the latter two raw material provinces.

The analysis of Tanged Point Technocomplex (TPT) settlement patterns in north-eastern Poland shows that all major site concentrations evidently overlap with the above-mentioned three regions with rafted sediments containing good quality flint raw material (Szymczak 1992). A somewhat different situation was noticed in north-western Poland where TPT settlement is concentrated in just a few territories, only some of them associated with areas of abundant raw material. The section of the Warta River near Poznań or regions of Western Pomerania, in which occupation is obviously concentrated on the densest accumulations of raw material, may serve as examples. This pattern is not repeated everywhere, however, as shown by the inventories of the Wojnowo region in western Poland, where there were evidently problems in procuring good quality flint (Kobusiewicz 1999). The situation in this region is therefore similar to the central Poland raw material province where only one of a few concentrations was directly connected with chocolate flint exploitation. The use of some other sources, such as in the Warsaw-Berlin Marginal Valley, is connected with the movement of raw materials along Final Palaeolithic reindeer migration routes (Schild 1975; Chmielewska 1978; Szymczak 1992).

The workshops described above have close counterparts in other areas of the European Plain. Sites at Bergheide in Brandenburg (eastern Germany) connected with flint exploitation and the site Finsterwalde, at which initial preparation of nodules took place, were all located in the frontal moraine zone of the Saale glaciation (Wechler / Wetzel 1987; Wechler 1988). On the other hand, in southern Lithuania there exist workshops of Tanged Point Technocomplex societies who exploited and prepared rafted Cretaceous flint from local occurrences at Eĭerynai (Rimantiene 1971), Margionys (Ostrauskas 2004) and Titnas (investigated by Satavicus).

Conclusions

The use of local raw materials by prehistoric communities on the Polish Plain demanded complex geological knowledge. It required the ability to detect areas in which substantial flint raw material concentrations existed, knowing the conditions of its occurrence and the ability to select nodules most suitable for production. This exceptional knowledge was shared by the communities of Magdalenian Culture and the Tanged Point Technocomplex, in which highly elaborate flint technologies based on the exploitation of carefully prepared blade cores necessitated access to high quality raw materials (Schild 1975; Kozłowski 2004). These populations were able to perfectly locate mass secondary accumulations of flint occurring in glacial rafts or in the form of erratics. In such places are found both sites for raw material exploitation and workshops dealing with initial preparation and distribution of exploited material. In terms of location, as well as typological and statistical structure, these workshops resemble those defined as »outside-the-house« or »mine-type« workshops known in areas adjacent to the southern parts of the Plain (cf. Ginter 1974). The concentration of settlement in the flint-bearing regions and especially the high density of sites with evident workshop elements lead us to suspect the existence of several source »basins« where Late Upper Palaeolithic people provided themselves with flint raw material. For the Magdalenian Culture this was the region of Silesia along the Upper Oder, while for communities of the Tanged Point Technocomplex sources were based on local occurrences of Cretaceous flint in glacial rafts, as well as on areas characterised by the mass occurrence of erratics such as the regions of Szczecin, Kocierz, Poznań and Miedzychód. The existence of such basins may furthermore be confirmed by the discovery of further workshops from more recent prehistoric times (Mesolithic, Neolithic and Bronze Age). The significance of these basins will be the subject of further research.

References

Bagniewski 1999: Z. Bagniewski, Mezolityczna enklawa osadnicza na Polanie Łęczyńskiej (Pojezierze Dobiegniewskie). Monografie Archeologiczne 5 (Wrocław 1999).

Balcer 1983: B. Balcer, Wytwórczość narzędzi krzemiennych w neolicie ziem Polski (Wrocław, Warszawa, Kraków, Gdańsk, Łódź 1983).

Bartkowski 1961: T. Bartkowski, Wiek teras w przełomowej dolinie Warty pod Poznaniem a stanowisko archeologiczne w Poznaniu Starołęce. Fontes Archaeologici Posnaniensis 12, 24-37.

Brodzikowski 1988: K. Brodzikowski, Sprawozdanie z badań geologicznych na stanowisku archeologicznym w rejonie Krosna Odrzańskiego. Śląskie Sprawozdania Archeologiczne 27, 11-16.

1989: K. Brodzikowski, Budowa geologiczna systemu terasowego rzeki Odry w rejonie stanowiska archeologicznego Strumienno 1 w okolicach Krosna Odrzańskiego (sprawozdanie z badań terenowych w sezonie 1986). Śląskie Sprawozdania Archeologiczne 29, 16-25.

Burdukiewicz 1988a: J. M. Burdukiewicz, Stanowisko paleolityczne w Strumiennie gm. Krosno Odrzańskie (wyniki badań w sezonie 1987). Śląskie Sprawozdania Archeologiczne 30, 7-14.

1988b: J.M. Burdukiewicz, Stanowisko paleolityczne w Strumiennie gm. Krosno Odrzańskie. Śląskie Sprawozdania Archeologiczne 27, 5-10.

1989: J. M. Burdukiewicz, Wyniki badań stanowiska paleolitycznego w Strumiennie gm. Krosno Odrzańskie (sezon 1986). Śląskie Sprawozdania Archeologiczne 29, 5-13.

Chmielewska 1978: M. Chmielewska, Późny paleolit pradoliny warszawsko-berlińskiej (Wrocław, Warszawa, Kraków, Gdańsk 1978).

Cyrek 1983: K. Cyrek, Surowce krzemienne w mezolicie dorzeczy Wisły i Górnej Warty. In: J.K Kozowski / S.K. Kozłowski (eds.),

Człowiek i środowisko w pradziejach (Warszawa 1983) 106-113.

Czarnecki 1970: M. Czarnecki, Z problematyki badań nad paleolitem i mezolitem Pomorza Zachodniego. Materiały Zachodniopomorskie 16, 31-71.

1971: M. Czarnecki, Wstępne badania wykopaliskowe paleolitycznego stanowiska w Kocierzu, pow. Gryfice. Materiały Zachodniopomorskie 17, 7-16.

Czekalska 1957: A. Czekalska, Wycieczka na Jurę. In Przewodnik do wycieczek XXVIII Zjazdu Polskiego Towarzystwa Geologicznego w r.1955, w Szczecinie. Rocznik Polskiego Towarzystwa Geologicznego 25/4, 343-347.

Furmanek 2005: M. Furmanek, Sprawozdanie z badań ratowniczych w Sowinie, stanowisko 7, województwo opolskie przeprowadzonych w 2005 roku (unpubl. manuscript).

Furmanek / Molenda / Rapiński 2001: M. Furmanek / G. Molenda / A. Rapiński, Wstępne wyniki badań na stanowisku schyłkowopaleolitycznym w Sowinie, pow. Niemodlin w 2000 roku. Śląskie Sprawozdania Archeologiczne 43, 485-490.

Galon 1972: R. Galon, Ogólne cechy rzeźby Niżu Polskiego. In R. Galon (ed.), Geomorfologia Polski II. Niż Polski (Warszawa 1972).

Galiński 1987: T. Galiński, An investigation into Paleolithic settlement of Pomeranian territories. In: J. M. Burdukiewicz / M. Kobusiewicz (eds.), Late glacial in Central Europe. Culture and environment. (Wrocław 1987) 143-163.

2000: T. Galiński, Stanowisko późnopaleolityczne w Kocierzy. Materiały Zachodniopomorskie 45, 7- 65.

2001: T. Galiński, Osadnictwo późnopaleolityczne i mezolityczne na stanowisku w Tanowie. Wykopy »łąkowe«. Materiały Zachodniopomorskie 46, 7-66.

Gieysztor-Szymczak 1981: E. Gieysztor-Szymczak, Badania wykopaliskowe na stanowisku na st.2 w Płonce- Strumiance, gm. Łapy, woj. Białystok. Reports of State Archaeological Museum in Warsaw (unpubl. manuscript).

1982: E. Gieysztor-Szymczak, Płonka-Strumianka, gm. Łapy, woj. białostockie. Stanowisko 2. Informator Archeologiczny 1981 (1982) 19-20.

1983a: E. Gieysztor-Szymczak, Płonka-Strumianka, gm. Łapy, woj. białostockie. Stanowisko 2. Informator Archeologiczny 1982 (1983) 15-16.

1983b: E. Gieysztor-Szymczak, Płonka-Kozły, gm. Łapy, woj. białostockie. Stanowisko 1. Informator Archeologiczny 1982 (1983) 18-19.

Ginter 1974: B. Ginter, Wydobywanie, przetwórstwo i dystrybucja surowców i wyrobów krzemiennych w schyłkowym paleolicie, północnej części Europy Środkowej. Przegląd Archeologiczny 22, 5-122.

Ginter 1984: B. Ginter, The Swiderian flint workshops in the upper Warta region. In: H. Berke / J. Hahn / C.-J. Kind (eds.), Jungpaläolithische Siedlungsstrukturen in Europa. Urgeschichtliche Materialhefte 6 (Tübingen 1984) 221-333.

Ginter / Kozłowski 1975: B. Ginter / J. K. Kozłowski, Technika obróbki i typologia wyrobów kamiennych paleolitu i mezolitu (Warszawa 1975).

Ginter et al. 2002: B. Ginter / M. Połtowicz / M. Pawlikowski / S. Skiba / J. Trąbka / A. Wacnik / M. Winiarska-Kabacińska/ P. Wojtal, Dzierżysław 35 – stanowisko kultury magdaleńskie na przedpolu Bramy Morawskiej. In: J. Gancarski (ed.), Starsza i środkowa epoka kamienia w Karpatach polskich (Krosno 2002) 111-146.

Kobusiewicz 1961: M. Kobusiewicz, Stanowisko z końca paleolitu i początku mezolitu z Poznania-Starołęki. Fontes Archaeologici Posnaniensis 12, 1-23.

1967: M. Kobusiewicz, Źródła surowców krzemiennych w paleolicie schyłkowym i mezolicie na terenie środkowozachodniej Niziny Wielkopolskiej, III Sympozjum Paleolityczne 1 (unpubl. mauscript).

1989: M. Kobusiewicz, Procurement of Flint in the Mesolithic of Polish Plain. In: C. Bonsall (ed.), The Mesolithic in Europe (Edinburgh 1989) 442-446.

1997: M. Kobusiewicz, Sources of flint on the West Polish Plain. In: R. Schild / Z. Sulgostowska (eds.), Man and Flint. Proceeding of the VIIth International Flint Symposium, Warszawa-Ostrowiec Świętokrzyski, September 1995 (Warszawa 1997) 83-90.

1999: M. Kobusiewicz, Ludy łowiecko-zbierackie Północno-Zachodniej Polski (Poznań 1999).

Kondracki 1965/1981: J. Kondracki, Geografia fizyczna Polski (Warszawa 1965; 1981).

2000: J. Kondracki, Geografia regionalna Polski (Warszawa 2000).

Kozarski 1995: S. Kozarski, Deglacjacja północno-zachodniej Polski: warunki i transformacja geosystemu (~20ka-1ka BP). Część I Opracowanie syntetyczne (Poznań 1995).

Kozłowski 1964: J. K. Kozłowski, Paleolit na Górnym Śląsku (Wrocław 1964).

2004: J. K. Kozłowski, Świat przed »rewolucją neolityczną«. Wielka Historia Świata 1 (Kraków, Warszawa 2004).

Krukowski 1920: S. Krukowski, Pierwociny krzemieniarskie górnictwa transportu i handlu w holocenie Polski I. Wiadomości Archeologiczne 5, 185-206.

1922: S. Krukowski, Pierwociny krzemieniarskie górnictwa transportu i handlu w holocenie Polski II. Wiadomości Archeologiczne 7, 34-57.

1939-1948: S. Krukowski, Paleolit. In: S. Krukowski / J. Kostrzewski / R. Jakimowicz (eds.), Prehistoria ziem polskich (Kraków 1948) 1-117.

Książkiewicz 1957/1968: M. Książkiewicz, Geologia dynamiczna (Warszawa 1957; 1968).

Liszkowski / Radaszewski 1999: J. Liszkowski / R. Radaszewski, Pojezierze Międzychodzko-Pniewskie. Historia geologiczna i ewolucja rzeźby. In: J. Biernacka / J. Skoczylas (eds.), Geologia i Ochrona Środowiska Wielkopolski, Rocznik LXXI Zjazdu Polskiego Towarzystwa Geologicznego (Warszawa 1999) 147-162.

Marks 1992: L. Marks, Osady i formy rzeźby lodowcowej i wodnolodowcowej. In: L. Lindner (ed.) Czwartorzęd. Osady, metody badań, stratygrafia (Warszawa 1992) 92-151.

Ostrauskas 2004: T. Ostrauskas, International conference »Interaction between East and West in Great European Plain during the Final Palaeolithic. Finds and concepts«. Archaeological and cultural sites in Lithuania. Field guide (unpubl. manuscript).

Płonka 1997: T. Płonka, Pracownie krzemieniarskie w Radgoszczy, stan.15, woj. gorzowskie. Badania w 1995 roku, Śląskie Sprawozdania Archeologiczne 39, 47-64.

1999: T. Płonka, Drugi sezon badań wykopaliskowych w Radgoszczy, stan. 15, gm. Międzychód, Śląskie Sprawozdania Archeologiczne 41,1999, 53-63.

Rimantiene 1971: R. K. Rimantiene, Paleolit i mezolit Litvy (Vilnius 1971).

Rühle 1961: E. Rühle, Przekrój geologiczny doliny Bugu na Podlasiu w okolicy Mielnika. Biuletyn Instytutu Geologicznego 169 (Warszawa 1961).

Schild 1964: R. Schild, Paleolit końcowy i schyłkowy. Materiały do prahistorii ziem polskich (Warszawa 1964).

1975: R. Schild, Późny paleolit. In: W. Chmielewski / W. Hensel (eds.), Prahistoria ziem polskich (Wrocław, Warszawa, Kraków, Gdańsk 1975).

1976: R. Schild, Krzemienne górnictwo i wymiana w pradziejach Polski widziana z perspektywy krzemienia czekoladowego Polski Środkowej. Acta Archaeologica Carpathica 16, 116-147.

1980: R. Schild, Introduction to dynamic technological analysis in chipped stone assemblages. In: R. Schild (ed.), Unconventional Archaeology (Wrocław 1980) 57-85.

2000: R. Schild, Paleolit schyłkowy na Niżu Polskim. In: M. Kobusiewicz / S. Kurnatowski (eds.), Archeologia i prahistoria Polska w ostatnim półwieczu (Poznań 2000) 39-46.

Schild / Królik / Tomaszewski 1997: R. Schild / H. Królik / J. Tomaszewski, A Raw material economy of the Paleolithic and Mesolithic occupants of Rydno complex. In: R. Schild / Z. Sulgostowska (eds.), Man and Flint. Proceeding of the VIIth International Flint Sympodium, Warszawa-Ostrowiec Świętokrzyski, September 1995 (Warszawa 1997) 285-293.

Sulgostowska 1989: Z. Sulgostowska, Prahistoria międzyrzecza Wisły, Niemna i Dniestru u schyłku plejstocenu (Warszawa 1989).

Sulimirski 1960: T. Sulimirski, Remarks Concerning the Distribution of Some Varieties of Flint in Poland. Światowit 20, 282-307.

Szmit 1929: Z. Szmit, 1929, Badania osadnictwa epoki kamiennej na Podlasiu. Wiadomości Archeologiczne 10, 36-117.

Szymczak 1992: K. Szymczak, Północno-wschodnia prowincja surowcowa kultury świderskiej. Acta Universitatis Lodziensis. Folia Archaeologica 15 (Łódź 1992).

Śliwończuk 1987: Z. Śliwończuk, Kruszywo naturalne. In: R. Osika (ed.), Budowa geologiczna Polski, (Warszawa 1987) 514-526.

Wechler 1988: K. P. Wechler, Zwei spätpaläolithische Feuersteinschlagplätze aus dem Altmoränengebiet der südwestlichen Niederlausitz. Veröffentlichungen des Museums für Ur- und Frühgeschichte Potsdam 22 (Potsdam1988) 7-15.

Wechler / Wetzel 1987: K. P. Wechler / G. Wetzel, Eine Fundstelle mit steinzeitlichem Bergbau auf Moränenfeuerstein von Bergheide, Kr. Finsterwalde. Veröffentlichungen des Museums für Ur- und Frühgeschichte 21 (Potsdam 1987) 7-30.

Wilczyński 1961: A. Wilczyński, Stratygrafia górnej jury w Czarnogłowach i Świętoszowie, Acta Geologica Polonica 12, 3-64.

Wyrwicka 1987: K. Wyrwicka, Surowce wapienne. In: R. Osika (ed.), Budowa geologiczna Polski (Warszawa 1987) 581- 617.

Abstract

The exploitation of local sources of flint on the Polish Plain during the Final Palaeolithic

In the 1960s M. Kobusiewicz observed that some Stone Age sites in north-western Poland were strikingly rich in flint raw materials. Many of them had attributes typical of sites connected with flint procurement, such as flint mines and flint workshops, and were similar to the better known »chocolate« and Jurassic flint quarries in central and southern Poland. This type of site on the Polish Plain is connected with concentrations of erratic flint, resulting from specific geomorphological processes.

Since then, especially during the last few years, dozens of new very similar sites have been discovered across the Polish Plain. Among them, ten to a dozen are identified as the result of Final Pleistocene hunter-gatherer activity. Discovery of such sites concentrated in limited areas leads us to hypothesize the existence of several flint »basins« which played a prominent role in providing raw material for the Late Glacial occupants of the Polish Plain.

Key-words

Final Palaeolithic, lithic raw materials, flint quarries, workshops.

EVA DAVID · JACQUES PELEGRIN

POSSIBLE LATE GLACIAL BONE »RETOUCHERS« IN THE BALTIC MESOLITHIC: THE CONTRIBUTION OF EXPERIMENTAL TESTS WITH LITHICS ON BONE TOOLS

The Mesolithic Zvejnieki complex (Latvia) yielded several archaeological layers dated to the Mesolithic with a rich bone and antler industry represented by tools and objects as well as manufacturing debris (David / Zagorska 2004). In the Preboreal occupation horizon of the settlement site, two chisels made of mammal limb bones (probably elk) show specific damage patterns that were not formerly registered by the two archaeologists who excavated the Zvejnieki site (Zagorska 1980; Zagorskis 1987; Zagorska / Zagorskis 1990; Zagorska 1992). Indeed, the »scratched« aspect they show is only visible beneath the manufacturing and use wear pattern of the chisels. The modifications are clearly different to traces resulting from taphonomically (biologic and abiotic) related factors observed on other bone products at Zvejnieki or other contemporaneous bone material (David 2007, 3-24). As has been previously suggested (David 2006a, 236), these traces might be related to an earlier use of the bone object for flint working, since they are evocative of the Palaeolithic-/Epipalaeolithic-like tool types classically described as »compresseurs«, »retouchoirs« or »percuteurs« (see Patou-Mathis / Schwab 2002). Indeed, apart from punches made on antler tines and light hammers formed from aurochs metapodial bones (David 2002), these types of »bones with impact traces« have not so far been recorded in the Early Mesolithic bone industry of northern Europe (David 2004a, 83). It is suggested that Mesolithic tool makers possibly used additional bone material left *in situ* by a previous Late Glacial human population.

Baltic »bones with impact traces« in context

Each of the two discussed pieces from the Zvejnieki site is made on the diaphysis of a limb bone. Their anatomically external and most convex face bears two distinct and diametrically opposed fields of damage patterns, restricted to each extremity (**Fig. 1**). They extend parallel to the long axis of the bone over a length of up to 3.6 cm with a breadth of 1.2 cm. Each field is formed by a concentration of deep impact traces which are aligned roughly parallel or slightly obliquely to the main axis of the bone. The longest impact trace is formed by a straight but irregularly marked depression measuring 5 mm and ca. 1 mm deep, with a clear or less regular cross section. These depressions were produced by a succession of similar actions, which formed an overlapping area of nick marks and hollows, as well as leaving deep secondary lines. These latter are thin and short parallel striae, regularly distributed transverse to the longest axis of a primary depression. The maximum length for a stria is around 2.2 mm. Their placement developed over a 0.5 cm long section with a regular decrease in their length until the end of the depression. The presence of these secondary striae seems to derive from a last phase of use after the deepest hollows had already damaged the compacta in adjacent areas. Given all these characteristics, it can be concluded that the location and patterning of these fields of damage are due to precise and recurrent percussive motions and that all aspects of the impact traces are consistent with human activity involving the interaction of the bone surface with a sharp-edged lithic.

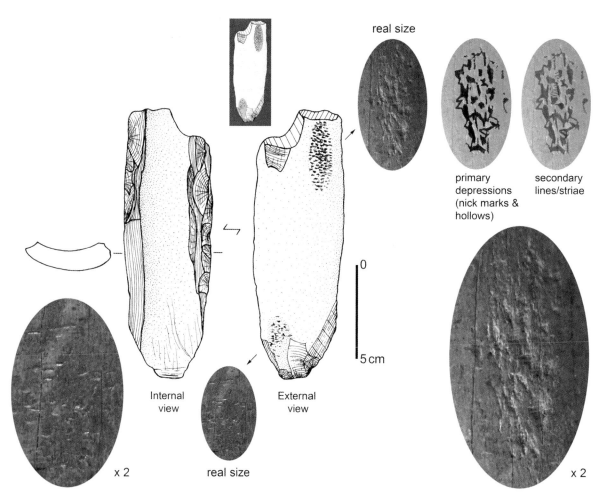

real size

primary
depressions
(nick marks &
hollows)

secondary
lines/striae

0

5 cm

Internal
view

External
view

x 2

real size

x 2

Fig. 1 The Early Mesolithic settlement of Zvejnieki (Latvia): A bevel-end tool (chisel) made on a mammal limb bone shows specific damage patterns related to an original use of the bone for flint working. They are visible beneath the traces subsequently left by the manufacturing/use of the chisel itself. Original drawing after David 2006-a, 243, n° 24. Photos and CAD: E. David.

It is not possible to say whether these patterns developed during the use of the bone in its intact state or whether the diaphysis was already split before use. The considered fields of use traces are located away from all fracture planes and do not intersect the negatives of bone flake removals visible on the internal anatomical face along both sides. The latter fracture patterns are apparently due to operations of débitage (Inizan et al. 1999, 138) in which the blanks for both chisels were produced using the »shaft-wedge-splinter« technique (David 2006a, 238-239). Transverse traces of scraping on the internal face are associated with the shaping sequence intended to sharpen the bevelled end of the chisel. All these manufacture techniques are fully characteristic of the Early Mesolithic bone and antler industry. However, they have also been recorded in the bone industry of some Late Glacial contexts in northern Germany and also in France (David 2004b, 123). A distinction between the bone and antler industries of different chronological periods, here the Final Palaeolithic and the Mesolithic, is therefore, as demonstrated for the Early and the Middle Mesolithic (David 2006b), not effective by means of manufacturing techniques only.

On both objects, a first pattern of use wear is represented by the polished aspect of the bevelled end. This almost completely obscures the previously described damage patterns from use as a knapping tool when they are located close to it. A second type of modification is represented by additional transverse fracture

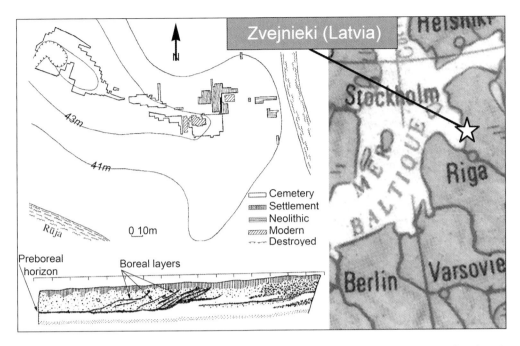

Fig. 2   The Early Mesolithic settlement of Zvejnieki (Latvia): Geographical location, excavated area (after Zagorskis 1987, 11) and stratigraphic data (after Zagorska 1992, 101).

planes on the upper end, as well as deep scars running from the active end of the tool extending onto the external face, suggesting that both objects have functioned as an intermediate piece, such as a wedge. The morphology of the two pieces and the nature and location of their active end determines them typologically as chisels. The overlaps of the traces of manufacture and use allows recognition of a chronology of events. Following the (first) use of the bone to interact with a lithic specimen it was flaked, shaped and (secondarily) used as a chisel until it was broken. The impact traces from a first use of the piece were overlain by the polish due to the secondary use as a chisel. This appears problematical to us, since to date we can recognize no equivalent feature in the bone material of the northern European Early Mesolithic period (David 2004a). While some tools may show secondary manufacturing processes related to their re-use, none of them show the specific damage patterns produced here by the first use of the two specimens. Might this mean that, at Zvejnieki, bone material of another chronological stage has become incorporated into that of the Early Mesolithic?

The sediment layers yielding the earliest human occupation at Zvejnieki (**Fig. 2**) have been clearly identified as a single stratigraphic unit during the excavation (Zagorska / Zagorskis 1990, 414). This has been dated by pollen analyses to the (Late) Preboreal (Zagorska 1980, 74). A bone from this layer directly dated to 8 500 ± 460 BP (Tn-296; Zagorska 1992, 100), calibrated 8 800-6 400 cal BC, is stratigraphically deeper than skeletal material of Mesolithic grave no. 305 dated to 8 240 ± 70 BP (Ua-3634; Zagorska 1997, 43), 7 480-7 070 cal BC. With two other graves (no. 170 and 154), the latter find and further, higher lying layers, represent a »middle« Mesolithic occupation of the settlement site (ibid.). The burials reveal a long tradition of funerary practices (Nilsson Stutz 2006) incorporating (bone) grave goods (Zagorska / Lõugas 2000) and food material for the whole Latvian Mesolithic period, i.e. until the introduction of ceramics in the 5th millennium cal BC (Eriksson et al. 2003). While none of the published records suggest that there is any stratigraphic evidence for random intrusive elements in the lower layer of the Zvejnieki site, could it be that the contextual integrity of the Early Mesolithic worked bone assemblage is unreliable?

As at other Early Mesolithic settlement sites in northern Europe, chisels form an important component of the Zvejnieki assemblage and represent 21 % of the total of manufactured bone and antler items in the discussed layer. This has yielded a total of 148 worked bone and antler specimens, 39 of which represent manufacture waste (David 2006a, 236). Apart from the two pieces« under discussion, the manufactured items are represented by awls, blades and knives, a punch, two narrow lissoirs, various types of bone chisels and projectile points, together with numerous tooth pendants. All are typical of other Mesolithic contexts in terms of both morphology and their representation. Moreover, the study of the associated waste has enabled reconstruction of the manner of their production and, by comparison with material from other Baltic and Russian sites, recognition that they form part of a north-eastern European technocomplex (David 2003, 117). The Zvejnieki worked bone assemblage therefore seems to represent a homogenous Early Mesolithic industry. However, the presence of four harpoons, two of which have subsequently also been secondarily reshaped into chisels is surprising in this context (David 2006a, Fig.8, 24.28). The blanks of these latter chisels were taken from a mammal limb bone and an elk jaw. By contrast, neither the species nor the anatomical unit of the two retouchers/chisels discussed above can be determined. Nor can it be decided whether they were originally Mesolithic tools reshaped as chisels by Mesolithic tool-makers or taken from an earlier occupation layer, which might possibly have been dated to the Late Glacial had it been recorded *in situ*. The latter hypothesis has been supported by new evidence from recent geological and palynological investigations at Zvejnieki and its surroundings.

At some parts of the Zvejnieki locality, the presence of an anthropogenically influenced Late Glacial soil is evoked by the presence of significant percentages of charcoal and by identification of ruderal species in pollen diagrams for the end of the Younger Dryas chronozone (Kalnina 2006, 71). Correspondence between the distribution of layers of clay-rich till, gyttja and peat and the shoreline water levels identified in several test pits suggest a rapid fall in water level between the transition Dryas III/Preboreal (10 200-9 200 BP) and the Atlantic chronozone, when the Burtnieki Lake began to stabilize (Eberhards 2006, 37). The Zvejnieki dwelling site is located in a region bordering the Burtnieki Lake on the side of a drumlin ridge, which forms a pathway to the Baltic Sea. From the beginning of the Holocene, fluctuations in the water level eventually transformed the Zvejnieki ridge into an island and the dwelling site was, from that period, either surrounded or submerged by water (ibid., 39). Moreover, a break in sedimentation has been recorded between the end of Dryas III and the time when Early Mesolithic communities became established. This hiatus possibly reflects rapid erosional processes which could have affected Late Glacial layers in some parts of the ridge (ibid., 62). The uncertain chronological resolution of these palaeoenvironmental episodes makes the data difficult to interpret, however it seems quite possible that eroded Final Palaeolithic anthropogenic layers were accessible during the Early Mesolithic occupation of Zvejnieki Island. This scenario would make it possible for opportunistic Mesolithic tool makers to obtain additional bone material from eroded Late Glacial layers close to their settlement site for the production of their own bone tools. However, is it in fact still possible to use a bone after long burial (ca. 1 000 years) in the ground?

The suitability of bone material for the manufacture of a tool is determined by its state of preservation. Dry bone implies an unreliable state of solidity and elasticity (see Vincent 1988, 188) and such material would certainly split soon after being shaped, especially if used as an intermediate piece, as is the case for the two chisels under discussion. The fracture patterns of these specimens instead suggest a good state of preservation. Indeed, their manufacture and use have produced waves of percussion and fracture planes in the *compacta* that have developed in precisely the same way as if the bone was fresh. By contrast, bones worked when dry would have broken into baton-shaped fragments or parallelepipeds. In view of the types of sediment in which originally Late Glacial bone material would have survived at Zvejnieki, i.e. gyttja or peat, there is no contradiction between its long term deposition and a relatively »fresh« state of preservation.

One must remember that most well known and well preserved north European prehistoric bone collections do indeed derive from such sediments (see David 2004a). However, once bone is removed from these anaerobic sediments it must be used immediately, since sudden exposure to oxygen would start to cause disintegration of its compacta by the degradation of collagen. By immediate use is meant within two or three days only (personal experience by E. D.; see also Vincent 1988). However, if stored under water bone can be used over a longer time (i.e. more than some weeks), since it will take longer for the bone to lose its organic matter. The rapid environmental changes recorded at Zvejnieki may have provided the optimal conditions required for the preservation of the bones, since they would have become buried relatively quickly in anaerobic sediment each time they were discarded (they are of course also still very well preserved even after 10 000 years).

In Europe, »bones with impact traces« identified as compressors or retouchers for lithic reduction are only recorded from Middle Palaeolithic to Final Palaeolithic contexts (de Beaune 1997, 177-192). Tools having the same function from Final Palaeolithic and Mesolithic contexts are only known in the form of pebbles (ibid.; Heuschen et al. 2006; Taute 1965). This suggests that the two Zvejnieki chisels could indeed have possibly been Late Glacial artefacts re-used by Mesolithic tool makers. Prehistoric activities germane to the use of »bones with impact traces« are now discussed in more detail.

Records on »bones with impact traces«

The first accurate descriptions of similar patterns of damage were made by H. Martin for bones from the La Quina site (Martin 1906). The recognition of pieces showing »…tissue modifications due to a concentration of impacts on silica matter…« started a debate on the Mousterian activities involved with these bones (Baudouin 1906, 197). Publication of the entire La Quina material made it clear that different patterns could be related to different activities (Martin 1907b). Indeed, similar patterns could be grouped according to their frequency on the same animal taxon (large bovids, cervids and equids), anatomical parts (epiphyses and diaphyses) and blanks (tool preforms and spalls).

Taking into account the morphology (convexity) of areas showing modifications, as well as their orientation, distribution and extension and interpreting this relative to details of the impact traces themselves, it was possible to record and identify damage patterns left by different activities: butchering, dismembering, cutting meat on bone anvils etc. (ibid.). All the observed activities showing bone interaction with lithics still remain of great interest because of the possibilities they offer for the discussion of prehistoric technological and cognitive abilities. In an examination of the type of traces observed mainly on the phalanges and limb bone diaphyses of large ungulates, H. Martin suggested that these bones were used as light hammers to knap flint or, more probably, as anvils during the sharpening of wooden sticks using flint tools (Martin 1907a, 272). These first functional hypotheses, if not accepted by all scientists at the time, clearly pose the question whether one and the same trace can in fact be obtained in different ways.

In the case of similar modalities of activity (for instance direct percussion) using the same raw materials – flint and bone – the definition of the material object used changes depending on whether it is being used actively or passively; the bone is a »compressor« or light hammer if the flint is passive, but an anvil, if the bone is passive. It is nevertheless supposed that impact traces on the bone are similar whichever way the bone has been employed (Martin 1907b, 115). If the traces observed on damage areas are not characteristic enough to distinguish the way they have been produced, it has also been argued that the intensity of use explains the different states of the impact traces (ibid.). One of the first experimental studies on bones developed this idea and applied it to the performed action itself, suggesting that the type of removal to be expected is probably linked to the intensity of the action carried out, for instance when shaping the working ends of lithic scrapers. Accordingly, the action of retouching using different degrees of force depending upon the type of retouch that is wanted (for example »Quina-type«), would alone explain the diversity of impact traces observed on bones »retouchers« used with direct percussion (Vincent 1993, 178). Other authors emphasize that the morphology of the lithic elements is directly related to the intensity of retouch and hence of the duration of their use (Dibble 1988). The number of episodes of retouch used to shape an edge (Verjux 1988) or the »degree of retouching« (Chase 1990) would be the reason for the large set of scraper forms observed in Mousterian industries, and, consequently, of the bone objects used to shape them.

From observations described from experimental studies, optimally in conjunction with corresponding related archaeological data, three main forms of impact traces are recorded on bones used to retouch lithics by direct percussion: hatching (»hachures«), nick marks (»entailles«) and cup-shaped hollows (»cupules«). With regard to their patterning, they are always concentrated together in zones or fields of damage located on the most plano-convex parts of the anatomically external face of the used bone fragment or splinter (Vincent 1993, 179-180). When it is used for retouching, the presence of ridges on the sharp-edged lithic piece removes even more bone matter (Armand / Delagnes 1997, 212). Fields of damage occur singly or multiply forming up to four zones located at the extremities of the blank, never touching its sides and always axially or diametrically opposed. This suggests that prehistoric stone workers produced fields of damage serially during short term use, turning the bone axially through 180° when the cortical matter or compacta of the first produced field became too damaged for the bone to be used efficiently. The lateral disposal of fields of damage indicates right or left handedness (see Semenov 1964, 173). The location of fields of impact traces may differ between bones used as »percuteurs« (i.e. for direct percussion) and those as »retouchoirs« (i.e. for pressure flaking), with the former damage fields located at the very extremities of the bone fragment or splinter (Hahn 1993, 374). W. Taute first emphasized patterning in the relationship between features of fields of damage and prehistoric cultures (Taute 1965). Considering only French sites, some chronological trends in the typology of nick marks have recently been recognized on bones. They are long and transverse during the Mousterian, whereas in the Aurignacian/Gravettian they become shorter and in the Magdalenian they remain short but are located axially (Schwab 2002; 2005).

The dimensions of nick marks resulting from retouching a flint edge by pressure seem narrower and shorter than those made by direct percussion (V. E. Shchelinskii after Plisson 1988, 131). For this modality, the presence of small »scratches« is also observed; these run transversely, at almost a right angle to the primary damage depression, and correspond to the slippage of the retouched flint edge during the act of retouching (ibid., 134).

F. Bordes indicated that there are two ways to shape flint points and scrapers using pressure technique, using either a »hand compressor« or an anvil (Bordes 1947, 20). The appearance of the retouch on the flint products produced by the two methods was not the same and the choice of method apparently determined the type of lithic edge produced. Use of bone as an anvil renders the retouch on lithic pieces less invasive than that produced by a »hand compressor« and the obtained trimmed edge is also more blunted. However, this type of anvil retouch may be useful for obtaining truncation (ibid.). It is not explained whether the impact traces obtained on bones were similar in all details.

The authenticity of all these patterns is nowadays clear and well defined by comparison with bone modifications resulting from taphonomic events, especially by animal agents (carnivores, ungulates and rodents) with a focus on the effects of gnawing (Malerba / Giacobini 1998). However, the way in which patterns are described could result in confusion when comparing data. For instance, H. Martin (1906, 273) mentions the presence of »secondary striae« perpendicular to the main impact traces. However, these are apparent-

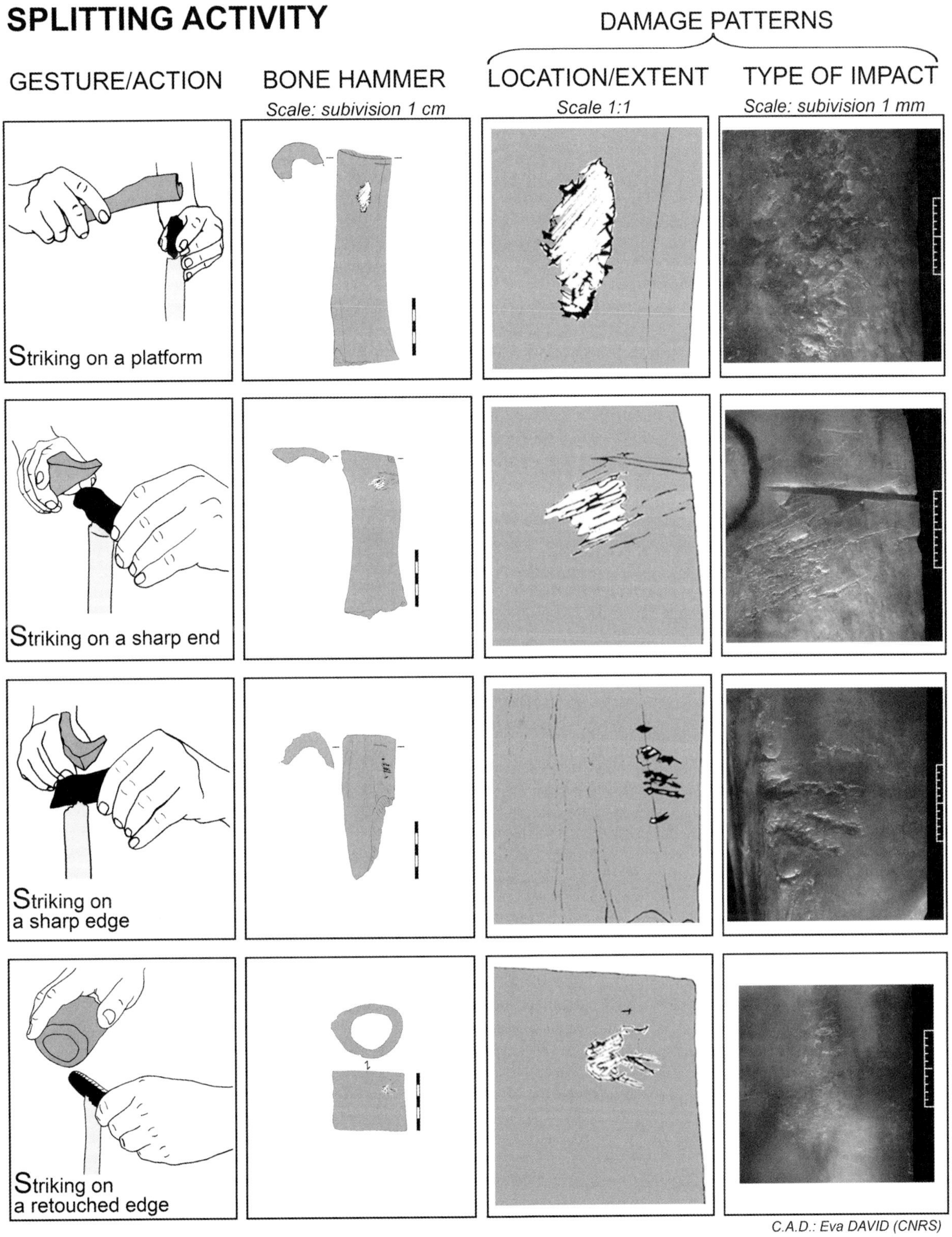

SPLITTING ACTIVITY

DAMAGE PATTERNS

GESTURE/ACTION	BONE HAMMER *Scale: subivision 1 cm*	LOCATION/EXTENT *Scale 1:1*	TYPE OF IMPACT *Scale: subivision 1 mm*

Striking on a platform

Striking on a sharp end

Striking on
a sharp edge

Striking on
a retouched edge

C.A.D.: Eva DAVID (CNRS)

Fig. 3 Results of experimental tests. The left column shows the use of fresh bones (grey) involving flint blades (black) for knapping activities and for splitting/carving wood (light grey). Photos: E. David. Drawings: E. David.

CARVING ACTIVITY

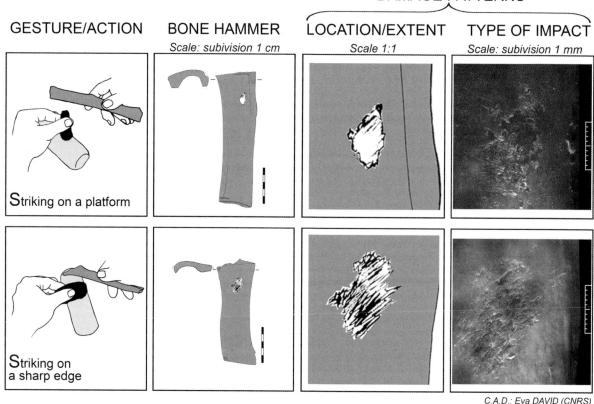

GESTURE/ACTION	BONE HAMMER *Scale: subivision 1 cm*	DAMAGE PATTERNS	
		LOCATION/EXTENT *Scale 1:1*	TYPE OF IMPACT *Scale: subivision 1 mm*

Striking on a platform

Striking on a sharp edge

C.A.D.: Eva DAVID (CNRS)

Fig. 4 Results of experimental tests. The left column shows the use of fresh bones (grey) involving flint blades (black) for knapping activities and for splitting/carving wood (light grey). Photos: E. David. Drawings: E. David.

ly striae located adjacent to the main concentration of nick marks. They could be a result of the shaping of wooden points rested upon the bone used as an anvil. When these were scraped with a forwards motion, striae would be formed on the bone by a follow through motion of the flint tool when it passed the wooden tip. The presence of so-called secondary lines has also been recorded in experiments with bone »retouchers« used with direct percussion to shape the working ends of Magdalenian-type end scrapers (Rigaud 1977, 19). The striae are also the result of incidental damage produced at the end of the retouch motion when the most prominent irregularities of the lithic edge come into contact with the bone surface. They are thus distributed adjacent to the first group of impact nick marks produced when flint is being removed. In the case of the Zvejnieki »bones with impact traces«, we have used »secondary lines or striae« to indicate traces visible precisely within the zone of the impact traces and thus intimately linked to these, to the nick marks and the hollows. These subsidiary »secondary lines or striae« are apparently the result of a stepped movement performed at the exact moment flint is removed. They are thus produced in tandem with the primary impact and are not a secondary feature produced incidentally at the end of the striking motion, as described above. For the latter phenomenon »adjacent« or »supplementary lines or striae« would be a better term.

Other functional possibilities, for example retouch by counterblow (Bordes 1947, 16), have not really been explored experimentally. Other hypotheses have also been put forward concerning »bones with impact traces«, but not so far investigated by experiments (summarized by S. A. de Beaune 1997, 169-176). Used objects dated to the Early Aurignacian, with similar damage patterns but made on other anatomical parts (carnivore teeth), have even been named differently (Mouton 1958; Mouton / Joffroy 1958, 70; Leroy-Prost 1975, 145; Castel et al. 2003). Antler should not to be considered here since the damage patterning caused by interaction with sharp-edged lithics is somewhat different (Averbouh / Bodu 2002).

On the evidence of available recorded data, the Zvejnieki »bones with impact traces« display patterns similar to those involving two different techniques of retouching lithic products with bones. These are the use of direct percussion and pressure. For both methods, two different ways of using the bone are possible - passive or active use. It is not yet clear if the observed Zvejnieki impact traces (nick marks, hollows and secondary striae) are exactly comparable in all details to published artefacts. A number of experimental tests was therefore carried out in order to understand better the modalities of interaction of both materials, bone and flint, when used for different purposes.

Experimental tests on bone tool-making tools

Experimental work was conducted in Nanterre, in 2006, by both authors. Fresh limb bones (tibia, femora) of a horse were used after being boiled for several minutes (with washing powder), after which remaining outer flesh was removed by careful scraping. Articular ends had already been already sawn off by the butcher, so it was only necessary to split the bone diaphyses axially to obtain long blanks. A number of other shafts left unsplit was also used. Ten experimental tests were carried out using flint (brown Bergerac and grey Senonian flint). Microscopic observations were made at the same degree of magnification. Each test was undertaken with reference to the notion of »choc utile d'éclatement« (»useful flaking impact«) developed by H. Martin (1907b, 115). This means that the recorded tests reflect technical actions reliably, since the technical effort expended indeed correlates with the efficiency of the action. The results of the experiments are illustrated synthetically (**Fig. 3-5**). The tests would need to be further documented as was done for a past experiment (Pelegrin 1991), but the current issue is less to discover the function of the Zvejnieki »bones with impact traces« than to explore the modalities of damage to bone matter in order to identify basic patterns.

Three types of experimental activity were conducted: the splitting and carving of wood and the knapping of flint, using bone as either a passive or an active object. During the active employment of bone, its use as a light hammer for direct percussion on flint (itself used as an intermediate piece) produced three types of impact traces depending on the part of the flint which was struck. Percussion to the narrow end of a blade (scraper) produced hatching (hachures), percussion to the striking platform (butt) yielded cup-shaped hollows (cupules) and percussion to a sharp edge delivered deep nick marks (entailles). In the case of almost all activities, a zone of damage patterns appeared consistently after a few operations. These zones developed in an approximately central position at an end of the bone (but without reaching it). When striking a retouched edge, nick marks did not develop so far as when retouching an end scraper. Alignment of all marks was transverse or transverse-oblique relative to the main axis of the bone. Detaching burin spalls created fewer deep nick marks, also centrally placed.

The passive employment of bone as an anvil upon which a flint edge is retouched by counterblow, did not produce a well defined field of damage traces and only light hatching became barely visible. Retouching flint by pressing its edge against the surface of the bone (the flint is thus more active than the bone object, although both pieces are held in the hands) creates an irregularly shaped field of damage marks marked mainly by secondary lines or striae.

Depending on the type of activity, when effective visual control of the blow or applied pressure was required, the field of damage tends to form more laterally relative to the central axis of the bone fragment or

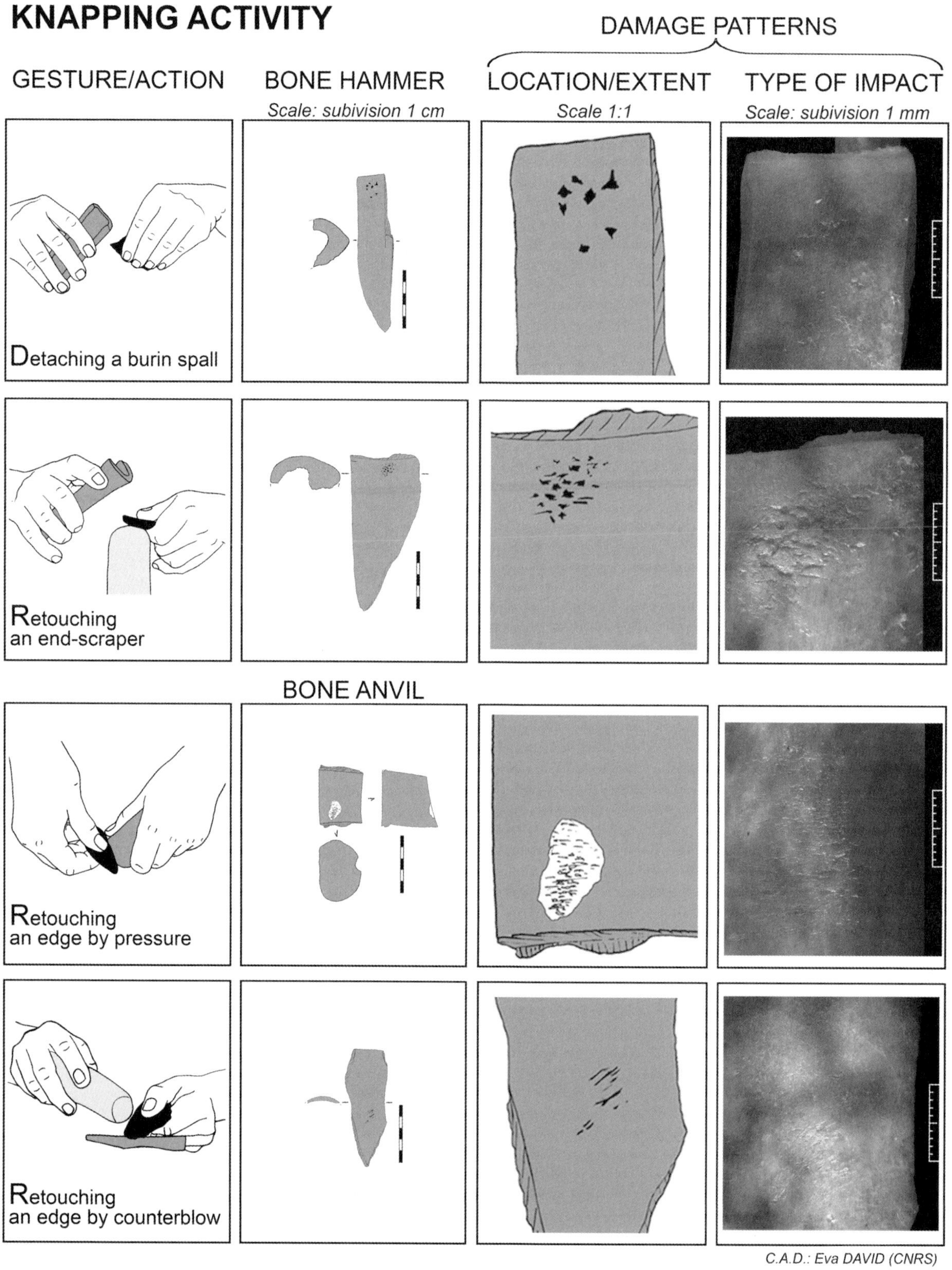

KNAPPING ACTIVITY

DAMAGE PATTERNS

GESTURE/ACTION	BONE HAMMER	LOCATION/EXTENT	TYPE OF IMPACT
	Scale: subivision 1 cm	Scale 1:1	Scale: subivision 1 mm

Detaching a burin spall

Retouching an end-scraper

BONE ANVIL

Retouching an edge by pressure

Retouching an edge by counterblow

C.A.D.: Eva DAVID (CNRS)

Fig. 5 Results of experimental tests. The left column shows the use of fresh bones (grey) involving flint blades (black) for knapping activities and for splitting / carving wood (light grey). Photos: E. David. Drawings: E. David.

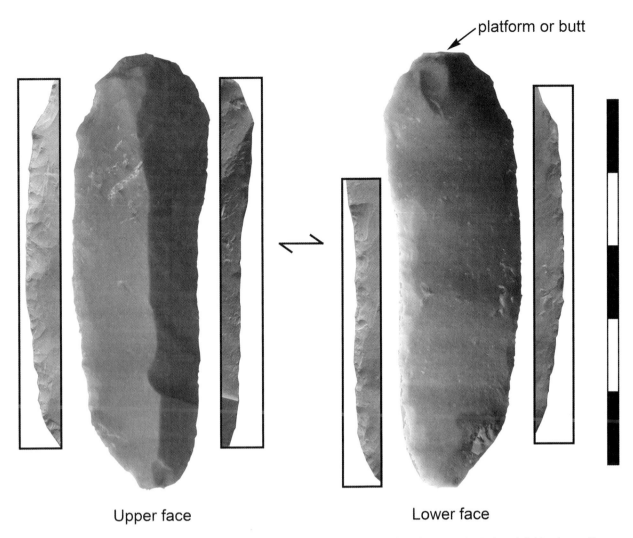

platform or butt

Upper face   Lower face

Fig. 6 Edges of an experimentally produced flint blade retouched by pressure on a fresh bone matrix. Scale: subdivision in cm. Photos: E. David.

splint. This was the case when striking the end of a blade (retouched or not) but equally so when retouching an edge by pressure. This latter is the only action that did eventually produce secondary lines or striae. For our purposes, three episodes of retouch were conducted for each edge of a blade (**Fig. 6**). An edge was first retouched along its entire length, the blade then reversed and retouched again, finally reversed and retouched a third time. During these actions, chips of flint were detached without any easy control of their length or depth. Although retouching a flint edge using a bone as a hand anvil (»retouch by pressure trimming«/retouche par égrisage ou ébarbage) does indeed produce a straight blunted edge similar to that suggested by F. Bordes in the case of retouch by counterblow (see above), the former method is the one most compatible with the traces observed on the two archaeological pieces from Zvejnieki. The observed secondary lines or striae do indeed derive from a rotating motion of the hand when transmitting pressure to the flint piece. In the course of this motion, detached flint chips are aligned lengthwise to the bone and the flint edge leaves nick marks. The question arises about the need to produce such retouched flint edges, which seem less regular and/or sharp than if produced by direct percussive retouch. Further investigations are required on the flint tool types from both Late and Post Glacial contexts in northern Europe. Zvejnieki »bones with impact traces« are possibly Late Glacial retouchers used for working lithic artefacts.

Since both flint and bone Late Glacial industries are rarely found in Latvia (Zagorska 2000, 154), thanks to an opportunistic behaviour of Mesolithic tool makers, the Zvejnieki site offers a chance to record a Final Palaeolithic bone industry and identify the technological patterns used to produce lithic tools. It would be valuable to obtain direct AMS dates for these objects.

References

Armand / Delagnes 1998: D. Armand / A. Delagnes, Les retouchoirs en os d'Artenac (couche 6c): Perspectives archéozoologiques, taphonomiques et expérimentales. In: J.-Ph. Brugal / L. Meignen / M. Patou-Mathis, Économie préhistorique: Les comportements de subsistance au Paléolithique, Actes des XVIIIe Rencontres Internationales d'Archéologie et d'Histoire d'Antibes 1997 (Sophia-Antipolis 1998) 205-214.

Averbouh / Bodu 2002: A. Averbouh / P. Bodu, Fiche percuteur sur partie basilaire de bois de cervidés. In: M. Patou-Mathis, Industrie de l'os préhistorique Cahier X, Compresseurs, Percuteurs, Retouchoirs (Paris 2002) 117-131.

Baudouin 1906: M. Baudouin, Discussion sur l'usage de l'os comme outil à l'époque moustérienne. Bulletin de la Société Préhistorique Française 3, 189-200.

de Beaune 1997: S. A. de Beaune, Les galets utilisés au Paléolithique supérieur. Gallia Prehist. Sup. 32 (Paris 1997).

Bordes 1947: F. Bordes, Etude comparative des différentes techniques de taille du silex et des roches dures. Anthropologie 51, 1-29.

Castel et al. 2003: J.-Ch. Castel / F.-X. Chauvière / S. Madelaine, Sur os et sur dents: Les »retouchoirs« aurignaciens de la Ferrassie (Savignac-de-Miremont, Dordogne). PALEO 15, 29-50.

Chase 1990: Ph. G. Chase, Tool-making, Tools and Middle Paleolithic Behavior. Current Anthropology 31/4, 443-447.

David 2002: E. David, Fiche percuteur sur métapodien d'Aurochs. In: M. Patou-Mathis, Industrie de l'os préhistorique Cahier X, Compresseurs, Percuteurs, Retouchoirs. (Paris 2002) 133-136.

2003: E. David, The Mesolithic Zvejnieki site (Latvia) in its European Context: Preliminary results delivered by a technological study of the bone and antler industry. Journal of Estonian Archaeology 7/2, 99-122.

2004a: E. David, Technologie osseuse des derniers chasseurs préhistoriques en Europe du Nord (Xe-VIIIe millénaires avant J.-C.): Le Maglemosien et les technocomplexes du Mésolithique. Ph.D. Monograph (Nanterre 2003).
http://web.mae.u-paris10.fr/recherche/mpEvaDavid.html

2004b: E. David, Fiche Transformation des matières dures d'origine animale dans le Mésolithique de l'Europe du Nord. In: D.

Ramseyer, Industrie de l'os préhistorique, Cahier XI, Matières et Techniques (Paris 2004) 113-149.

2006a: E. David, Technical behaviour in the Mesolithic (9th-8th millenium cal. BC): The contribution of the bone and antler industry from domestic and funerary contexts. In: L. Larsson / I. Zagorska, Back to the origin, New research in the Mesolithic-Neolithic Zvejnieki cemetery and environment, Northern Latvia. Acta Archaeologica Lundensia Series in 8°, 52 (Stockholm 2006) 235-252.

2006b: E. David, Contributions of the Bone and Antler Industry for Characterizing the Early Mesolithic in Europe. In: C.-J. Kind (ed.), After the Ice Age. Settlements, subsistence and social development in the Mesolithic of Central Europe, Proceedings of the International Conference 2003, Rottenburg, Baden-Württemberg. Materialhefte zür Archäologie in Baden-Württemberg 78 (Stuttgart 2006) 135-145.

2007: E. David, Principes de l'étude technologique des industries osseuses et critères de diagnose des techniques mésolithiques. Séminaire de technologie osseuse de l'Université Paris X Nanterre (Paris 2007).
http://cel.archives-ouvertes.fr/cel-00129410

David / Zagorska 2004: E. David / I. Zagorska, Zvejnieku Mezolīta Apmetne un Kapulauks Eiropas Kontekstā: Kaula un Raga Industrijas Tehniskā Izpētes Pirmie Rezultāti. Journal of Latvian Archaeology 2, 5-26.

Dibble 1988: H. L. Dibble, The interpretation of Middle Paleolithic scraper reduction patterns. In: L. Binford / J.-Ph. Rigaud, L'Homme de Neandertal, La technique 4. Actes du Colloque International de Liège 1986. E.R.A.U.L. 31 (Liège 1988) 49-58.

Eberhards 2006: G. Eberhards, Geology and development of palaeolake Burtnieks during the Late Glacial and Holocene. In: L. Larsson / I. Zagorska (eds.), Back to the origin, New research in the Mesolithic-Neolithic Zvejnieki Cemetery and environment, Northern Latvia. Acta Archaeologica Lundensia Series in 8°, 52 (Stockholm 2006) 25-51.

Eriksson et al. 2003: G. Eriksson / L. Lõugas / I. Zagorska, Stone Age hunter-fisher-gatherers at Zvejnieki, northern Latvia: radiocarbon, stable isotope and archaeozoology data. Before farming 2003, 1-25.

Hahn 1993: J. Hahn, Erkennen und bestimmen von Stein- und

Knochenartefakten. Einführung in die Artefaktmorphologie. Archaeologica Venatoria 10 (Tübingen 1993).

Heuschen et al. 2006: W. Heuschen / F. Gelhausen / S. B. Grimm / M. Street, Ein verzierter Retuscheur aus dem mittleren Siegtal (Nordrhein-Westfalen). Archäologisches Korrespondenzblatt 36, 1-12.

Inizan et al. 1999: M.-L. Inizan / M. Reduron-Ballinger / H. Roche / J. Tixier, Technology and Terminology of Knapped Stone. Préhistoire de la Pierre taillée 5 (Nanterre 1999).

Kalnina 2006: L. Kalnina, Palaeovegetation and human impact in the surroundings of the ancien Burtnieks lake as reconstructed from pollen analysis. In: L. Larsson / I. Zagorska (eds.), Back to the origin, New research in the Mesolithic-Neolithic Zvejnieki Cemetery and environment, Northern Latvia. Acta Archaeologica Lundensia Series in 8°, 52 (Stockholm 2006) 53-73.

Leroy-Prost 1975: Ch. Leroy-Prost, L'industrie osseuse aurignacienne. Essai régional de classification: Poitou, Charentes, Périgord. Gallia Préhist. 18, 1975, 1-156.

Malerba / Giacobini 1998: G. Malerba / G. Giacobini, Les retouchoirs sur éclats diaphysaires du Paléolithique moyen et supérieur de trois sites de l'Italie nord orientale (Grotte de San Bernardino, Abri Fumane et Abri Tagliente). In: M. Patou-Mathis (ed.), L'industrie sur os du Paléolithique inférieur et moyen: Nouvelles méthodes d'analyses, Actes du Workshop 4, XIIIe Congrès de l'Union Internationale des Sciences Préhistoriques et Protohistorique 6/1, Forli 1996 (Forli 1998) 167-171.

Martin 1906: H. Martin, Maillets ou enclumes en os provenant de la couche moustérienne de la Quina (Charente). Bulletin de la Société Préhistorique Française 3, 1906, 155-162.

1907a: H. Martin, Présentation d'ossements utilisés de l'époque moustérienne. Bulletin de la Société Préhistorique Française 4, 1907, 269-277.

1907b: H. Martin, Industrie osseuse. Recherches sur l'évolution du Moustérien dans le Gisement de La Quina (Charente) 1 (Paris 1907-1910).

Mouton 1958: P. Mouton, Un nouvel outil de l'Aurignacien typique, les »cousoirs« sur canines de grands fauves. In: Congrès Préhistorique de France, Compte rendu de la XVe session, Poitiers-Angoulême 1956 (Paris 1958) 756-757.

Mouton / Joffroy 1958: P. Mouton / R. Joffroy, Le gisement aurignacien des Rois à Mouthiers (Charente). Gallia Suppl. 9 (Paris 1958).

Nilsson Stutz 2006: L. Nilsson Stutz, Unwrapping the dead. Searching for evidence of wrappings in the mortuary practices at Zvejnieki. In: L. Larsson / I. Zagorska (eds.), Back to the origin, New research in the Mesolithic-Neolithic Zvejnieki Cemetery and environment, Northern Latvia. Acta Archaeologica Lundensia Series in 8°, 52 (Stockholm 2006) 217-233.

Patou-Mathis / Schwab 2002: M. Patou-Mathis / C. Schwab, Fiche générale. In: M. Patou-Mathis, Industrie de l'os préhistorique Cahier X, Compresseurs, Percuteurs, Retouchoirs (Paris 2002) 11-20.

Pelegrin 1991: J. Pelegrin, Aspects de démarche expérimentale en technologie lithique. In: 25 ans d'études technologiques en Préhistoire: Bilan et perspectives, Actes des XIe Rencontres Internationales d'Archéologie et d'Histoire d'Antibes, Juan-les-Pins 1989 (Juan-les-Pins 1991) 57-63.

Plisson 1988: H. Plisson, Technologie et tracéologie des outils lithiques moustériens en Union soviétique: Les travaux de V.E. Shchelinskii. In: L. Binford / J.-Ph. Rigaud (eds.), La technique. L'Homme de Neandertal 4. Actes du Colloque International de Liège 1986. E.R.A.U.L. 31 (Liége 1988) 121-168.

Rigaud 1977: A. Rigaud, Analyses typologique et technologique des grattoirs magdaléniens de la Garenne à Saint-Marcel (Indre). Gallia Prehist. 20/1, 1-43.

Schwab 2002: C. Schwab, Les »os à impressions et à éraillures« de la Grotte d'Isturitz (Pyrénées-Atlantiques, France). In: M. Patou-Mathis / P. Cattelain / D. Ramseyer, L'industrie osseuse pré- et protohistorique en Europe, Approches technologiques et fonctionnelles, Actes du Colloque 1.6., XIVe Congrès de l'U.I.S.P.P. Liège 2001. Bulletin du Cercle archéologique Hesbaye-Condroz 26, 9-18.

2005: C. Schwab, Les »os à impressions« magdaléniens d'Isturitz (Pyrénées-Atlantiques) et de la Vache (Ariège). In: V. Dujardin, Industrie osseuse et parures du Solutréen au Magdalénien d'Europe, Table ronde sur le Paléolithique supérieur récent, Angoulême (Charente) 2003. Société Préhistorique Française Mémoire 34 (Paris 2005) 291-300.

Semenov 1964: S. A. Semenov, Prehistoric technology (London 1964).

Taute 1965: W. Taute, Retoucheure aus Knochen, Zahnbein und Stein vom Mittelpaläolithikum bis zum Neolithikum. Fundberichte aus Schwaben, N. F. 17, 76-102.

Verjux 1988: Ch. Verjux, Les denticulés moustériens. In: L. Binford / J.-Ph. Rigaud (eds.), La technique. L'Homme de Neandertal 4. Actes du Colloque International de Liège 1986. E.R.A.U.L. 31 (Liège1988) 196-204.

Vincent 1988: A. Vincent, L'os comme artefact au Paléolithique moyen: Principes d'étude et premiers résulats. In: L. Binford / J.-Ph. Rigaud (eds.), La technique. L'Homme de Neandertal 4. Actes du Colloque International de Liège 1986. E.R.A.U.L. 31 (Liège 1988) 185-196.

1993: A. Vincent, L'outillage osseux au Paléolithique moyen: Une nouvelle approche (Nanterre1993).

Zagorska 1980: I. Zagorska, Das Frühmesolithikum in Lettland. Veröffentlichungen des Museums für Ur- und Frühgeschichte Potsdam 14/15, 1980, 73-82.

1992: I. Zagorska, The Mesolithic in Latvia. Acta Archaeologica 63, 1992, 97-117.

1997: I. Zagorska, The first radiocarbon datings from Zvejnieki Stone Age burial ground, Latvia. Iskos 2, 42-46.

2000: I. Zagorska, The Earliest Settlement of Latvia. Pact 57 1/6, 131-156.

Zagorska / Lõugas 2000: I. Zagorska / L. Lõugas, The tooth pendant head-dresses of Zvejnieki cemetery. Muinasaja Teadus 8, 223-245.

Zagorska / Zagorskis 1990: I. Zagorska / F. Zagorskis, The Bone and Antler Inventory from Zvejnieki II, Latvian SSR. In: C. Bonsall (ed.), The Mesolithic in Europe. Papers presented at the Third International Symposium, Edinburgh 1985 (Edinburgh 1990) 414-423.

Zagorskis 1987: F. Zagorskis, Zvejnieku akmens laikmeta kapulauks (Riga 1987).

Abstract

Possible late glacial bone »retouchers« in the Baltic Mesolithic: the contribution of experimental tests with lithics on bone tools

The Early Mesolithic layer of the Zvejnieki site (Latvia) yielded two bevel-end tools showing specific damage patterns, which can be related to a primary use of the bone for flint working. They are more evocative of Final Palaeolithic types described as »compresseurs«, »retouchoirs« or »percuteurs«. As these types of bone tools are not recorded so far from the European Early Mesolithic, patterns on the artefacts are compared here with data provided by new experimental tests. Some criteria for functional identification are proposed. Integrating results of recent palaeoenvironmental studies in Northern Latvia, it is suggested here that Mesolithic tool makers possibly re-used bone material left *in situ* by previous Late Glacial human populations.

Key-words

Early Mesolithic, retouchers, compressors, tools, hammers, experiments.

MICHAŁ KOBUSIEWICZ

THE LYNGBY POINT AS A CULTURAL MARKER

The Bromme culture, sometimes known also as the Bromme-Lyngby culture, was first identified by the German prehistorian Gustav Schwantes (1923). Wolfgang Taute (1968) described it much more precisely and his proposed definition has been generally accepted. The main, and practically the only distinguishing artefact (fossile directeur) for the flint inventories of Bromme culture is the so called Lyngby point. This point type differs from other tanged points mainly in its size. According to Taute Lyngby points are greater than 5.5 cm in length and/or 1.7 cm in breadth. Taute (1968, 12) also assigned the form the description »narrow« (when over 5.5 cm long but less than 1.7 cm wide) and »short« (less than 5.5 cm, but with a width of over 1.7 cm) (**Fig. 1**). I propose to term larger specimens combining both larger dimensions (more than 5.5 cm length and 1.7 cm breadth) »long«. The more or less separate tang is generally located at the proximal end of the blank and usually characterized by steep direct retouch, more rarely by alternating retouch. The bulb of percussion is sometimes preserved and in such cases the end of the tang is wider. The piercing pointed end is rarely retouched. Taute states that the narrow and short specimens are transitory forms between the large type of Lyngby point and the Ahrensburgian point.

The flint technology of the Brommian consists of exploiting normally single platform cores, sometimes conical in shape, more rarely with opposed platforms which are worked with a hard or soft hammer. The resulting blanks are mostly large, thick blades or elongated flakes. The relatively limited dating evidence available suggests that the Bromme Culture can be dated to the second half of the Allerød and the early phase of Dryas III (Eriksen 2002). Some scholars identify the so called Lyngby axe made of reindeer antler with the Bromme culture, but, since up to now it has been very difficult to obtain precise dates for these objects, it is safer to attribute them more generally to any culture of the Tanged Point Technocomplex of the Allerød or Dryas III (see Clausen 2004; 2005; Brinch Petersen 2009).

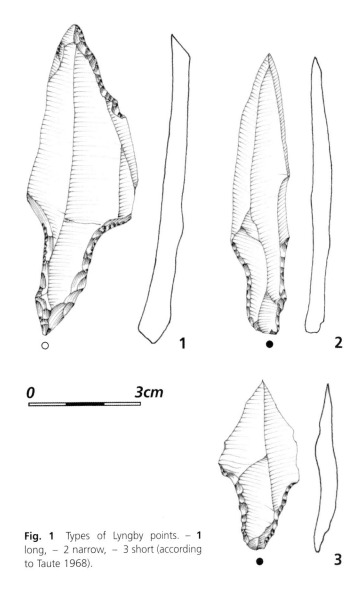

Fig. 1 Types of Lyngby points. – **1** long, – **2** narrow, – **3** short (according to Taute 1968).

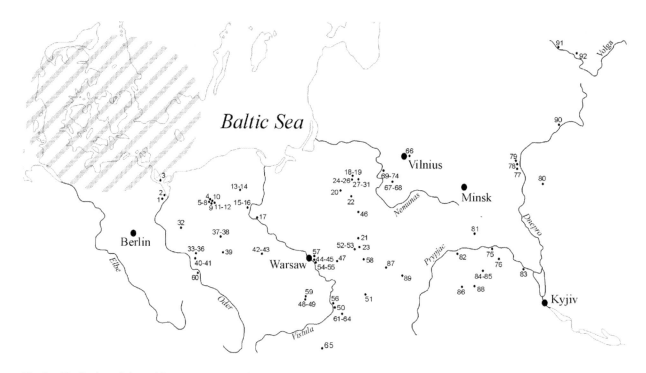

Fig. 2 Distribution of sites with one or more Lyngby point in the central and eastern part of the North European Plain. The hatched territory marks the core area of the Bromme Culture.

Poland: – 1 Szczecin-Krzekowo, – 2 Szczecin-Bukowo, – 3 Świnoujście, – 4 Gudowo 3a , – 5 Jaglisko 1, – 6 Jaglisko 3, – 7 Jaglisko 3a, – 8 Jaglisko 19, – 9 Rędocin 15, – 10 Lubiszewo 4, – 11 Wierzchowo 1a, – 12 Złocieniec »b«, – 13 Chocimski Młyn 1, – 14 Męcikał 3, – 15 Pałcz II, – 16 Bydgoszcz Czersko Polskie, – 17 Toruń »Wzgórza Piaskowe (Sandy hills)«, – 18 Zusno, – 19 Toczyłowo, – 20 Ełk, – 21 Wólka, – 22 Woźna Wieś 1, – 23 Mielnik, – 24 Puchówka 9, – 25 Rajgród 25, – 26 Dręstwo 9/10, – 27 Wołkusz 3, – 28 Wołkusz 5, – 29 Burdeniszki 1d/e, – 30 Burdeniszki 4, – 31 Rygol 1, – 32 Strumienno 1c, – 33 Pomorsko 1, – 34 Kargowa »e«, – 35 Smolno Wielkie 1, – 36 Wojnowo 2, – 37 Potrzanowo 5, – 38 Zielątkowo 4, – 39 Zwola 1, concentration 1, – 40 Siedlnica 17, I/73, – 41 Siedlnica 17, II/78, – 42 Witów 1, concentration III, – 43 Ruszków, – 44 Całowanie IV, trench III. – 45 Całowanie level V, – 46 Borsukówka, – 47 Świdry Wielkie I, – 48 Nowy Młyn Ia, – 49 Nowy Młyn Ib, – 50 Jacentów 10, – 51 Dorohucza II, – 52 Stańkowicze I, – 53 Stańkowicze II, – 54 Czemierniki 3, – 55 Nowa Praga, – 56 Dąbrówka, – 57 Białka, – 58 Borsuki 3, – 59 Grzybowa Góra X/59+IV/60, – 60 Bobrowice, – 61 Chwałowice, – 62 Dzierzkowice Wola, – 63 Gródek 1c, – 64 Trzciniec, – 65 Pakoszówka.

Lithuania: – 66 - Vilnius I, – 67 Erfierynas 15, – 68 Erfierynas 16, – 69 - Maksauka 6, – 70 Meragežeris 8, – 71 Kašetos, – 72 Gribasa, – 73 - Derażnica 31, – 74 Ilgis.

Belarus: – 75 Nobel, – 76 Krasnosielie, – 77 Janowo, – 78 Koromka, – 79 Bierestieniewo, – 80 Greńsk, – 81 Opol II, – 82 Pidliszczyna.

Northern Ukraine: – 83 Pribor, – 84 Lipa, – 85 Rudnia, – 86 Goromowka, – 87 Newir, – 88 Bolszoj Midsk, – 89 Lutka.

Russia: – 90 Anosowo, – 91 Podoł III, – 92 Troickie, – 93 Ust-Tudowka I.

Taute's »Lyngby Kreis« comprised a group of flint assemblages characterized by a small number of retouched tool types. For this group Lyngby points were represented either exclusively or clearly outnumbered other types of tanged points. An example is provided by the assemblages of the »Segebro-Bromme Gruppe«. They are concentrated in a narrow territory of Jutland, the Danish Islands, southern Sweden, Schleswig-Holstein and the island of Rügen (Taute 1968, Karte 9). The second group of the Lyngby Kreis, known as the »Tolk-Sprenge Gruppe«, differs from the Bromme-Segebro by the presence, alongside the Lyngby points, of Ahrensburgian points and smaller quantities of backed blades, which however never exceed the number of tanged points. If backed blades predominate, the assemblage should then, by definition, no longer be considered Brommian but as part of the Federmessergruppen Culture. Taute himself stated that only the proportion of tanged to backed points distinguishes Tolk-Sprenge assemblages from those of Federmessergruppen type. To my mind this distinction is purely arbitrary. Geographically, assemblages of the Tolk-Sprenge Gruppe occur further south than those of the Segebro-Bromme group, extending from northern Germany to the Netherlands in the west and eastwards to the central Oder River. Various scholars follow Taute's interpretation; for example Andersen (1988) refers to the territory of Segebro-Bromme as the »core area« of the Bromme Culture, while Eriksen (2002, Fig. 6) describes it as the location of the classical Brommian.

Review of the evidence

Major progress in Central and Eastern European Final Palaeolithic research over the last three decades following Taute's seminal publication has enabled some of the more problematic issues presented in this paper to be seen in a new light. For example, new discoveries relating to Taute's Lyngby Kreis (Bromme Culture) have shown that Lyngby points occur, sometimes in large numbers, outside and even occasionally extremely far from the area generally recognized as the territory of the classical Bromme Culture (**Fig. 2**). They appear on the Polish Plain, in Lithuania, Belarus, northern Ukraine and even reach the sources of the Volga River in Russia, almost 400 km to the North West of Moscow and some 1 400 km as the crow flies from the core area in Jutland. In these instances Lyngby points have been recorded in assemblages originating both from controlled excavations and, more often as surface finds. They can appear individually or in small numbers in several different cultural contexts.

Table 1 indicates the very widespread distribution of Lyngby points across the central and eastern parts of the European Plain. Of course, it must be acknowledged that the list is by no means exhaustive. A more scrupulous search would probably bring many others to light but this list is sufficient as the basis for further discussion and establishing some preliminary conclusions.

In the first place, these data significantly enrich Taute's map of Lyngby points which numbered 98 sites with single Lyngby points, 21 sites with two to three Lyngby points, nine sites with four to nine and one site (Bromme) with over 50 points, all in the area between the Rhine and the Neman rivers (Taute 1968). In this paper I shall not analyze the occurrence of Lyngby points in the territory south and west of the core area. For eastern Germany these data are published by Gramsch (1988). It would also be appropriate to mention the abundant finds of Bromme-like tanged projectile points from France described by de Sonneville-Bordes (1988) as »nordic related«. These have been found south of the Loire valley as far as the Garonne River and to the east and west of the Massif Central. They appear as single finds or in small numbers in late Upper Palaeolithic assemblages dated by D. de Sonneville-Bordes to Dryas II and the beginning of Allerød, which would make them slightly older than the classical Bromme sites.

Lyngby-type tanged points are known too from Hengistbury Head on the central south-coast of England. The excavators qualify these finds as belonging to the Backed Blade Technocomplex *sensu lato* and dating to the Bølling and Allerød (Barton / Bergman 1988). Smaller specimens of tanged points in Britain are believed to be more recent, Dryas III or younger (Barton / Roberts 2002).

Returning to the question of the prehistory of Central and Eastern Europe: here, the discovery of Lyngby points far from the accepted core area of the Bromme Culture has been interpreted by many scholars as representing traces of the physical presence of human groups which arrived in these regions from southern Scandinavia. For these researchers, finds of such points mark the trails of newcomers who wandered across vast expanses of the Plain as far east as the source of the Volga. For example, in 1971 R. Rimantiene distinguished a group of site assemblages with Lyngby points in the Middle Neman Basin in Lithuania. She named them Baltic Magdalenian and remarked on the obvious resemblances to the western European Brommian. For her, these connections represented the physical presence of Bromme people arriving from

Northern belt of the Polish Plain	Szczecin-Krzekowo, Szczecin-Bukowo, Świnoujście, Gudowo 3a, Jaglisko 1, Jaglisko 3, Jaglisko 3a, Jaglisko 19, Rędocin 15, Lubiszewo 4	Bagniewski 1997
	Wierzchowo 1a, Złocieniec »b«, Chocimski Młyn 1, Męcikał 3, Pałcz II, Bydgoszcz Czersko Polskie	Kobusiewicz 1999
	Toruń – »wzgórza piaskowe (sandy hills)«	Marciniak 1982
	Zusno,Toczyłowo, Ełk, Wólka, Woźna Wieś 1, Mielnik	Sulgostowska 1989
	Puchówka 9, Rajgród 25, Dręstwo 9/10	Siemaszko 1999
	Wołkusz 3, Wołkusz 5, Burdeniszki 1 d/e, Burdeniszki 4, Rygol 1	Szymczak 1999
Central belt of the Polish Plain	Strumienno 1c, Pomorsko 1, Kargowa »e«	Kobusiewicz 1970
	Smolno Wielkie 1, Wojnowo 2, Potrzanowo 5, Zielątkowo 4, Zwola 1, skup. 1	Fojud / Kobusiewicz 1978; Kobusiewicz 1999
	Siedlnica 17 I/73, Siedlnica 17 II/78	Burdukiewicz 1999
	Witów 1, skup. III, Ruszkow	Chmielewska 1978
	Całowanie IV wyk. III	Schild 1988
	Całowanie level V	Schild 1975
	Borsukówka	Sulgostowska 1989
	Świdry Wielkie	Sawicki 1936
	Nowy Młyn Ia, Nowy Młyn Ib	Kozłowski / Kozłowski 1977
	Jacentow 10, Dorohucza II	Libera 1990
	Stańkowicze I, Stańkowicze II	Szmit 1929
	Czemierniki 3, Nowa Praga, Dąbrówka, Białka, Borsuki 3	Libera 1995
Southern belt of the Polish Plain	Grzybowa Góra X/59+IV/60	Schild 1975
	Bobrowice	Burdukiewic 1979
	Chwałowice	Libera 1990
Uplands of south eastern Poland	Dzierzkowice Wola, Grodek 1c, Trzciniec, i Pakoszówka koło Sanoka	Libera 1995
Lithuania (Middle Neman Basin)	Vilnius I, Erżarynas 15,16, Maksauka 6, Mergeżeris 8, Kašetos, Gribasa, Dereżnica 31, Ilgis 1	Rimantiene 1971; Sulgostowska 1989; Zaliznyak 1995; 1998
Belarus	Nobel, Krasnosielie, Janowo, Koromka, Bierestieniewo, Opol II, Greńsk, Pidliszczyna	Sulgostowska 1989; Zaliznyak 1995
North-western Ukraine	Pribor 4, Lipa, Rudnia, Goromowka, Nienenkowo, Newir, Listka, Bolszoj Midsk, Lutka	Zaliznyak 1995; 2005
Western Russia (Tver district by the sources of the Volga River)	Ust Tudovka I, Anosowo, Troickie 3 Podoł III	Zaliznyak 1999; 2005
		Sinitsina 1999

Table 1 Distribution of Lyngby points across the central and eastern parts of the European Plain.

southern Scandinavia along the southern Baltic coast (Rimantiene 1971). In 1976, S. K. Kozłowski reported that the Lithuanian assemblages were the eastern extension of the eastern (Polish) group of the Bromme Culture (Kozłowski 1976), while a year later he referred to them as Bromme *sensu largo* and illustrated their distribution on a map (Kozłowski / Kozłowski 1977). In 1999 L. Zaliznyak reiterated Rimantiene's hypothesis asserting that Bromme people had reached Lithuania and Belarus as far as the Neman, Prypec and Dniepr basins. He also sees their distribution extending as far east as the upper Volga (Zaliznyak 1999). More recently J. K. Kozłowski (2004) has added his support to this hypothesis, arguing that Bromme groups

Poland	Bierzwnik 19 (LA), Jaglisko 1 (LA), Jaglisko 3 (LAF), Jaglisko 3a (LF), Ełk (LA), Puchówka (LAS), Mielnik (LA), Woźna Wieś (LF), Wólka (LS), Wołkusz 5 (LS)*, Strumienno 1c (LA), Pomorskoi 1 (LAS), Smolno Wielkie 1 (LAS), Wojnowo 2 (LAS), Kargowa »e« (LF) Witów 1 concentration III (LAS), Siedlnica 17 I/73 (LF), Siedlnica 17 II/78 (LF), Zwola 1, skup. 1 (LAS), Dąbrówka (LS), Dorohucza II (LS), Nowa Praga (LS), Gródek (LS), Świdry Wielkie I (LS), Całowanie, level V, (LAS), Stańkowicze I (LS), Stańkowicze II (LS)
Lithuania	Dereżnica (LS), Kašetos (LAS),Ezjarynas 15 (LAS), Erżarynas 16 (LAS), Gribasa (LS).
	From Belarus: Krasnosielce (LAS), Nobel concentration 2 (LS), Nobel concentration 5 (LAS), Lutka (LAS), Kut (LAS)), Janowo (LAS), Pidliszczyna (LA)
North western Ukraine	Pribor 4 (LAS), Rudnia (LS), Bolszoj Midsk (LA)
Western Russia	Podoł III (LS)

Table 2 Assemblages containing Lyngby points and other forms of armature. − L = Lyngby point or points, − A = Ahrensburgian point or points, − S = Swiderian point or points, − F = Federmesser type backed blade or backed blades. * Regarding other sites of the Wolkush culture, K. Szymczak (1999) writes that they contain Ahrensburgian or similar tanged points.

moved east into Lithuania and Belarus along a corridor which today lies submerged under the southern Baltic. Z. Bagniewski (1997), equally, has no doubts that Brommian settlement arrived from the west, spreading into Polish Pomerania and farther east, and even marks numerous islands of Bromme settlement on the map of Europe (Bagniewski 1997). A slightly different hypothesis has been proposed by K. Szymczak (1995). After excavating several assemblages containing Lyngby points in north eastern Poland he recognized an entirely new cultural unit which he termed the Perstunian Culture. On the basis of typology he dated it to the Allerød and drew parallels with the Baltic Magdalenian of R. Rimantiene (1971). He considered both of these units to be clearly related to the Brommian (Szymczak 1995). Finally, in discussing the assemblages from Grzybowa Gora V/59+IV/60 in Central Poland at the southern limit of the Plain, R. Schild (1975) believes they were probably made by a group of Bromme explorers who arrived there on a 800 km long-distance quest for the red colouring agent haematite (Schild 1975). In this case, there would seem at least to be some logic in the interpretation.

Given the ideas presented above, it is in my opinion worth giving some of these views serious consideration. For instance, did Scandinavian hunters really migrate as far as the banks of the Volga? Was this a real event based on historical fact?

Let us take a look at the assemblages containing Lyngby points (**Table 2**). Apart from a few exceptions, which I will discuss later, all occurrences (except single finds) also contain Ahrensburgian or Swiderian points or backed blades, or sometimes all of these types in combination. In addition to these typological elements, there exist distinctive forms of lithic core which are referred to »Masovian« or »Swiderian« types. These are two-platform and opposed platform blade cores which occur in addition to single platform examples.

In Central and Eastern Europe a few assemblages are known to contain only Lyngby points. Proceeding from west to east they are: Grzybowa Góra X/59+IV/60 in central Poland, Vilnius I in Lithuania and Anosovo and Troickie 3 in western Russia. These assemblages are rather small and this might explain the lack of other typological elements. Anosovo is predominantly a workshop site and as such atypical. Double platform cores of Swiderian type are present at the Russian sites.

In summary, the above description clearly shows that Lyngby points are dispersed over a vast area of the European Plain. They are often accompanied by other types of tanged points, such as Ahrensburgian or Swiderian forms, or other »atypical« specimens whose shapes differ from the former points. Moreover, these combinations may also include backed blades of Federmesser or other types and even Hamburgian shouldered points. To further complicate matters, typical Lyngby points are found in assemblages attributed to other well-known cultures of the Tanged Point Technocomplex. For example, in the Swiderian they occur at Świdry Wielkie I near Warsaw (Sawicki 1936) or Witów I, concentration III (Chmielewska 1978), at Eggstedt and Stellmoor in northern Germany they appear in the Ahrensburgian (Taute 1968) and they occur in Federmesser contexts at Siedlnica 17, trench I/73 and Siedlnica 17, trench II/78 in western Poland (Burdukiewicz 1979).

In many cases, it seems clear that the apparent association of different point types is due to various kinds of mixing processes caused either by multiple occupations or by the way in which the finds were collected. These cases have little value for scientific discussion. However, it should also be emphasized that some of the assemblages with Lyngby points and other types of tanged points actually come from carefully controlled excavations, mainly in Poland, where research has been very intensive over the past few decades. Examples of this kind include Jaglisko 1, Jaglisko 3, Jaglisko 3a, Woźna Wieś 1, Pomorsko 1, Wołkusz 3, Wołkusz 5, Strumienno 1c, Siedlnica 17, I/73, Siedlnica 17, II/78, Witów 1 skup. 3, Całowanie IV, Wykop III and Całowanie. Although we cannot be one hundred percent certain in all cases, especially for river terraces with sandy-gravels or in dune formations, I believe there is in many instances a strong case for the homogeneity of these assemblages.

Concluding discussion

What sort of conclusions can be drawn from the evidence reviewed above? A long time ago it was suggested that Lyngby points had a special role in mediating intercultural relations; this was highlighted in particular by B. Ginter (1966) who regarded such points as having a special cultural status. In 1974 he stated that »…we cannot exclude that the Lyngby point had a common intercultural value. It is known in many cultures starting from the west European Magdalenian, through the Federmesser, Ahrensburgian and up to the Ukrainian Swiderian…« (my translation). According to Ginter, the concept of the Lyngby Point should be separated from the concept of the Bromme Culture, as most of the points have nothing to do with this culture (Ginter 1966; 1974). R. Schild (1975) largely concurred with this view in noting that the occurrence of single finds of Lyngby points in north-eastern Europe could only be correlated with Bromme settlement to a limited degree. In a similar vein, one should not overestimate the importance of a few tools of the same type found in different cultural contexts in order to prove extensive cultural diffusion (Otte 1988). I entirely agree with the above opinions. The projectile point which we refer to as the Lyngby point was simply a perfect and efficient hunting weapon for tipping either spears or arrows. As such, it would have been common to the hunting toolkits of a wide range of tundra hunters. Derived from the west European Magdalenian its use spread right across the European Plain. It survived in this large form until the Early Mesolithic, for example in northern Germany at Pinnberg in layers Ia and Ib (Rust 1958), at Ust Tudovka on the upper Volga in Russia (Żhilin / Krawtcow 1991, after Sinitsina 1999) and at Kotitsky V, where it is found in the Late Mesolithic (Sinitsina 1999). Furthermore, this projectile point form is even known from the Neolithic record (Taute 1968).

Secondly, the variation in size and shape seen in these points may be due to a number of factors, including differences in precise function (e. g. whether used as a spear or arrowhead) or the local wealth and quality of raw material (the largest Lyngby points are known in Demark and in the upper Volga region, both abundant in good flint sources) and finally maybe even due to the skills of individual flint knappers.

Thirdly, it is important to emphasize that the Lyngby point is clearly and very methodically connected to use in the park-tundra environments of the European Plain, although such items do sporadically occur outside the Plain.

Fourthly, I do not regard the Lyngby point as any form of cultural marker. As an efficient weapon it was generally adopted by many tundra hunters. Its occurrence is not a proxy for the presence of a Scandinavian Bromme population, just as the presence of a Kalashnikov automatic rifle does not mean a Russian presence in the Middle East. Following on from this, we know of many good examples in prehistory of products that were used over a very wide area and were not culturally connected, for example small backed blades which appeared independently at the end of Pleistocene in both Europe and North Africa. Another illustration is at the end of the Mesolithic, when trapezoidal microliths became dominant over the whole of the European Plain. This is why for a long time flint assemblages containing trapezes were called »Tardenoisian«, in the same way that the collections containing Lyngby points are now called »Brommian«. It follows that there was no mass migration of people from Scandinavia across Lithuania and Belarus to the upper Volga. Incidentally, such an interpretation would require other influences and overpopulation was certainly not one of them.

Fifthly, the environment in the tundra zone was rather monotonous and without much differentiation, although southern Scandinavia was probably warmer than the upper Volga region. There was thus no need for different ways of adaptation and therefore no impetus for creating differences in culture. By the same token, it seems clear to me that there were no significant differences between the Ahrensburgian and Swiderian cultures (Kobusiewicz 2002). I am also uncertain as to whether a separate Bromme Culture really existed. Yes, we have several sites where large points are predominant, but they also contain some typological elements of other cultures of the so-called Tanged Point Technocomplex which are regarded as distinctive from the Bromme. The scarcity of other retouched tools in association with Lyngby points at the Bromme sites, which was already stressed by Taute, might be explained by a high specialization in the activities which took place there. This is a feature in common with similar assemblages from the upper Volga region (Podoł III). Possibly the tool kits in both areas had similar hunting functions.

As a final point, our aim as archaeologists is to reconstruct the history of prehistoric human populations. Exaggerated conclusions based on the analysis of differences and resemblances of flint artefacts can be misleading, leading to the false presumption that, by analogy to genetic processes, changes in the shape of flint tools are foreseeable, which is definitely misleading. The shapes of tools and their methods of production do not submit to the laws of nature in the same way as genetics. Equally, humans do not always react automatically or in the same way to environmental or other pressures. For example, after the retreat of glaciers Europe became »microlithic«, whereas there was no obvious reaction in typological terms to the same processes of deglaciation in North America (Bower / Kobusiewicz 2002).

In trying to reconstruct the history of European hunter-gatherers at the end of the Pleistocene we have, until now, had to rely almost exclusively on the surviving record of flint artefacts and this has led to a major bias in interpretation and sometimes to attempts to draw knowledge from them at any price. In consequence, I feel that the cognitive potential of flint artefact typology, at least from the area and time under discussion, is now totally exhausted. Continuing on this course will only lead to serious misconceptions and create further artificial entities (cultures). We send their creators on a chase around the world, to force out some of their neighbours or to assimilate the others, undergo acculturation, flourish or decay. Of course, most probably such processes did take place in the past, but we do not yet understand them and we shall never find out any more about them by simply re-shuffling stone artefacts in every possible way.

I realize that what I am saying may raise considerable opposition and objections. Nevertheless I still insist (Kobusiewicz 2002) that the way forward in trying to recognize the possible prehistoric cultural division of Final Palaeolithic and Mesolithic populations is not to speculate on flint typology, but to try hard to learn about all possible aspects of hunter-gatherer lifestyles, including subsistence patterns, organization of settlement, social organization, spiritual life, physical anthropology and so on. Only when we collect enough such data and when the chronology of events becomes more precise, will we then be able to understand the genuine relations between human groups of the time. Only by adopting this more enlightened attitude will it be possible to create a new, more objective picture of the cultural differentiation of Final Palaeolithic and Mesolithic Europe. How to achieve this much desired aim is a different story.

References

Andersen 1988: S. Andersen, A survey of the Late Palaeolithic of Denmark and southern Sweden. In: M. Otte (ed.), De la Loire à l'Oder. Les civilisations du paléolithique final dans le nord-ouest européen. British Archaeological Reports (International Series) 444 (Oxford1988) 523-566.

Bagniewski 1997: Z. Bagniewski, O schyłkowo paleolitycznych kulturach kompleksu z liściakami na Pomorzu. Acta Universitatis Wratislaviensis No.1924, Studia Archeologiczne 29 (Wrocław1997) 25-92.

Barton / Bergman 1988: R. N. E. Barton / C. A. Bergman, The Upper Palaeolithic Tool Assemblage from Hengistbury Head. In: M. Otte (ed.), De la Loire à l'Oder. Les civilisations du paléolithique final dans le nord-ouest européen. British Archaeological Reports (International Series) 444 (Oxford 1988) 447-463.

Barton / Roberts 2002: R. N. E. Barton / A. J. Roberts, Ensembles à pointes pédonculées du tardiglaciaire et technologies associées dans le sud de la Grande-Bretagne. In: M. Otte / J. K. Kozołwski (eds.), Préhistoire de la Grande Plaine du nord de l'Europe. E.R.A.U.L. 99 (Liège 2002) 69-81.

Bower / Kobusiewicz 2002: J. R. F. Bower / M. Kobusiewicz, A Comparative Study of Prehistoric Foragers in Europe and North America. Cultural Responses to the End of the Ice Age. Mellen Studies in Anthropology 6 (Leviston, Quinston, Lampeter 2002).

Brinch Petersen 2009: E. Brinch Petersen, The human settlement of southern Scandinavia 12 500-8 700 cal BC. This volume, 89-129.

Burdukiewicz 1979: J. M. Burdukiewicz, Zur Problematik des Spätpaläolithikums im Südwesten der VR Polen. Veröffentlichungen des Museums für Ur- und Frühgeschichte Potsdam 12, 1979, 9-38.

1999: J. M. Burdukiewicz, Tanged points in the Sudeten foreland. In: S. K. Kozłowski / J. Gurba / L. Zaliz (eds.), Tanged Points Cultures in Europe (Lublin 1999) 102-109.

Chmielewska 1978: M. Chmielewska, Późny paleolit pradoliny warszawsko-berlińskiej (Wrocław, Warszawa, Kraków, Gdańsk 1978).

Clausen 2004: I. Clausen, The Reindeer antler axe of the Allerød period from Klappholz LA 63, Kreis Schleswig-Flenburg / Germany. Is it a relict of the Federmesser, Bromme or Ahrensburg culture? In: Th. Terberger / B. V. Eriksen (eds.), Hunters in a changing world. Environment and Archaeology of the Pleistocene - Holocene Transition (ca. 11 000-9 000 B.C.) in Northern Central Europe. Workshop of the U.I.S.P.P.-Commission XXXII at Greifswald, 2002. Internationale Archäologie, Arbeitsgemeinschaft, Symposium, Tagung, Kongress 5 (Rahden / Westfalen 2004) 141-161.

2005: I. Clausen, Das allerødzeitliche Rengeweihbeil aus Klappholz LA 63, Kreis Schleswig-Flensburg. Ein Relikt der Federmesser-, der Bromme- oder der Ahrensburger Kultur? Offa 59-60, 2002-2003 (2005) 15-39.

Eriksen 2002: B. V. Eriksen, Reconsidering the geochronological framework of Lateglacial hunter gatherer colonization of southern Scandinavia. In: B. V. Eriksen / B. Bratlund (eds.), Recent studies in the Final Palaeolithic of the European plain. Proceedings of a U.I.S.P.P. Symposium, Stockholm 1999. Jutland Archaeological Society Publications 39 (Århus 2002). 25-42.

Fojud / Kobusiewicz 1978: R. Fojud / M. Kobusiewicz, Osadnictwo z epoki kamienia w Zwoli, woj. Poznańskie. Wiadomości Archeologiczne 43, 1978, 18-30.

Ginter 1966: B. Ginter, Przyczynek do znajomości zachodniej strefy przemieszania przemysłowego cyklu mazowszańskiego. Zeszyty Naukowe Uniwersytetu Jagiellońskiego CXLIX. Prace Archeologiczne 8, 23-38.

1974: B. Ginter, Spätpaläolithikum in Oberschlesien und im Flussgebiet der oberen Warta. Zeszyty Naukowe Uniwersytetu Jagiellońskiego CCCXXXvII. Prace Archeologiczne, Zeszyt 17 (Warszawa, Kraków 1974).

Gramsch, 1988: B. Gramsch, Paléolithique final dans la région entre Oder et l'Elbe. In: M. Otte (ed.), De La Loire à l'Oder. Les civilisations du Paléolithique final dans le nord-ouest européen, British Archaeological Reports (International Series) 444 (Oxford 1988) 511-122.

Kobusiewicz 1970: M. Kobusiewicz, Paleolit schyłkowy w środkowo-zachodniej Wielkopolsce. Światowit 31, 19-100.

1999: M. Kobusiewicz, Ludy zbieracko-łowieckie północno-zachodniej Polski. Poznańskie Towarzystwo Przyjaciół Nauk (Poznań 1999).

2002: M. Kobusiewicz, Ahrensburgian and Swiderian: two different modes of adaptation? In: B. V. Eriksen / B. Bratlund (eds.), Recent studies in the Final Palaeolithic of the European plain. Proceedings of a U.I.S.P.P. Symposium, Stockholm 1999. Jutland Archaeological Society Publications 39 (Århus 2002) 117-122.

Kozłowski 2004: J. K. Kozłowski, Świat przed rewolucją neolityczną. Wielka historia świata 1 (Kraków 2004).

Kozłowski / Kozłowski 1977: J. K. Kozłowski / S. K. Kozłowski, Epoka kamienia na ziemiach polskich. Państwowe Wydawnictwo Naukowe (Warszawa 1977).

Kozłowski 1976: S. K. Kozłowski, Quelques remarques sur le Brommien. Acta Archaeologica 46, 1977, 134-142.

Libera 1990: J. Libera, Liściaki typu Lyngby w inwentarzach krzemiennych na obszarze międzyrzecza środkowej Wisły i Bugu. Lubelskie Materiały Archeologiczne 3, 13-28.

1995: J. Libera, Późny paleolit i mezolit środkowo-wschodniej Polski, cz. I. Analiza (Lublin 1995).

Marciniak 1982: M. Marciniak, Kultury archeologiczne paleolitu schyłkowego i mezolitu w dolinie dolnej Wisły (od Torunia do Grudziądza). M. A. Thesis University Toruń (1982).

Otte 1988: M. Otte, Bilan d'un rencontre. In: M. Otte (ed.), De la Loire à l'Oder. Les civilisations du Paléolithique final dans le nord-ouest européen. British Archaeological Reports (International Series) 444 (Oxford 1988) 723-731.

Rimantiene 1971: R. K. Rimantiene, Paleolit i mezolit Litwy (Vilnius 1971).

Rust 1958: A. Rust, Die Funde vom Pinnberg. Offa-Bücher 14 (Neumünster 1958).

Sawicki: 1936: L. Sawicki, Przemysł świderski I ze stanowiska wydmowego Świdry Wielkie I. Przegląd Archeologiczny 5, 1-23.

Schild 1975: R. Schild, Późny paleolit. In: W. Chmielewski / W. Hensel (eds.). Prahistoria ziem polskich. Paleolit i mezolit. (Wrocław, Warszawa, Kraków, Gdańsk 1975) 159-338.

1988: R. Schild, Processus de changement dans le paléolithique final des plaines septentrionales. In: M.Otte (ed.), De la Loire à l'Oder. Les civilisations du Paléolithique final dans le nord-ouest européen. British Archaeological Reports (International Series) 444 (Oxford 1988) 595-602.

Schwantes 1923: G. Schwantes, Die Zivilisation von paläolithischem Gepräge in Holstein. Mitteilungen Anthropologischer Gesellschaft 57, 158-161.

Siemaszko 1999: J. Siemaszko, Tanged points in the basin of Lega and Ełk Rivers. In: S. K. Kozłowski / J. Gurba / L. Zaliznyak (eds.), Tanged Points Cultures in Europe (Lublin 1999) 186-193.

Sinitsina 1999: G. Sinitsina, Problems of the Valdai Mesolithic. In: S. K. Kozłowski / J. Gurba / L. Zaliznyak (eds.), Tanged Points Cultures in Europe (Lublin 1999) 318-324.

Sonneville-Bordes 1988: D. Sonneville-Bordes, Les pointes d'affinités nordiques dans le paléolithique final au sud de la Loire. In: M. Otte (ed.), De la Loire à l'Oder. Les civilisations du Paléolithique final dans le nord-ouest européen. British Archaeological Reports (International Series) 444 (Oxford 1988) 621-654.

Sulgostowska 1989: Z. Sulgostowska, Prahistoria międzyrzecza Wisły I Niemna u schyłku plejstocenu. Państwowe Wydawnictwo Naukowe (Warszawa 1989).

Szmit 1929: Z. Szmit, Badania osadnictwa epoki kamiennej na Podlasiu. Wiadomości Archeologiczne, 10, 36-109.

Szymczak 1995: K. Szymczak, Epoka kamienia Polski północno wschodniej na tle środkowo europejskim (Warszawa 1995).

1999: K. Szymczak, Late Palaeolithic cultural units with Tanged Points in Northeastern Poland. In: S. K. Kozłowski / J. Gurba / L. Zaliznyak (eds.), Tanged Points Cultures in Europe (Lublin 1999) 93-101.

Taute 1968: W. Taute, Die Stielspitzen-Gruppen im nördlichen Mitteleuropa. Ein Beitrag zur Kenntnis der späten Altsteinzeit. Fundamenta A5 (Köln, Graz 1968).

Zaliznyak 1995: L. Zaliznyak, The Swidrian Reindeer-Hunters of Eastern Europe. Beiträge zur Ur-und Frühgeschichte Mitteleuropas 5 (Wilkau-Hasslau 1995).

1998: L. Zaliznyak, Pieredistoria Ukrainy X-V tis. de n. e. Biblioteka Ukraincia (Kijev 1998).

1999: L. Zaliznyak, Finalnyj paleoloit pivnicznowo zachodu shidnoj Evropy (Kijev 1999).

2005: L. Zaliznyak, Finalnyj paleolit i mezolit kontinentalnoj Ukrainy (Kiev 2005).

Žhilin / Krawcow: 1991: M. G. Žhilin / A. E. Krawcow. Rannij komplex stojanki Ust Tudowka I. In: F. W. Wasiliew (ed.), Archeologia wierchnewo Powołża (Nowgorod 1991) 3-18.

Abstract

The Lyngby point as a cultural marker

The massive, so-called Lyngby tanged point is the fossile directeur of the Bromme culture. However, this type of point, evidently typical for the classical territory of the Bromme culture, is also often found in assemblages typologically quite different from the Brommian, being collected or excavated far to the East of the core area of this culture in areas such as Lithuania, Ukraine, Belarus and even western Russia. These points usually occur in small numbers or as single pieces. Many scholars interpret their presence as proof of far reaching migrations or even raids by Bromme culture groups outside their own native territory. The analysis of such finds leads us to the conclusion that the Lyngby tanged points in fact represent a very useful and efficient intercultural invention appreciated by hunters of many different populations. The widespread distribution of Lyngby points, which covers a vast area far beyond the Bromme »homeland«, demonstrates a cultural unification of the European Plain at the end of Pleistocene probably caused by similar, repetitive natural environmental conditions.

Key-words

Late Palaeolithic, Bromme culture, Lyngby point, intercultural items.

KRZYSZTOF KOWALSKI · TOMASZ PŁONKA

NEW ORNAMENTED ARTEFACTS FROM THE POLISH LOWLAND AND FINAL PALAEOLITHIC SYMBOLISM

In our paper we present two newly discovered ornamented artefacts from northern Poland and consider their significance for research into Final Palaeolithic symbolism and the symbolic culture of the North European Plain. In our opinion their significance touches upon three crucial problems:

– Finding the sources of symbolic culture.
– Grasping a system or systems of symbolism between 13 000 and 10 000 BP.
– The importance of the system or systems for the origin of Mesolithic symbolic culture.

In our paper we use the term »symbolic culture« in P. Chase's sense (Chase 1999). In his opinion symbolic culture »…is the creation of an intellectual environment populated by phenomena that owe their very existence to symbolism«. Symbolic culture is multi-directional and penetrates all branches of human activity. In archaeological evidence the intellectual environment is visible through finds such as art pieces, ornaments, ochre, graves and exotic materials.

Our concept of the Final Palaeolithic symbolic culture of the North European Plain from ca. 13 000 to 10 000 BP is based on quite modest sources of information, many of them in the form of stray finds. These are often contrasted with the symbolic artefacts of the Magdalenian known from Middle and Late Magdalenian sites of the Central European uplands.

Symbolic finds and their interpretation

The scarcity of Final Palaeolithic symbolic finds on the Plain is often interpreted in two different ways (cf. Bosinski 1982; Svoboda et al. 2002, 249; Gamble 1999). The first interpretation sees a connection with the state of preservation of the archaeological evidence. Most Final Palaeolithic sites of the Plain are located in sandy areas where artefacts made of organic materials will have decayed. Moreover, the isolated sites where organic materials have survived are too rare for the reconstruction of the use of symbolic artefacts. In consequence adherents of this interpretation assume that the symbolic artefacts could originally have been quite numerous, although this cannot be confirmed because organic artefacts have decayed.

Advocates of the second interpretation propose that the scarce archaeological evidence is the true reflection of a real reduction in the occurrence of symbolic artefacts/behaviour during the Final Palaeolithic following the Magdalenian period. This happened as a consequence of the considerable mobility of the Final Palaeolithic hunters on the Plain. Firstly, this high mobility was not conducive to the production of symbolic pieces because of problems with the transport of larger artefacts; secondly, the aggregations of many people, which are favourable for the production and expression of symbolic behaviour, are expected to have been rare and of short duration. This model of explanation was used e. g. by J. K. Kozłowski (1997) as an explanation for earlier behavioural differences with regard to artistic expression in a comparison of the Gravettian and Epigravettian.

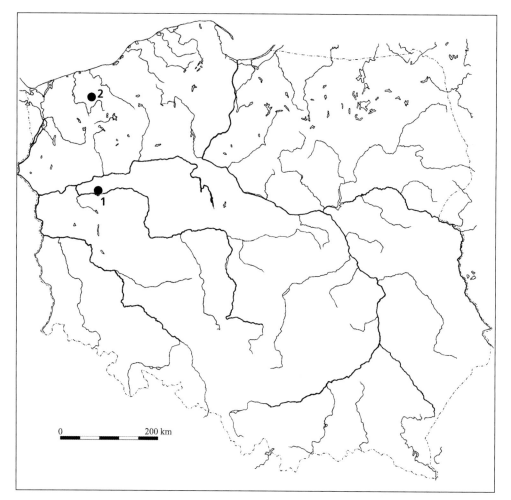

Fig. 1 New sites with symbolic artefacts on the Polish Lowland. – 1 Radgoszcz 15, – 2 Rusinowo.

A stone from Radgoszcz 15

The artefact was discovered on the site Radgoszcz 15, in north-western Wielkopolska, on the Warta River (Płonka 1997), in Torun-Eberswalde ice marginal valley (**Fig. 1**). It is made of plain green sandstone and measures ca. 8.5 by 10.5 cm, with one of its sides being broken (**Fig. 2**). The stone was found at a depth of 30 cm in a concentration of flint artefacts below the humus layer of the modern top soil. The flint concentration is similar to other neighbouring ones and shows characteristics of the Tanged Point culture of the Younger Dryas, specifically of the Ahrensburgian and Swiderian. The artefacts point to a specialized workshop where flint cores were prepared and blades produced.

One of the stone surfaces is covered with straight and curved lines of different generations (**Fig. 2**). The oldest lines are worn, showing that the artefact was used over a longer period of time. The best preserved group was incised later and consists of three lines which intersect in the form of a St. Andrew's cross (**Figs. 2-3**). The cross-section of the oldest line of this group is U-shaped. At both ends short strokes run at an acute angle to the original line. The strokes at the top have a cross section similar to the one of the main line. By contrast, the strokes at the bottom are very thin and were produced spontaneously when the main line was incised. The line is crossed by two younger, parallel lines, both V-shaped in cross-section. The ends of these two younger lines cross each other and so we can also identify the order of their incision. The older line is bifurcated; unfortunately the break of the stone destroyed the ends of both lines.

Is it legitimate to consider this stone as a symbolic artefact, i.e. can it be referred to Final Palaeolithic symbolic culture in the sense we have given in the introduction? Such types of incised lines are well known on stones, pebbles and cortex of flint nodules from the Palaeolithic and the Mesolithic periods in Europe. We suggest that the meaning of such simple marking varied greatly, depending on the particular situation, i.e. the context. In the case of the Radgoszcz stone we can suppose that the marking relates to the symbolism surrounding the flint processing – the artefact was found in the concentration of flint debris. The site is

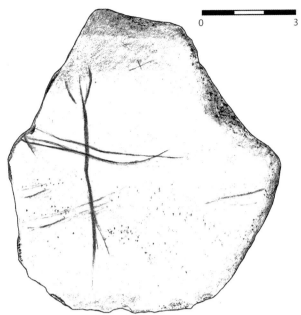

Fig. 2 A sandstone artefact from Radgoszcz 15 (drawing by Nicole Lenkow).

Fig. 3 Radgoszcz 15. Intersecting lines.

located in a region very rich in Baltic flint (Kobusiewicz 1967; 1989; 1997; Płonka 1997) and, as described above, we can interpret Radgoszcz 15 as a workshop for the processing of flint cores and/or the production of blades to be taken away to other locations.

An antler artefact from Rusinowo

The second piece (**Fig. 4**) was found at Powalice, Pomerania, in a heap of chalk which had been transported onto a field as fertilizer by a farmer. According to information provided by the farmer, the dumped material had been dug from a chalk quarry near Rusinowo, in the Mostowa river valley, several kilometres away from Powalice.

The unusual artefact was made probably from a tine and palmate section cut from an elk antler which had belonged to an imposing individual. The artefact is more than 40 cm long and weighs 900 g. Its state of preservation is excellent: some parts of the surface are slightly weathered but most traces of its production and the incised lines of the ornamentation are very well preserved.

We have analysed this outstanding artefact, both with regard to its technology of production and ornamentation, as well as traces of its use. The research programme also includes radiocarbon dating, pollen analysis and chemical analyses of a dark substance recognized in the incised lines, which might represent an inlay. This work is in progress and, for the time being, we would like to focus on the style of ornamentation covering the artefact. Decoration is visible on both sides of the piece but is only found on the surface of the tine. It is not present on the palmate sections showing a natural antler surface.

The centre of the ornamental composition is formed by groups of zigzag lines perpendicular or aligned slightly obliquely relative to the axis of the artefact (**Fig. 4**). These groups (six on one and seven on the opposite face of the artefact) are made up of different numbers of zigzag lines. The lines are not regular; they are composed of strokes of different length, in places extending over the edges of the tine.

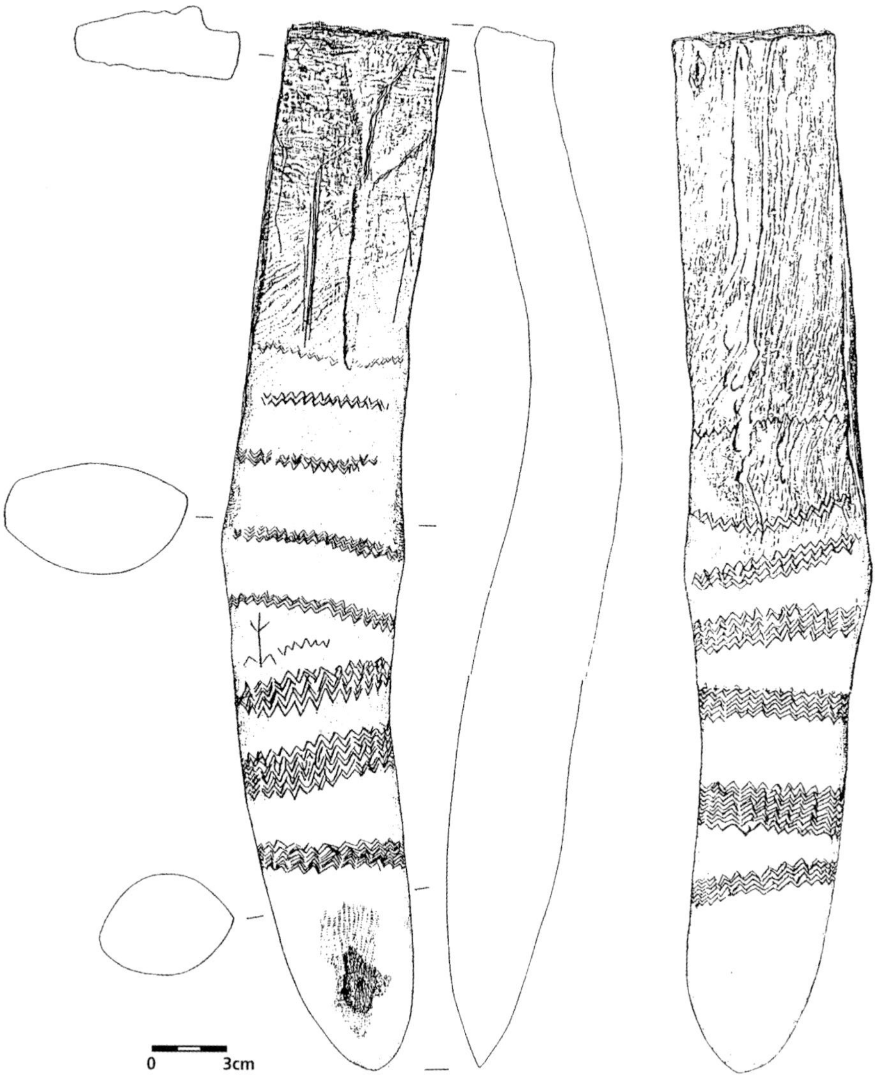

Fig. 4 Rusinowo. Ornamented antler artefact.

On one face of the object, between two groups of zigzag lines we recognize a representation of a human figure depicted next to a single zigzag line. The linear and schematic style of the representation allows two interpretations:

– It is a representation of a male with upraised arms; the male is presented *en face* or from the rear; a stroke between his legs represents a penis (the figure is then upside down in **Fig. 4**)

– It is a representation of a female with spread legs, possibly at the moment of childbirth (the figure is correctly oriented in **Fig. 4**)

In our opinion the latter interpretation is more probable; we can see this scene on many archaeological and ethnological artefacts from many countries (Guthrie 2005, 353 and 360). This type of representation is also represented on other stray finds from northern Europe dated to the Mesolithic. We can mention anthropomorphic figures on a knife from Stensby on Funen, an amber pendant found close to Hjørring, Jutland (Płonka 2003, Fig. 56.1, 86.1) and on a flint nodule from Holmegård V (Fischer 1975). The two latter depictions also resemble the stroke-style of our representation on the antler from Rusinowo. On the other hand, figures of persons with upraised arms are also found in Mesolithic art. They have no sex attributes, so we cannot be sure whether they represent males or females (cf. Płonka 2003, Figs. 9.1, 18, 69.2). Nevertheless, we suggest that the most convincing argument for our female identification is the position of a single zigzag line pointing to the pubic region, probably connected with birth and fertility. In this case, the artefact was positioned for observation with its tip fixed in the ground or in a container dug in the ground.

The ornamentation of the artefact is an elaborate composition, representing a narrative; it tells a story, real or perhaps mythical, centred on the human presented in action among zigzags, which are most often connected with water and the symbolism of life and/or fertility.

The finished form of the ornamentation poses questions about the period of time over which the decoration was incised. Was it during a single continuous action, or was it produced over several sessions as A. Marshack has suggested in discussions of many Palaeolithic and Mesolithic artefacts? In Marshack's opinion the second scenario is confirmed by the identification of many different flint points used to incise the ornamentation (Marshack 1970; 1983; 1991; 1993). In our case, we also found that several flint points were used, but in our opinion Marshack's interpretation of different ornamentation phases is unconvincing. In the light of our own experiments, an incising point becomes blunted or damaged in 15 to 20 minutes and the user would reshape the point or use a new one. Therefore the use of different points is not a conclusive argument for the production of an ornament in different stages. In the case of our artefact, we can rather presume that the ornament was produced during one session only. Given its elaborate and compact composition, we are convinced that it was not a product of a cumulative process.

The dating of the antler artefact is a very interesting aspect. When we first saw it we expected it to be of early Mesolithic age[1]. In the interim, we have received a somewhat unexpected radiocarbon date measured by the Poznań AMS Laboratory. The result (Poz-14541: 10 700 ± 60 BP) of 10 901-10 690 calBC (95.4 % probability, OxCal 4.0 online, April 2008) assigns the find to the end of the Allerød or the beginning of the Younger Dryas. The date is some 600 radiocarbon years earlier than that of a similar artefact from Wustermark 22 in the Havelland area (Beran 2001, 183, Fig. 5.7)[2]. In our opinion we can rule out that a fossil antler was used to produce the artefact from Rusinowo. In the Late Glacial zigzag motives became very popular and are represented on bone and antler harpoons as well as stone artefacts (Kozłowski 1977; Galiński 1990; Le Goffic 2001). We believe that it is useful to take a closer look at a schist plate found at the site Lann-Gazel at Trémaouézan, Brittany (Le Goffic 2001). One of the sides of the piece is incised with straight and zigzag lines. The latter are composed of short strokes and the zigzags run close one to the other. The stone was found associated with Final Palaeolithic backed points of Azilian type. Irrespective of the great distance between Brittany and Pomerania, we can propose that ornamentation composed of closely running zigzag lines became more popular at the end of the Pleistocene and later, in the early Mesolithic.

A pollen spectrum obtained from a chalky sediment sample preserved in the spongy matter of the antler suggests a cold climate (82.9 % arboreal pollen, mainly *Pinus* and *Betula*; 17.1 % non arboreal pollen)[3]. From just a single sample we cannot determine the period according to pollen alone.

Discussion and conclusions

Finally we would like to consider some general questions concerning Final Palaeolithic symbolic culture or cultures specific to different periods of the Final Palaeolithic and different territories of the Plain. In our opinion, irrespective of any differences we can find common elements. Both pieces presented here belong to a category of non-utilitarian artefacts, whereas most of the ornamented objects from the Plain are harpoon heads, i.e. tools (Kozłowski 1977; Galiński 1990). Both the presented artefacts show different forms of symbolic transmission; the stone with different generations of incised lines probably represents a more immediate form (**Figs. 2-3**) in a context auxiliary to flint production. In accordance with ethnological evidence, stones are more commonly used in action as magical sources, and only more rarely as a hierophany (cf. Eliade 1966).

The antler artefact is a more complex form (**Fig. 4**). It is an exceptional object and probably served its purpose for a long time in the society in which it played an important role. We find such types of artefacts on the European Plain from the beginning of its re-settlement after the last glaciation, for example in the shape of a baguette from Poggenwisch (Rust 1951; 1958, 93-113; Bosinski 1978) and the amber figurines from Weitsche (Veil / Breest 1995; 1997; Veil / Breest / Grootes 2007). We suggest looking at them from the point of view of the information that they convey, i.e. treating style as a medium of information (Wobst 1977; Conkey 1978; 1980; 1985; Gamble 1982; 1986; 1999; Barton / Clark / Cohen 1994). Certainly, this approach is one of several possible ones. From this point of view the artefact from Rusinowo is very rich in meaning and, according to Wobst's observations (Wobst 1977), it is less probable that it was produced simply for family needs. We suggest its rich narrative composition was designed to be presented to a larger group of people. Such types of artefact could play a central role during temporary social aggregations. We can suspect that the artefacts were of ritual importance. If we follow this interpretation, the artefact from Rusinowo would be an example of an emblematic style, and as such addressed to a specific group of recipients (Wiessner 1983; 1984; Barton / Clark / Cohen 1994). This interpretation contradicts Wiessner's opinion, according to which this type of art would rather exemplify the assertive style, i.e. the style indicative of the person in possession of the ornamented piece.

As discussed above, a small number of Final Palaeolithic symbolic artefacts is interpreted in different ways. We can see that even at sites with well preserved organic materials, for example Poggenwisch, symbolic artefacts are not so numerous as at Magdalenian sites in the Central European uplands. We should consider whether this reduction is due to a form of control over symbolic artefacts, with some specific persons allowed to produce and use them, at least those forms closely related to myths and ritual. Such suppositions, admittedly from a different point of view, were made with reference to Magdalenian and earlier sites with ornamented stone slabs (cf. Davidson 1997, 129-130).

Let us proceed to the sources of the ornamental composition on the antler artefact. Among the Magdalenian ornamented artefacts from Central Europe, a rib from the Maszycka Cave presents a similarly complicated and ordered incised geometrical design, although without a human representation (Marshack 1993). Such complex and ordered Magdalenian geometrical incisions are extremely rare[4]. We therefore think that the concept of a fully geometric and dynamic human representation, presented *en face* or from the rear, is not characteristic of the Magdalenian. In summary up, the Rusinowo ornamentation is a mature example of a Final Palaeolithic symbolic culture specific to the European Plain.

Finally, let us point to the clear relationship between the composition on the Rusinowo antler and features of the early Mesolithic art of north-western Europe: regular composition, bands of zigzag lines, the style of human representation and its positioning among geometrical designs (Liversage 1967; 1968; Brinch Petersen 1973; Płonka 2003). In our opinion, this is an important indication that most of the Final Palaeolithic population of the Plain remained here and did not desert the region to follow reindeer herds as they migrated north at the beginning of the Holocene (cf. Schild 1996, 290-294). The artefact from Rusinowo is one of the proofs that Mesolithic symbolism has its roots in the Late Glacial social life of communities on the Great Plain. We should also point to the other tradition which survived; that of the manufacture of animal figurines from amber (Veil / Breest / Grootes 2007).

Our main conclusions are: Final Palaeolithic symbolic culture took the form of an entity different from that of the Magdalenian of Central Europe, although they shared some concepts of representation and motifs In the Final Palaeolithic we still meet with complex ornamented artefacts, the production and use of which, important for ritual, could have been subject to social controls

The geometrical style of ornamentation of the Final Palaeolithic societies of the Great Plain influenced the rise of the Mesolithic art of north-western Europe

Notes

1 This idea was also expressed by Erik Brinch Petersen (»evidently Maglemose«) when he saw a slide of the artefact in a lecture at the U.I.S.P.P. congress at Lisbon in September 2006.
2 We would like to thank Dr. Bernhard Gramsch for information on the dating.
3 Pollen analysis was carried out by dr Małgorzata Malkiewicz from the Laboratory of Palaeobotany, Institute of Geology, University of Wrocław.

4 Swiss Magdalenian sites are not counted here. We meet complex and ordered geometrical designs at the Kniegrotte (Bosinski 1982, Plate 73) and Pekárna (Valoch 2003, Plate 4, 9).

References

Barton / Clark / Cohen 1994: M. C. Barton / G. A. Clark / A. E. Cohen, Art as information: Explaining Upper Paleolithic art in western Europe. World Archaeology 26/2, 185-207.

Beran 2001: J. Beran, Spätpaläolithische und mesolithische Funde der Rettungsgrabung Wustermark 22 im Havelland, Die Kunde N F. 52, 173-188.

Bosinski 1978: G. Bosinski, Der Poggenwischstab. Bonner Jahrbücher 178, 83-92.

1982: G. Bosinski, Die Kunst der Eiszeit in Deutschland und in der Schweiz. Kataloge vor- und frühgeschichtlicher Altertümer 20 (Bonn 1982).

Brinch Petersen 1973: E. Brinch Petersen, A survey of the Late Palaeolithic and the Mesolithic of Denmark. In: S. K. Kozłowski (ed.), The Mesolithic in Europe (Warsaw 1973) 77-127.

Chase 1999: P. Chase, Symbolism as reference and symbolism as culture. In: R. Dunbar / C. Knight / C. Power (eds.), The Evolution of Culture. An Interdisciplinary View (Edinburgh 1999) 34-49.

Conkey 1978: M. W. Conkey, Style and information in cultural evolution: Toward a predictive model for the Palaeolithic. In: C. L. Redman / M. J. Berman / E. V. Curtin / W. T. Langhorne / N. M.

Versaggi / J. C. Wanser (eds.), Social Archaeology (New York 1978) 61-85.

1980: M. W. Conkey, The identification of prehistoric hunter-gatherer aggregation sites: The case of Altamira. Current Anthropology 21/5, 609-630.

1985: M. W. Conkey, Ritual communication, social elaboration, and the variable trajectories of Paleolithic material culture. In: T. D. Price / J. A. Brown (eds.), Prehistoric Hunter-Gatherers (Orlando 1985) 299-323.

Davidson 1997: I. Davidson, The power of pictures. In: M. W. Conkey / O. Soffer / D. Stratmann / N. G. Jablonski (eds.), Beyond Art: Pleistocene Image and Symbol. Memoirs of the California Academy of Sciences 23 (San Francisco 1997) 125-159.

Eliade 1966: M. Eliade, Traktat o historii religii (Warszawa 1966).

Fischer 1975: A. Fischer, An ornamented flint-core from Holmegård V, Zealand, Denmark. Notes on Mesolithic ornamentation and flint-knapping. Acta Archaeologica 45, 1974 (1975) 155-168.

Galiński 1990: T. Galiński, Póênoplejstoceńskie i wczesnoholoceńskie harpuny i ostrza kościane i rogowe na południowych wybrzeżach Bałtyku między ujściem Niemna i Odry. Materiały Zachodniopomorskie 32, 7-69.

Gamble 1982: C. S. Gamble, Interaction and alliance in Palaeolithic society. Man N. S. 17, 92-107.

1986: C. S. Gamble, The Palaeolithic settlement of Europe (Cambridge 1986).

1999: C. S. Gamble, The Palaeolithic societies of Europe (Cambridge 1999).

Guthrie 2005: R. D. Guthrie, The Nature of Paleolithic Art (Chicago 2005).

Kobusiewicz 1967: M. Kobusiewicz, Źródła surowców krzemiennych w paleolicie schyłkowym i mezolicie na terenie środkowozachodniej Niziny Wielkopolskiej. In: III Sympozjum Paleolityczne, referaty 1 (Kraków 1967) 57-65.

1989: M. Kobusiewicz, Procurement of flint in the Mesolithic of the Polish Plain. In: C. Bonsall (ed.), The Mesolithic in Europe. Papers presented at the Third International Symposium Edinburgh 1985 (Edinburgh 1990) 442-446.

1997: M. Kobusiewicz, Sources of flint on the west Polish Plain. In: R. Schild / Z. Sulgostowska (eds.), Man and Flint. Proceedings of the VIIth International Flint Symposium (Warszawa 1997) 83-90.

Kozłowski 1997: J. K. Kozłowski, Le deuxième pléniglaciaire et l'évolution de l'art paléolithique. L'Anthropologie 101/1, 24-35.

1977: S. K. Kozłowski, Jednorzędowe harpuny typu hawelańskiego w basenie Morza Bałtyckiego. Archeologia Polski 22/1, 73-95.

Le Goffic 2001: M. Le Goffic, Trémaouézan, Lann-Gazel. Notices d'archéologie finistérienne 130, 98-100.

Liversage 1967: D. Liversage, Ornamented Mesolithic artefacts from Denmark. Acta Archaeologica 37, 1966 (1967) 221-237.

1968: D. Liversage, Art mésolithique au Danemark. Archéologia, Trésors des âges 25, 56-59.

Marshack 1970: A. Marshack, New techniques in the analysis and interpretation of Mesolithic notation and symbolic art. In: Valcamonica Symposium. Actes du Symposium International d'Art Préhistorique (Capo di Ponte 1970) 479-494.

1983: A. Marshack, European Upper Paleolithic - Mesolithic symbolic continuity. A cognitive, comparative study of ritual marking. In: Acts of the Valcamonica Symposium III (1979): The Intellectual Expressions of Prehistoric Man: Art and Religion (Capo di Ponte 1983) 111-119.

1991: A. Marshack, The Roots of Civilization. The Cognitive Beginnings of Man's first Art. Symbol and Notation (2nd revised ed.) (New York 1991).

1993: A. Marshack, Maszycka iconography. A study of the dispersed symbol systems of the Magdalénien à navettes. In:

S. K. Kozłowski (ed.), Maszycka Cave. A Magdalenian site in southern Poland. Jahrbuch des RGZM 40/1, 205-216.

Płonka 1997: T. Płonka, Pracownie krzemieniarskie w Radgoszczy, stan. 15, woj. gorzowskie. Badania w 1995 roku. Śląskie Sprawozdania Archeologiczne 39, 47-64.

2003: T. Płonka, The Portable Art of Mesolithic Europe. Acta Universitatis Wratislawiensis 2527 (Wrocław 2003).

Rust 1951: A. Rust, Eine jungpaläolithische Gesichtsplastik aus Ahrensburg-Poggenwisch. Hammaburg 3, 1-3.

1958: A. Rust, Die jungpaläolithischen Zeltanlagen von Ahrensburg (Neumünster 1958).

Schild 1996: R. Schild, Radiochronology of the Early Mesolithic in Poland. In: L. Larsson (ed.), The Earliest Settlement of Scandinavia and its Relationship with Neighbouring Areas. Acta Archaeologica Lundensia Series in 8°, 24 (Stockholm 1996) 285-304.

Svoboda et al. 2002: J. Svoboda / P. Havlíček / V. Ložek / J. Macoun / R. Musil / A. Pfiichystal / H. Svobodová / E. Vlček, Paleolit Moravy a Slezska. Dolnovestonické studie 8 (2nd revised ed.) (Brno 2002).

Valoch 2003: K. Valoch, Das Magdalénien in Mähren. 130 Jahre Erforschung. Jahrbuch des RGZM 48/1, 2001 (2003), 103-159.

Veil / Breest 1995: S. Veil / K. Breest, Figurfragmente aus Bernstein vom Federmesser-Fundplatz Weitsche bei Lüchow, Ldkr. Lüchow-Dannenberg (Niedersachsen). Archäologisches Korrespondenzblatt 25/1, 29-47.

1997: S. Veil / K. Breest, La figuration animale en ambre de gisement Federmesser de Weitsche, Basse-Saxe (Allemagne) et son contexte archéologique: Les résultats de la fouille 1996. Bulletin de la Societé Préhistorique Française 94, 387-392.

Veil / Breest / Grootes 2007: S. Veil / K. Breest / P. Grootes, ^{14}C-dating the assemblage with amber elk and pendant at the Federmesser site Weitsche, Lower Saxony. In: 49th Annual Meeting of the Hugo Obermaier Society for Quaternary Research and Archaeology of the Stone Age, Trento 2007 (Erlangen 2007) 30.

Wiessner 1983: P. Wiessner, Style and social information in Kalahari San projectile points. American Antiquity 48/2, 1983, 253-276.

1984: P. Wiessner, Reconsidering the behavioral basis for style: A case study among the Kalahari San. Journal of Archaeological Research 3/3, 190-234.

Wobst 1977. H. M. Wobst, Stylistic behavior and information exchange. In: Ch. E. Cleland (ed.), For the Director: Research Essays in Honor of James B. Griffin. Anthropological Papers, Museum of Anthropology, University of Michigan 63 (Ann Arbor 1977) 317-342.

Abstract

New ornamented artefacts from the Polish Lowland and Final Palaeolithic symbolism

The paper presents two newly discovered ornamented artefacts from northern Poland and considers their significance for research on Final Palaeolithic symbolism and symbolic culture of the North European Plain. The first artefact is a plain green sandstone pebble discovered on the site Radgoszcz 15 (Wielkopolska) which belongs to the Tanged Point complex. The second object is a stray find from Rusinowo, Pomerania, AMS dated to ca. 10 910-10 680 cal BC (Poz-14541: 10 700 ± 60 BP). Both pieces belong to a category of non-utilitarian artefacts. The antler artefact represents an exceptional object of more complex form. It was probably in use for a longer time period and played an important role for society. Its ornamentation is a mature example of the Final Palaeolithic symbolic culture, specific for the Central European Plain. Finally, we can identify clear relations between the composition on the antler and the early Mesolithic art of north-western Europe: regular composition, bands of zigzag lines, the style of human representation and its positioning among geometrical designs. In conclusion we can see very clearly the Palaeolithic roots of the Mesolithic style of incised artefacts.

Key-words

Final Palaeolithic, Mesolithic, decorated antler artefact, symbolism, symbolic culture.

THOMAS TERBERGER · NICK BARTON · MARTIN STREET

THE LATE GLACIAL RECONSIDERED – RECENT PROGRESS AND INTERPRETATIONS

We conclude this volume on Late Glacial research from the North European Plain and adjacent regions by reporting on a number of recent studies that also provide a context for reviewing current progress in this field. We begin by considering a number of unifying themes which characterise the study of the Late Glacial and are taken into account by many of the papers presented in this volume. In this review we will touch briefly on the related topics of chronostratigraphy, the natural environment and selected aspects of cultural development during the Late Glacial period.

Chronostratigraphy and the Late Glacial environmental background

Despite progress made in the radiometric and relative dating of the Late Glacial and early Holocene there is still no general consensus on a chronostratigraphic framework for the period. Indeed, today we are confronted with a proliferation of geo- and biostratigraphic schemes, often correlated with absolute ages derived from radiocarbon dating or varve counting, the former occasionally expressed as calendric ages calibrated by sometimes unspecified methods (**Table 1**).

Nevertheless, it is clear that the extension of the dendrochronological calendar back into the Late Glacial and the increased coverage of Greenland ice core records allow ever greater precision in the development of calendric time scales (Johnsen et al. 1992; Street / Baales / Weninger 1994; Björck et al. 1998; 2002). We therefore predict that these developments will soon lead to general acceptance of a standard radiometric time scale for Late Glacial and early Holocene climatic events at a supra-regional scale and, in optimal scenarios, enable their correlation with local environmental and archaeological phenomena. Clearly, recurring problems caused by plateaux in the radiocarbon record will continue to cloud the detailed picture and single radiocarbon dates will remain far less valuable than serial measurements from controlled stratigraphic sequences. Such difficulties might eventually be circumvented using techniques such as tephrochronology which would allow precise time-lines to be established for archaeological sites over wide geographic areas and in relation to limnic, marine and ice core evidence (Lowe 2001; Blockley et al. 2007). Even allowing for such high-precision developments, the timing of the major climatic events shown by Greenland ice cores is already well established and we suggest that these can broadly be correlated with the traditionally used northern European pollen zones (**Table 2**).

The originally defined Late Glacial pollen zones (e.g. Iversen 1954 and see **Table 1**) have been subject to revision (e.g. Litt / Stebich 1999) and their general applicability has been increasingly questioned. This debate is perhaps best exemplified by a general dissatisfaction with the definition of the Bølling chronozone, for which much confusion still exists (summary in de Klerk 2004), which indeed led to a recommendation not so long ago to drop the term Bølling altogether (Usinger 1998, 61). Proposals to establish a revised (and rather complicated) biostratigraphical framework based on varved lake sequences (Litt / Stebich 1999; Litt et al. 2001) drew critical comments, but were widely discussed (e.g. Terberger et al. 2004). In joining this debate we concur that the Bølling interstadial as defined at the eponymous locality should be viewed as an early phase of the Allerød interstadial (Usinger 1985; 1998). This would equate to GI 1c3 in the ice core

	Denmark			British Isles	Northern Germany		
van der Hammen (1957)	Iversen (1954; 1973)	Mangerud et al. (1974)		Lowe / Gray (1980)	Menke (1968)	Bokelmann / Heinrich / Menke (1983)	Menke (in Bock et al. 1985)
Late Glacial	Younger Dryas	Younger Dryas (III)	Late Weichselian	Younger Dryas begins 11000 ¹⁴C BP	Younger Dryas stadial	Jüngere Tundrenzeit	Jüngere Dryaszeit	WS 4 Jüngere Dryaszeit
	Allerød interstadial	Allerød (II)			Lateglacial interstadial	Alleröd-Interstadial	Alleröd-Interstadial	WS 3 Alleröd (Ala-Alc)
		Older Dryas (Ic)		Allerød begins 11800 ¹⁴C BP		Mittlere Tundrenzeit	Mittlere Dryaszeit	WS 2b Mittlere Dryaszeit
		Bølling (Ib)				Bölling-Interstadial (Phase 2)	Bølling-Interstadial	WS 2a Bölling
	Older Dryas	Oldest Dryas (Ia)		Older Dryas begins 12000 ¹⁴C BP		Bölling-Interstadial (Phase 1)	Ältere Dryaszeit	WS 1b Ältere Dryaszeit
	Bølling interstadial (*sensu lato*)			Bølling begins 13000 ¹⁴C BP		»Grömitz-Oszillation« »Meiendorf-Intervall«	Meiendorf-Intervall/ Interstadial	WS 1a Meiendorf-Intervall/ Interstadial
Pleniglacial			Middle Weichselian			Pleniglazial, Endphase		WH Pleniglacial

Table 1 Selection of the suggested chronostratigraphic and biostratigraphic frameworks for the late glacial period in northern Europe. Terminology following the original authors. PAZ = Pollen Assemblage Zone; WH = Weichsel-Hochglazial (pleniglacial); WS = Weichsel-Spätglazial (late glacial).

record (**Table 2**), while the initial warming of the Late Glacial interstadial (GI 1e) should be equated with the Meiendorf interstadial, although even this interpretation is not accepted by de Klerk for the Bølling type locality due to recently obtained older radiocarbon ages for the base of the sequence ~ 12500 ¹⁴C BP, which date it to well before the onset of the Allerød (de Klerk 2004, 281).

Other recently published high resolution pollen analyses for north-eastern Germany (Endtmann 2004; de Klerk 2008) generally confirm traditional interpretations of Late Glacial vegetation development. A pollen record from a kettle hole near Reinsberg, northern Vorpommern (Helbig / De Klerk 2002) reveals a possible initial phase of vegetation characterized by *Armeria* at the onset of the Late Glacial climatic amelioration, but this requires further confirmation.

Relevant data have been published from sites in the Central Rhineland buried by tephra of the East Eifel Laacher See volcano (Baales / Bittmann / Wiethold 2001; Baales et al. 2002; Bittmann 2007; Scharf / Bittmann / Böttger

Northern Germany		Netherlands			West Eifel region
Usinger (1985)	Usinger (1998)	De Klerk (2002); Terberger et al. (2004)	van Geel / Coope / van der Hammen (1989)	Hoek (2001)	Litt et al. (2001); Litt / Schmincke / Kromer (2003)
Younger Dryas		Open vegetation phase III (11000-10000 ^{14}C BP/3000-11450 calBP)	Late Dryas (III) begins 10950 ^{14}C BP	Biozone 3 (begins 10950 ^{14}C BP/13.0 ka calBP)	PAZ 4 (begins 12680 varve years BP)
Bølling-Allerød Complex — c	Allerød-Interstadial PAZ 6-14	Lateglacial *Betula*/*Pinus* forest phase (11900-11000 ^{14}C BP/13900-13000 calBP)	Allerød (II) begins 11900 ^{14}C BP	Biozone 2b (begins 11250 ^{14}C BP/13.2 ka calBP)	PAZ 3c1-3c3 (begins 13350 varve years BP)
Bølling-Allerød Complex — b					PAZ 3b (begins 13540 varve years BP)
Bølling-Allerød Complex — a				Biozone 2a (begins 11900 ^{14}C BP/14.0 ka calBP)	PAZ 3a (begins 13670 varve years BP)
Helianthemum-Betula nana PAZ	*Helianthemum-Betula nana* PAZ 3-5	Open vegetation phase II (12000-11900 ^{14}C BP/14000-13900 calBP)	Earlier Dryas (Ic) begins 12150 ^{14}C BP	Biozone 1c (begins 12100 ^{14}C BP/14.1 ka calBP)	PAZ 2 (begins 13800 varve years BP)
Hippophaë-Betula nana PAZ	Meiendorf-Interstadial *Betula nana-Hippophaë* PAZ 2	*Hippophaë* phase (12450-12000 ^{14}C BP/14750-14000 calBP)	Bølling s.s. (Ib) begins 12400 ^{14}C BP	Biozone 1b (begins 12450 ^{14}C BP/14.8 ka calBP)	PAZ 1a, 1b (begins ca. 14450 varve years BP)
Artemisia-Poaceae PAZ	*Artemisia*-Poaceae PAZ 1	Open vegetation phase I (12900-12450 ^{14}C BP/15200-14750 calBP)	Ia (incl. Bølling s. l.) begins 13930 ^{14}C BP	Biozone 1a (begins 12900 ^{14}C BP/15.5 ka calBP)	Pleniglacial
		Late Pleniglacial	Pleniglacial	LP	

2005; Schirmer 1999). Further to the west, biostratigraphical sequences have also been published from sediments in maar basins of the West Eifel volcanic field (Litt / Schmincke / Kromer 2003; Litt / Stebich 1999; Litt et al. 2001). Tree remains from the Reichwalde site in Saxony, eastern Germany, have demonstrated that pine forests had already started to grow in the North European Plain by the end of the earlier part (Meiendorf) of the Late Glacial Interstadial. Reichwalde has also made important contributions to the study of dendrochronology and climatic development of this period (Friedrich et al. 2001; Vollbrecht 2005). Tree remains from Brandenburg demonstrate that pine forests could survive in more protected areas even in the climatically more rigorous conditions of the Younger Dryas (Gautier 1995-1996; 1999). Nevertheless new studies are now required to take into account local variations in vegetation in different landscape settings such as till plain river valleys (see Kolstrup 1994; 2002). Detailed studies of this kind have already been begun for certain time slices such as the period around the Laacher See eruption (Theuerkauf 2002).

Calibrated age	Ice core terminology	Pollen Zone	Events
7 100 BC- 3 750 BC		Atlantic	Middle Holocene Oscillation 6 250 BC
8 600 BC- 7 100 BC		Boreal	
9 640 BC- 8 600 BC		Preboreal	(cold) Preboreal Oscillation 9 350 BC
10 760 BC- 9 640 BC	GS I	Younger Dryas	
11 015 BC-10 760 BC	GI 1a	Allerød »3«	Laacher See Tephra 10 950 BC
11 240 BC-11 015 BC	GI 1b		Inner Allerød Cold Period
11 575 BC-11 240 BC	GI 1c1	Allerød »2«	
11 625 BC-11 575 BC	GI 1c2		cold period
11 950 BC-11 625 BC	GI 1c3	Allerød »1« not Bølling	
12 090 BC-11 950 BC	GI 1d	Older Dryas	
12 720 BC-12 090 BC	GI 1e	Meiendorf	
	GS 2	Oldest Dryas	

Table 2 Suggested correlation of Late Glacial and early Holocene climatic events recorded in the Greenland GRIP ice core (Johnsen et al. 1997) and the classic northern European pollen zone biostratigraphy (ages following Street et al. 2002).

Progress can also be reported for studies of the Late Glacial faunal record. Direct AMS radiocarbon dating of various indicator species has been conducted in southern Scandinavia (Larsson et al. 2002). On the basis of the extended record the presence of reindeer has been recently discussed in a study (Aaris-Sørensen / Mühldorff / Brinch Petersen 2007) which may demonstrate the survival of the species into the Preboreal for some hundred years (Brinch Petersen this volume). By contrast, evidence for reindeer in the (early) Preboreal from archaeological sites in northern Germany cannot be demonstrated convincingly so far (Terberger 2006a). A continuing matter of discussion concerns the seasonal migration of reindeer on the plain. Baales (1996) postulates springtime migrations from the plain to calving areas in the more southerly upland Mittelgebirge zone and occupation of the more northern plain in winter. Brinch Petersen (this volume) argues for east - west directed migrations (and vice versa) with springtime occupation of southern Scandinavia. Clearly, if several populations are involved and taking into account the length of the period concerned different scenarios could be possible.

The onset of forestation during the second part of the interstadial (GI 1c/Allerød) reflects the more humid character of the climate. In more southern areas such as the Neuwied Basin, in Germany, the fauna becomes more »Holocene« in character with the appearance of species such as red deer, elk and beaver, although horse remains part of the fauna until the end of this phase. At Reichwalde in eastern Germany a bone close to a fireplace related to an early Federmessergruppen occupation was also identified as roe deer (Vollbrecht 2005, 370). The northern areas of the plain show more limited faunal variability with mainly red deer and elk. However, beaver seems to be present at some sites such as Alt Duvenstedt 120B in Schleswig-Holstein (Clausen 2004, 153). Recently I. Clausen published an antler axe of »Lyngby type« dating to the Allerød (Clausen 2004). The piece demonstrates the probably limited presence of reindeer at this time which is in accordance with evidence from elsewhere including Zealand (Petersen 2006, 59).

The important role of elk as game during the open woodland conditions of the Allerød phase of the Late Glacial Interstadial is confirmed throughout the region under consideration by repeated finds of faunal remains from Federmessergruppen and Bromme sites and is also demonstrated by two new pieces of art from the period. The amber sculpture from Weitsche in Lower Saxony is one of the rare pieces of figurative art of the Allerød period and has been identified as an elk (Veil / Breest 1995; 2000; 2002; S. Veil, lecture at Trento, April 2004). It is plausible that the species was the game of choice at that time. A surface find from the Rhineland can probably be assigned to a Federmessergruppen context. The engraved representations of an animal in silhouette on both faces of a flat stone retoucher seem to represent either a female elk or a male following shedding of the antlers (Heuschen et al. 2005).

Radiocarbon dating of faunal material at the Central Rhineland sites Gönnersdorf and Andernach-Martinsberg has been expanded within the context of several projects, so that there is now quite an extensive number of results for species associated with both intensive Magdalenian and Federmessergruppen occupations and, potentially, with ephemeral occupations of the sites chronologically intermediate to these (Street 2007; Street / Terberger 2002; 2004). The latest series of dates from the sites (Stevens et al. 2009) was obtained in conjunction with investigations of stable isotopes of large herbivores from Late Glacial sites in North-western and Central Europe (Belgium, Central Rhineland, Swabian Alb). First results from stable isotopes on horse and reindeer have been published (Stevens / Hedges 2004; Stevens et al. 2008).

It should be noted here that, while AMS radiocarbon dating of bone and antler is now routinely employed, improvements in preparation techniques such as the application of ultrafiltration suggest that many previously obtained dates might be in need of reassessment (Jacobi / Higham / Lord this volume). It remains to be seen to what extent this will have wider implications for mapping the chronological and geographical distribution of Late Glacial mammal species and their human predators.

Specialist studies of Late Glacial fauna from the region under consideration have treated morphometrical aspects of Late Glacial populations of horse (Bignon 2006; this volume; Bignon et al. 2005; Bignon / Eisenmann 2006) and reindeer (Weinstock 2000a; 2000b; 20002), while first investigations into the genetics of Late Glacial mammal populations have also been initiated (Dalén et al. 2007; Sommer et al. 2008). Comparison of the DNA of late glacial specimens of arctic fox from Belgium, the Central Rhineland and Russia with that of recent Scandinavian animals (Dalén et al. 2007) suggests local extinction of the former population rather than northerly migration or range transposition as a response to climatic change at the end of the Pleistocene. The genetics of recent European red deer populations was studied against the background of the directly ^{14}C dated late Pleistocene record for this species (Sommer et al. 2008). The timing of their late glacial re-immigration to northern Europe from southern refugia has the potential to serve as a proxy for the logistics of Final Palaeolithic human groups since almost all dated records of red deer are from archaeological contexts and thus directly associated with human activity.

To the edge of the Plain and beyond – the Resettlement of Late Glacial landscapes by human populations

An earlier synthetic approach to the Late Glacial recolonisation of north-western and central Europe and the North European Plain used the frequencies of radiocarbon dates to suggest a subdivision of this process into a pioneer phase and a residential phase (Housley et al. 1997). The validity of this approach has been questioned (Pollard / Blockley / Donahue 2000; Housley / Gamble / Pettitt 2000) and alternative approaches are proposed by some workers (Jacobi / Higham / Lord this volume). The original model must also be refined in view of evidence for probably short-lived phases of resettlement in Central Europe post-dating the LGM but anterior to and unconnected with the Magdalenian (Street / Terberger 1999; Terberger / Street 2002).

Claims for the earliest Magdalenian from north-western and central Europe remain limited to a few rare cases, some of which can be rejected on grounds of the unproven association of the radiocarbon results with human activity (e. g. Miller / Noiret this volume for Belgium). Only a small number of sites can potentially be assigned to the period before 13 800 BP / 15 000 calBC, among them Munzingen in southern Germany (Padtberg 1925; Pasda 1995) and the Maszycka cave in Poland (Kozłowski et al. 1995; Połtowicz-Bobak this volume). Fourteen dates from the former site have a broad spread between 16 060 ± 140 (OxA-4785) and 9 080 ± 80 (OxA-4789), undermining confidence in their reliability. Nevertheless, certain clusters appear to be present within this range, raising the possibility that the Upper Rhine Graben may have been visited on repeated occasions during the early Late Glacial, perhaps by Magdalenian groups from eastern France crossing the Belfort Gap. This scenario might be lent support by similarly early dates from other southern German sites such as Hohle Fels Schelklingen (H-5313-4898: 15 760 ± 140 BP) or Spitzbubenhöhle (H-4149-3348: 15 230 ± 100 BP) (but see critical discussion in Housley et al. 1997).

Even if the intervening traces (e. g. from southern Germany) are questionable the presence of a Middle Magdalenian occupation far to the east at the Maszycka cave (two radiocarbon dates and the typological evidence of characteristic navettes: Allain et al. 1985) must imply that Magdalenian groups traversed central Europe at this time, already reaching the limit of the subsequent Upper Magdalenian *oikoumene*. Therefore there still remains much potential for future research into the existence and character of an earlier phase of Magdalenian resettlement of Central Europe (possibly involving only sporadic use of the landscape). The Upper Magdalenian is much better defined and placed in chronological context by a greater number of AMS radiocarbon dates, the systematic analysis of which has led to a better understanding of the timing of the appearance of more intensive Magdalenian occupation in north-western and central Europe (i. e. Charles 1996; 1998 Höck 2000; Küßner 2006; Miller / Noiret this volume), which is today generally accepted to have started before the onset of the Late Glacial Interstadial.

The border of Magdalenian expansion is marked by the northern limit of the Mittelgebirge and the Magdalenian does not extend beyond this onto the plain itself. This is illustrated graphically by the site of Gadenstedt in Lower Saxony, located at the very limits of the upland zone (Siemoneit / Veil 1999; Veil / Veil 2005). Whether this restriction reflects limitations due to e.g. geological substrate, hydrology, less-differentiated topography and possibly impoverished ecology on the plain or any combination of such factors remains one of the major unanswered questions for our understanding of human adaptation and expansion at this period.

The discovery of new sites in Poland contributes to a clearer understanding of the dynamic nature and extension of the eastern Magdalenian. It is clear, for example, that the relevance and intensity of settlements in areas such as Silesia and greater Poland have been greatly underestimated in the past (Połtowicz 2006; Połtowicz-Bobak this volume). The site of Wilczyce, pow. Sandomierz, presents a rich inventory of artefacts associated with items of personal adornment and art from an autumn/winter base camp that was probably used more than once (Fiedorczuk / Schild 2002; Fiedorczuk et al. 2007). Remains of a child burial recovered at the Wilczyce site (pers. comm. R. Schild, Rzeszów Commission XXXII meeting September 2005) provide rare evidence for the inhumation of the dead in the Central Europe Magdalenian (Street / Terberger / Orschiedt 2006, 572) and confirm that children were important members of the community in the Upper Palaeolithic (see Einwögerer et al. 2006).

While it now appears certain that human groups in the Magdalenian tradition had occupied the upland zone as far as its northern border by the end of GS 2 (most recently Terberger at al. 2009), the timing and mechanisms of subsequent movements of human populations onto the open expanse of the North European Plain remain less clear. In this context, the roots of the Hamburgian and its relationship to the Magdalenian have been discussed by Burdukiewicz and Schmider (2000). New results are to be expected from detailed lithic technological analyses still in progress (Weber 2006; dissertation in prep.), which might also provide new insights into the development of Hamburgian weapon technology.

It is possible that the site of Schweskau (Breest / Veil 1991) presents a rare insight into this early northward expansion. The lithic industry retains some features of the Magdalenian (e.g. en éperon butts, elongate borers) but has lost others. Perhaps most strikingly, the absence of backed bladelets and presence of shouldered points similar to those of the classic Hamburgian demonstrates a shift in hunting weapon technology (Breest / Veil 1991, 97). In some ways this parallels developments in northern France where a late facies of the Magdalenian also adopts shouldered points.

Schweskau can probably be interpreted as a short stay hunting camp and it is feasible that it represents an early incursion of humans into the lowlands at a time when they still maintained certain Magdalenian traditions while having abandoned others. In this interpretation, the Schweskau humans were in a state of transition and could equally well be described as the youngest Magdalenians or oldest Hamburgians. Certainly the location of the site is within the territory of the latter group but well to the north of that of the former. However, the absence of fine chronological resolution at Schweskau means that this proposal remains unproven.

The age of the earliest Hamburgian in northern Germany and southern Scandinavia is still a matter of controversy but a recent evaluation of the available chronological information, including new radiocarbon dating results (Grimm / Weber 2008), suggests the reoccupation of the plain shortly before the climatic amelioration at the onset of Greenland Interstadial 1e (ca 12 700 calBC) to be the most likely scenario.

Excavations at a kettle hole at Slotseng in southern Jutland have provided important new information on the Hamburgian, including organic material (Holm 2003). A date of ca 12 520 ^{14}C BP / 12 850 calBC (AAR-906) on material recovered from a core sample (Holm 1996) led to speculation on an early phase of recolonisation in areas as far north as Jutland. However, more recently obtained dates on excavated material from Slotseng now appear to cast doubt on the older date (Brinch Petersen this volume; Grimm / Weber 2008). It seems increasingly probable that the north-eastern territories of southern Scandinavia, the present Danish archipelago, were first recolonised during the Havelte phase of the Hamburgian (Petersen 2006), while reliable evidence for the earliest occupation of Scania is unknown before the Allerød.

The relationship of the classic Hamburgian and the Havelte phase is better understood following fieldwork by I. Clausen (1997) at open air sites at Ahrenshöft in Schleswig-Holstein. A stratigraphic sequence indicates that the layer with Hamburgian shouldered points underlies a layer with Havelte tanged points and suggests that the latter can be dated to ca 12 300-12 000 BP / 12 400-12 000 calBC (Clausen 1997; Grimm / Weber 2008). New excavations at Ahrenshöft by M. J. Weber may clarify the situation further. The appearance of tanged Havelte points is suggested by Grimm and Weber (2008) to be possibly due to the adoption of the bow towards the end of the 13th millennium calBC, with these forms representing some of the earliest arrowheads. The concentration of Havelte sites in the Netherlands, northern Germany and southern Scandinavia can also be interpreted in favour of their representing a north-western regional facies of the Hamburgian which could have also extended out into the now submerged »Doggerland« region (Brinch Petersen this volume).

The question of the recolonisation of north-eastern Germany and Pomerania also remains open. While Cziesla (2001) and Brinch Petersen (this volume) do not anticipate the discovery of any Hamburgian or Havelte sites in the region (see also Tromnau 2006), Terberger and Lübke (2004; 2007) prefer to attribute the absence of sites to a gap in research, especially in the case of the younger moraine landscape of north-eastern Germany. In this connection, it is interesting to acknowledge new discoveries in Poland that extend the distribution of the Hamburgian further to the east (Kabaciński / Kobusiewicz 2007). However, there are still no convincing sites east of the Noteć and the middle Vistula valley (Bobrowski / Sobkowiak-Tabaka 2006). Faunal remains from the Polish site of Mirkowice challenge the traditional view of a Hamburgian subsistence strategy dominated by reindeer hunting (Kabaciński / Sobkowiak-Tabaka this volume; see also Brinch Petersen this volume).

The Late Glacial recolonisation of the British Isles (or rather peninsula) and neighbouring areas of Europe has recently been reviewed in Barton et al. (2003). More than 50 AMS radiocarbon determinations are available on cut-marked bone and antler associated with lithic assemblages of Creswellian type (e. g. Barton et al. 2003; Jacobi 2004). While the oldest of these might suggest that resettlement of the peninsula could have taken place shortly after 13 000 BP ^{14}C, the majority of the dates is younger than this and a more reliable estimate for the appearance of the Creswellian might be around 12 600 BP (also Jacobi / Higham / Lord this volume). The oldest Creswellian dates should therefore be somewhat younger than those for Magdalenian sites in the closest neighbouring regions of Belgium and northern France. The existence of an extensive dry land connection with north-western Europe at this time (Coles 1998) would have facilitated contact between these regions and the area to the north-west and the recognizable similarities between the lithic, bone, antler and ivory equipment of the Creswellian and that of the continental late Magdalenian provide convincing arguments for a filiation of the former from the latter complex (Garrod 1926; Barton et al. 2003; Jacobi 2004).

It is noticeable that the distribution of Creswellian sites in England and Wales is closely associated with the margins of upland areas. This is not interpreted as merely reflecting the distribution of caves (with Creswellian sites) in limestone areas but is argued to resemble the pattern of distribution of Magdalenian sites in similar ecotonal locations at the northern edge of the upland Mittelgebirge on the margins of the North European Plain (Barton et al. 2003). It therefore seems possible that the Creswellian way of life remained similar to that of the Magdalenian further to the south. Subsistence seems to have been based on hunting large mammals (horse and red deer in particular) supplemented by a range of other species. Specific differences in the technical equipment consist of acquired features (bitruncated trapezoidal blades) or loss of others (backed bladelets).

A new insight into an important feature of the resettlement of north-western Europe is provided by the discovery of parietal art in areas where this has not been hitherto documented. At Church Hole cave (Creswell Crags) engravings are attributed to the Late Glacial and hence the Creswellian (Pettitt / Bahn / Ripoll 2007; Bahn / Pettitt 2009), while recent discoveries at Grotte Margot in western France provide some of the northernmost examples of Magdalenian French cave art (Pigeaud et al. 2006).

Diversification and consolidation of settlement in the second part of the Late Glacial Interstadial (GI 1d-1a)

Towards the end of the Late Glacial, the Upper Palaeolithic technological and typological features common to the late Magdalenian, Hamburgian and Creswellian are replaced by Final Palaeolithic elements in a process commonly described as »azilianisation«. This change is exemplified by the replacement of the previous technologies and traditions by the Arch-Backed Piece technocomplexes (e. g. Azilian / Federmessergruppen / Tjongerian / Penknife Point groups etc.). It is becoming increasingly clear that this shift occurs towards the beginning of or even prior to the woodland phase of the Late Glacial Interstadial (ca GI 1d/1c). The reasons for these transformations are unclear, although the processes of climatic change, which led to a vastly altered environment over a very short period of time, will surely have played a major role in this phenomenon. Not only does the motive force behind technological, cultural and economic changes remain poorly understood; evidence for transitional phases between the latest Upper Palaeolithic and the Final Palaeolithic is also very rare. This is particularly noticeable in the German Central Rhineland, where rich Magdalenian and Federmessergruppen sites are separated by at least some 1 000 radiocarbon years and very different in almost all their details, but where dated evidence for the intervening phase is restricted to an ephemeral, potentially short-stay occupation at the Gönnersdorf (Street et al. 2002; 2003; 2006) and perhaps Andernach (Stevens et al. 2009) or burials at Bonn-Oberkassel (Henke / Schmitz / Street 2006) and Neuwied-Irlich (Baales 2002).

In northern France the oldest Federmessergruppen phase (phase ancienne) retains features in common with the latest Magdalenian that may have developed in the earlier interstadial (Coudret / Fagnart 2004; 2006). Assemblages assigned to this phase are represented at the open-air sites of Hangest-sur-Somme quarry III.1 (lower layer), Le Closeau (lower layer) in the Paris Basin (Bodu 2000) and the Grotte du Cheval at Gouy (Bordes et al. 1974). They are characterized by symmetrical curved forms pointed at both ends (bi-pointes à dos courbe), although the assemblage from Hangest III.1 reveals a diversity of single and double pointed curved backed forms and an abundance of straight backed bladelets. The existence of shouldered and truncated points amongst the backed tools at Hangest III.1 may be significant in chronological terms (Fagnart / Coudret 2000). AMS radiocarbon dates from Le Closeau and the Grotte du Cheval place the occupations in a phase immediately preceding the beginning of the Allerød. A similar age may be inferred for Hangest III.1 (lower layer) which is stratified beneath the Allerød soil (Fagnart / Coudret 2000), although the published radiocarbon dates seem anomalously young.

There is as yet scant evidence from the British Isles concerning the timing of the initial appearance of industries containing backed points (Barton / Roberts 1996), although three statistically identical results from King Arthur's Cave in the Wye Valley (OxA-1562: 12 120 ± 120 BP; OxA-1563: 12 210 ± 120 BP; OxA-6844: 12 250 ± 100 BP) on bones from a layer containing lithic material with backed pieces (Barton 1996, fig. 4; Bronk Ramsey et al. 2002) may suggest that the transition from the Creswellian was quite early. There are also no unequivocal absolute dates for open-air sites containing backed points or other straight backed forms. The largest and best known of these is Hengistbury Head and the adjacent location of Nea Farm (Barton et al. 2009) which share typological affinities with one another and with sites in Northern France such as Hangest-sur-Somme quarry III.1 (Fagnart / Coudret 2000). However one of the striking differences continues to be in the presence of large tanged »Lyngby« points in the Hengistbury assemblage which either implies some admixture of potentially later material or the presence of a regionally distinct facies of the Final Palaeolithic so far unknown outside Britain.

In Germany, evidence for an early appearance of backed-point industries had already been reported from Schleswig-Holstein (Bokelmann / Heinrich / Menke 1983). Recent work at Reichwalde in Saxony has produced confirming evidence for an early date for assemblages with backed-points, among them broad, symmetrical »bipointe« forms and trapezoidal specimens (Vollbrecht 2005). Extensive investigations (field walking, excavation) have been conducted at Reichwalde and also at the Weitsche site noted above, the latter site being one of the most extensive Federmessergruppen settlement areas in the western part of the North European Plain. Unfortunately most concentrations here have been disturbed by ploughing, although it has recently been possible to detect a preserved original find layer by systematic drilling so that further important information might be expected from the site in future (S. Veil pers. communication). Large scale investigations of Federmessergruppen sites have also been conducted in the lowland regions of Belgium (De Bie / van Gijls 2006; De Bie / van Gijls / Deforce this volume).

The presence of Federmessergruppen sites in southern Scandinavia is quite limited (Brinch Petersen this volume) and their age is unclear. By contrast, the Brommian is represented by an appreciable number of sites (Eriksen 2002), although organic remains are rare and radiocarbon dates are only available for a very limited number of these. We might expect the Brommian, with elk as the typical game, to appear at ca 11 500 calBC; whether this tradition overlaps chronologically with the Federmessergruppen in the region is unknown. The subsequent transition towards the Ahrensburgian tradition is also not very well defined (Brinch Petersen this volume).

The Late Glacial Stadial and the transition to the Holocene - From Tanged-Point Groups to the Maglemosian

The discovery of a typical Ahrensburgian assemblage in a Late Glacial soil in the Sorge valley, Schleswig-Holstein, has led to renewed discussion of the emergence of the Ahrensburgian. The site, Alt Duvenstedt LA 121, can probably be assigned to the transition from the interstadial to the Younger Dryas stadial or to the early part of the latter (Clausen 1995; Kaiser / Clausen 2005; Terberger 2006a). Unfortunately there are no faunal remains to provide an environmental context for the early Ahrensburgian.

While a considerable number of Tanged-Point group (Ahrensburgian, Swiderian) sites is known from the northern German and Polish parts of the plain, the evidence from southern Scandinavia and, in particular, the British Isles is still very limited (Barton / Roberts 2002). The paucity of sites may reflect a more sporadic occupation of the north. Nonetheless, AMS-dating of faunal remains from different kettle holes at Hässlaberga demonstrate repeated human presence in southernmost Sweden during the Younger Dryas (Larsson this volume; Larsson et al. 2002).

New sites have been reported from Dværgebakke in Jutland (Møbjerg / Rostholm 2006), the most northern Ahrensburgian site, and from Lolland (Petersen 2006, 65; Hansen / Pedersen 2006), but preservation conditions at the latter site are only moderate (Brinch Petersen this volume). Small excavations have been conducted on two sites in eastern Mecklenburg-Vorpommen providing helpful geoscientific information on the Finow soil, which is interpreted as the equivalent of the Usselo horizon in north-western Europe (Bogen et al. 2003). More extensive field studies have been conducted some years ago at Groß Lieskow in southern Brandenburg, where a Federmessergruppen and an Ahrensburgian find layer were documented in a stratigraphic sequence (Pasda 2002).

A single decorated find reported from Rusinowo, Pomerania, is assigned by an AMS date to the transitional period from the Allerød to the Younger Dryas (ca 10 700 calBC) and probably within an early Ahrensburgian context (Kowalski / Płonka this volume). The geometric style of zigzag-decoration finds parallels on a younger, dated piece of elk antler found at the site Wustermark 22 in Brandenburg (Beran 2002) and both objects suggest that the Maglemose style of ornamentation is rooted in the Late Glacial. Bone points provide a further example for a »Mesolithic« artefact type that can be associated with the Younger Dryas. A barbed point of Duvensee type from Bützsee in Brandenburg is directly AMS-dated to ca 9 900 calBC (OxA-8743: 10 185 ± 65 BP) (Cziesla / Pettitt 2003; Cziesla 2004).

Our picture of the Ahrensburgian is still dominated by the site of Stellmoor in the Ahrensburg tunnel valley, where numerous faunal remains indicate intensive hunting of reindeer herds in the late Younger Dryas/early Preboreal period, especially during their autumn migrations (Rust 1943; Bratlund 1990; Bokelmann 1991). The richness of the site is probably related to favourable living conditions at that time in this area. It may be no coincidence that we also find the first reliable evidence for the recolonisation of more northerly parts of Scandinavia close to the start of the Preboreal (Bjerck 1995; Blankholm 2004; Rankama 2003; Fuglestvedt 2007). While there is also evidence for occupation of the inland areas in the extreme north during the Preboreal (Rankama / Kankaanpää 2004), colonisation was a dynamic process and seems to have been effected along the western coast up to Varanger Fjord. However, an alternative dispersal route from an eastern source might also have to be taken into consideration (Kankaanpää / Rankama 2009).

The phenomenon of the latest Ahrensburgian or Epi-Ahrensburgian (e. g. Gob 1991) is of particular interest because it seems to represent some of the earliest evidence for the Preboreal occupation of northern Europe. In Britain, northern France and northern Germany the existence of geographically extensive social networks is suggested by the widespread appearance of shared cultural traditions that precede those of the Maglemosian (cf. Brinch Petersen this volume). The lithic technologies are often characterised by long blades in combination with a variety of small backed material and microliths (Wymer 1976; Taute 1968; Barton 1989; Fagnart 1997; Jöris / Thissen 1997). These »long blade« industries, which are often located near good raw material sources, have now also been reported from Jutland at the Nørregard VI site (Sørensen / Sternke 2004). Unfortunately no reliable dating evidence is available but it is likely that they occupy the same broad time range as the British and French sites which can be dated to the very end of the Younger Dryas and to the earliest Holocene (Barton / Roberts 2004).

Further information on human behaviour at the end of the Late Glacial is provided by early Preboreal bone dumps, mainly of elk, detected in a kettle hole close to Lundby on southern Zealand (Hansen / Brinch Petersen / Aaris-Sørensen 2004; Hansen / Pedersen 2006). Sites of the initial Mesolithic on the plain have become more numerous and the typical elk antler adze of early Maglemose style found at sites such as Star Carr, Lundby and Friesack (Hansen / Pedersen 2006; Pratsch 2006, 53) can stand as a symbol for the rather uniform nature of early Mesolithic assemblages that become widespread soon after the onset of the Preboreal. It appears increasingly probable that cultural patterns at the transition to the early Holocene were more complex than conventional wisdom has sometimes suggested (Brinch Petersen this volume; Terberger 2004; 2006b)

Final remarks

Several case studies have been presented in the past several years synthesizing regional settlement and subsistence systems of Late Glacial human groups on the Great Plain and along its southern periphery. Among the most recent of these are papers on aspects of Magdalenian and Federmessergruppen occupation of the Paris Basin and other regions of northern France (Audouze 2006; Bodu / Debout / Bignon 2006; Coudret / Fagnart 2006; Julien 2006; Olive / Pigeot 2006), Belgium (De Bie / van Gijls 2006) and Germany (Street et al. 2006).

The present volume complements these works with contributions on the Magdalenian of Poland (Połtowicz-Bobak), the Magdalenian and Federmessergruppen occupation of Belgium (Miller / Noiret; De Bie / van Gijls / Deforce) and on the chronology and character of the settlement of southern Scandinavia (Brinch Petersen; Larsson) and the British Isles (Jacobi / Higham / Lord). Other papers presented here address specific questions of ecology and subsistence (Bignon; Kabaciński / Sobkowiak-Tabaka) and raw material procurement, whether these are of a lithic nature (Bobrowski) or involve secondary use of Late Glacial organic materials by later hunter-gatherers (David / Pelegrin). Themes of a more strictly socio-cultural nature are treated by Kobusiewicz, who questions critically whether it is legitimate to interpret the Lyngby point as an expression of cultural or indeed ethnic identity, and by Kowalski and Płonka, who discuss specific new finds of Late Glacial art from the north-eastern region of the North European Plain.

References

Aaris-Sørensen / Mühldorff / Brinch Petersen 2007: K. Aaris-Sørensen / R. Mühldorff / E. Brinch Petersen, The Scandinavian reindeer (*Rangifer tarandus* L.) after the last glacial maximum: time, seasonality and human exploitation. Journal of Archaeological Science 34, 914-923.

Allain et al. 1985: J. Allain / R. Desbrosse / J. K. Kozłowski / A. Rigaud, Le Magdalénien à navettes. Gallia Préhistoire 28/1, 37-124.

Audouze 2006: F. Audouze, Essai de modélisation du cycle annuel de nomadisation des Magdaléniens du Bassin parisien. Bulletin de la Société Préhistorique Française 103/4, 683-694.

Baales 1996: M. Baales, Umwelt und Jagdökonomie der Ahrensburger Rentierjäger im Mittelgebirge. Monographien des RGZM 38 (Mainz, Bonn 1996).

2002: M. Baales, Der spätpaläolithische Fundplatz Kettig. Untersuchungen zur Siedlungsarchäologie der FedermesserGruppen am Mittelrhein. Monographien des RGZM 51 (Mainz 2002).

Baales / Bittmann / Wiethold 2001: M. Baales / F. Bittmann / J. Wiethold, Vom Laacher See-Vulkan vor 12 960 Jahren verschüttete Bäume bei Kruft. Heimat-Jahrbuch Kreis Mayen-Koblenz 2001, 161-165.

Baales et al. 2002: M. Baales / O. Jöris / M. Street / F. Bittmann / B. Weninger / J. Wiethold, Impact of the Late Glacial eruption of the Laacher See volcano, Central Rhineland, Germany. Quaternary Research 58, 273-288.

Bahn / Pettitt 2009; P. Bahn / P. Pettitt, Britain's Oldest Art: The Ice Age Cave Art of Creswell Crags (Swindon 2009).

Barton 1989: R. N. E. Barton, Long blade technology in southern Britain. In: C. Bonsall (ed.), The Mesolithic in Europe (Edinburgh 1989) 264-271.

1996: Fourth Interim report on the survey and excavations in the Wye valley 1996. Proceedings of the University of Bristol Spelaeological Society 20 / 3, 263-273.

Barton et al. 2003: R. N. E. Barton / R. M. Jacobi / D. Stapert / M. J. Street, The Late-glacial reoccupation of the British Isles and the Creswellian. Journal of Quaternary Science 18/7, 631-643.

2009: R. N. E. Barton / S. Ford / S.N. Collcutt / J. Crowther / R. I. Macphail / E. Rhodes / A. Van Gijn, A Final Upper Palaeolithic site at Nea Farm, Somerley, Hampshire (England) and some reflections on the occupation of Britain in the Lateglacial Interstadial. Quartär 56, 7-35.

Barton / Roberts 1996: R. N. E. Barton / A. J. Roberts, Reviewing the British Late Upper Palaeolithic: new evidence for chronological patterning in the Lateglacial record. Oxford Journal of Archaeology 15/3, 245-265.

2002: R. N. E. Barton / A. J. Roberts, Ensembles à pointes pédonculées du tardiglaciaire et technologies associées dans le sud de la Grande-Bretagne. In M. Otte / J. K. Kozłowski (eds.),

Préhistoire de la Grande Plaine du nord de l'Europe. E.R.A.U.L 99 (Liège 2002) 69-81.

2004: R. N. E. Barton / A. J. Roberts, The Mesolithic period in England: Current perspectives and new research. In A. Saville (ed.), Mesolithic Scotland and its Neighbours: The Early Holocene Prehistory of Scotland, its British and Irish context and some Northern European perspectives (Edinburgh 2004) 339-358.

Beran 2002: J. Beran, Spätpaläolithische und mesolithische Funde der Rettungsgrabung Wustermark 22 im Havelland, Die Kunde N. S. 52, 173-188.

Bignon 2006: O. Bignon, De l'exploitation des chevaux aux stratégies de subsistance des magdaléniens du Bassin parisien. Gallia Préhistoire 48 (Paris 2006) 181-206.

this volume: O. Bignon, Regional populations and exploitation of large herbivores in the Paris Basin during the Late Glacial: in search of an integrated model. In: M. Street / R. N. E. Barton / Th. Terberger (eds.), Humans, environment and chronology of the Late Glacial of the North European Plain. Proceedings of Workshop 14 of the 15th U.I.S.P.P. Congress, Lisbon 2006. (Mainz 2009) 27-38.

Bignon et al. 2005: O. Bignon / M. Baylac / J.-D. Vigne / V. Eisenmann, Geometric morphometrics and the population diversity of Late Glacial horses in Western Europe (*Equus caballus arcelini*): phylogeographic and anthropological implications. Journal of Archaeological Science 32, 375-391.

Bignon / Eisenmann 2006: O. Bignon / V. Eisenmann, Western European Late Glacial horse diversity and its ecological implications. In: M. Mashkour (ed.), Equids in Time and Space. Papers in Honour of Véra Eisenmann. Proceedings of the 9th Conference of the International Council of Archaeozoology, Durham August 2002 (Oxford 2006) 161-171.

Bittmann 2007: F. Bittmann, Reconstruction of the Allerød vegetation of the Neuwied Basin, western Germany, and its surroundings at 12 900 cal B.P. Vegetation History and Archaeobotany 16/2-3, 139-156.

Bjerck 1995: H. Bjerck, The North Sea Continent and the pioneer settlement of Norway. In: A. Fischer (ed.), Man and Sea in the Mesolithic. Coastal settlement above and below the present sea level. Proceedings of the International Symposium, Kalundborg, Denmark 1993. Oxbow Monographs 53 (Exeter 1995) 131-144.

Björck et al. 1998: S. Björck / M. J. C. Walker / L. C. Cwynar / S. Johnsen / K.-L. Knudsen / J. J. Lowe / B. Wohlfarth, An event stratigraphy for the Last Termination in the North Atlantic region based on the Greenland ice-core record: a proposal by the INTIMATE group. Journal of Quaternary Science 13, 283-292.

Björck et al. 2002: J. Björck / Th. Andrén / St. Wastegård / G. Possnert / K. Schoning, An event stratigraphy for the Last Glacial-Holocene transition in eastern middle Sweden: results from investigations of varved clay and terrestrial sequences. Quaternary Science Reviews 21, 1489-1502.

Blankholm 2004: H.-P. Blankholm, Earliest Mesolithic Site in Northern Norway? A Reassessment of Sarnes B4. Arctic Anthropology 41, 41-57.

Blockley et al. 2007: S. P. E. Blockley / C. S. Lane / A. F. Lotter / A. M. Pollard, Evidence for the presence of the Vedde Ash in Central Europe, Quaternary Science Reviews 26 (25-28), 3030-3036.

Bobrowski this volume: P. Bobrowski, The exploitation of local sources of flint on the Polish Plain during the Final Palaeolithic. In: M. Street / R. N. E. Barton / Th. Terberger (eds.), Humans, environment and chronology of the Late Glacial of the North European Plain. Proceedings of Workshop 14 of the 15th U.I.S.P.P. Congress, Lisbon, September 2006. (Mainz 2009) 141-153.

Bobrowski / Sobkowiak-Tabaka 2006: P. Bobrowski / I. Sobkowiak-Tabaka, How far East did Hamburgian Culture Reach? Archaeologia Baltica 7, 11-20.

Bock et al. 1985: W. Bock / B. Menke / E. Strehl / H. Ziemus, Neue Funde des Weichsel-Spätglazials in Schleswig-Holstein. Eiszeitalter und Gegenwart 35, 161-180.

Bodu 2000: P. Bodu, Que sont devenus les Magdaléniens du Bassin parisien? Quelques éléments de réponse sur le gisement azilien du Closeau (Rueil-Malmaison, France). In: B. Valentin / P. Bodu / M. Christiansen (eds.), L'Europe centrale et septentrionale au tardiglaciaire: Confrontation des modèles régionaux de peuplement. Actes de la Table-ronde internationale. Colloque Nemours 1997. Mémoires du Musée de Préhistoire d'Ile de-France 7 (Nemours 2000) 315-339.

Bodu / Debout / Bignon 2006: P. Bodu / G. Debout / O. Bignon, Variabilité des habitudes tardiglaciaires dans le Bassin parisien : l'organisation spatiale et sociale de l'Azilien ancien du Closeau. Bulletin de la Société Préhistorique Française 103/4, 711-728.

Bogen et al. 2003: Ch. Bogen / A. Hilgers / K. Kaiser / P. Kühn / G. Lidke, Archäologie, Pedologie und Geochronologie spätpaläolithischer Fundplätze in der Ückermünder Heide (Mecklenburg-Vorpommern). Archäologisches Korrespondenzblatt 33, 1-20.

Bokelmann 1991: K. Bokelmann: Some new thoughts on old data on humans and reindeer in the Ahrensburgian Tunnel Valley in Schleswig-Holstein, Germany. In: N. Barton / A. J. Roberts / D. A. Roe (eds.), The Late Glacial in north-west Europe: Human adaptation and environmental change at the end of the Pleistocene. Council for British Archaeology Research Report 77 (Oxford 1991) 72-81.

Bokelmann / Heinrich / Menke 1983: K. Bokelmann / D. Heinrich / B. Menke, Fundplätze des Spätglazials am Hainholz-Esinger Moor, Kreis Pinneberg. Offa 40, 199-240.

Bordes et al. 1974: F. Bordes / M.-J. Graindor / Y. Martin / P. Martin, L'industrie de la grotte ornée de Gouy (Seine-Maritime). Bulletin de la Société Préhistorique Française 71/4, 115-118.

Bratlund 1990: B. Bratlund, Rentierjagd im Spätglazial. Offa 47, 7-34.

Breest. / Veil 1991: K. Breest / S. Veil, The Late Upper Palaeolithic site of Schweskau, Ldkr. Lüchow-Dannenberg, Germany, and some comments on the relationship between the Magdalenian and Hamburgian. In: N. Barton / A. J. Roberts / D. A. Roe (eds.), The Late Glacial in north-west Europe: Human adaptation and environmental change at the end of the Pleistocene. Council for British Archaeology Research Report 77 (Oxford 1991) 82-99.

Brinch Petersen this volume: E. Brinch Petersen, The human settlement of southern Scandinavia 12 500-8 700 cal BC. In: M. Street / R. N. E. Barton / Th. Terberger (eds.), Humans, environment and chronology of the Late Glacial of the North European Plain. Proceedings of Workshop 14 of the 15th U.I.S.P.P. Congress, Lisbon, September 2006. (Mainz 2009) 89-129.

Bronk Ramsey et al. 2002: C. Bronk Ramsey / T. F. G. Higham / D. C. Owen / A. E. G. Pike / R. E. M. Hedges, Radiocarbon dates from the Oxford AMS system: Archaeometry Datelist 31. Archaeometry (Oxford) 44/3, Supplement 1.

Burdukiewicz / Schmider 2000: J. M. Burdukiewicz / B. Schmider, Analyse comparative des pointes à cran hambourgiennes du Bassin de l'Oder et des pointes à cran magdaléniennes du Bassin Parisien. In: B. Valentin / P. Bodu / M. Christensen (eds.), L'Europe centrale et septentrionale au Tardiglaciaire: confrontation des modèles régionaux de peuplement. Actes de la table-ronde internationale de Nemours 1997. Mémoires du Musée de préhistoire d'Île-de-France 7 (Nemours 2000) 97-108.

Charles 1996: R. Charles, Back into the North: the radiocarbon evidence for the human recolonisation of the north-western Ardennes after the Last Glacial Maximum. Proceedings of the Prehistoric Society 62 (London 1996) 1-17.

Charles 1998: R. Charles, Late Magdalenian Chronology and Faunal Exploitation in the North-Western Ardennes. British Archaeological Reports (International Series) 737, 1-246.

Clausen 1995: I. Clausen, Alt Duvenstedt, Kreis Rendsburg-Eckernförde, LA 121. Ein Ahrensburger Kulturvorkommen in allerødzeitlichem Boden. Archäologische Nachrichten aus Schleswig-Holstein 6, 103-126.

1997: I. Clausen, Neue Untersuchungen an späteiszeitlichen Fundplätzen der Hamburger Kultur bei Ahrenshöft, Kr. Nordfriesland (ein Vorbericht). Archäologische Nachrichten aus Schleswig-Holstein 8, 8-49.

2004: I. Clausen, The Reindeer antler axe of the Allerød period from Klappholz LA 63, Kreis Schleswig-Flensburg/ Germany. Is it a relict of the Federmesser, Bromme or Ahrensburg Culture? In: Th. Terberger / B. V. Eriksen (eds.), Hunters in a changing world. Environment and Archaeology of the Pleistocene - Holocene Transition (ca. 11 000-9 000 B.C.) in Northern Central Europe. Workshop of the U.I.S.P.P.-Commission XXXII at Greifswald, 2002. Internationale Archäologie, Arbeitsgemeinschaft, Symposium, Tagung, Kongress 5 (Rahden / Westfalen 2004) 141-164.

Coles 1998: B. J. Coles, Doggerland, a speculative survey. Proceedings of the Prehistoric Society 64, 45-82.

Coudret / Fagnart 2004: P. Coudret / J.-P. Fagnart, Les fouilles du gisement paléolithique final de Saleux (Somme), Revue archéologique de Picardie 1-2, 3-17.

2006: P. Coudret / J.-P. Fagnart, Données préliminaires sur les habitats des groupes de la tradition à Federmesser du bassin de la Somme. Bulletin de la Société Préhistorique Française 103/4, 729-740.

Cziesla 2001: E. Cziesla, Zur Besiedlungsgeschichte von Berlin-Brandenburg: Die Anfänge. In: B. Gehlen / M. Heinen / A. Tillmann (eds.), Zeit- Räume. Gedenkschrift für Wolfgang Taute. Archäologische Berichte 14 (Bonn 2001) 381-396.

2004: E. Cziesla, Late Upper Palaeolithic and Mesolithic cultural continuity - or: bone and antler objects from the Havelland. In: Th. Terberger / B. V. Eriksen (eds.), Hunters in a changing world. Environment and Archaeology of the Pleistocene - Holocene Transition (ca. 11 000-9 000 B.C.) in Northern Central Europe. Workshop of the U.I.S.P.P.-Commission XXXII at Greifswald, 2002. Internationale Archäologie, Arbeitsgemeinschaft, Symposium, Tagung, Kongress 5 (Rahden / Westfalen 2004) 165-182.

Cziesla / Pettitt 2003: E. Cziesla / P. B. Pettitt, AMS-^{14}C-Datierungen von spätpaläolithischen und mesolithischen Funden aus dem Bützsee (Brandenburg). Archäologisches Korrespondenzblatt 33, 21-38.

Dalén et al. 2007: L. Dalén / V. Nyström / C. Valdiosera / M. Germonpré / M. Sablin / E. Turner / A. Angerbjörn / J. L. Arsuaga / A. Götherström, Ancient DNA reveals lack of postglacial habitat tracking in the arctic fox. Proceedings of the National Academy of Sciences of the USA 104/16, 6726-6729.

David / Pelegrin this volume: E. David / J. Pelegrin, Possible Late Glacial Bone »Retouchers« in the Baltic Mesolithic: the Contribution of Experimental tests with lithics on bone tools. In: M. Street / R. N. E. Barton / Th. Terberger (eds.), Humans, environment and chronology of the Late Glacial of the North European Plain. Proceedings of Workshop 14 of the 15th U.I.S.P.P. Congress, Lisbon, September 2006 (Mainz 2009) 155-168.

De Bie / van Gijls 2006: M. De Bie / M. van Gijls, Les habitats des groupes à Federmesser (azilien) dans le Nord de la Belgique. Bulletin de la Société Préhistorique Française 103/4, 781-790.

De Bie / van Gijls / Deforce this volume: M. De Bie / M. van Gijls / K. Deforce, Human occupation in a Late Glacial landscape. The Federmessergruppen site compleyx at Lommel Maatheide (Belgium). In: M. Street / R. N. E. Barton / Th. Terberger (eds.), Humans, environment and chronology of the Late Glacial of the North European Plain. Proceedings of Workshop 14 of the 15th U.I.S.P.P. Congress, Lisbon, September 2006 (Mainz 2009) 77-87.

de Klerk 2004: P. de Klerk, Confusing concepts in Lateglacial stratigraphy and geochronology: origin, consequences, conclusions (with special emphasis on the type locality Bøllingsø). Review of Palaeobotany and Palynology 129, 265-298.

2008: P. de Klerk, Patterns in vegetation and sedimentation during the Weichselian Late-Glacial in north-eastern Germany. Journal of Biogeography 35/7, 1308-1322.

Einwögerer et al. 2006: T. Einwögerer/ H. Friesinger / M. Händel / Ch. Neugebauer-Maresch / U. Simon / M. Teschler-Nicola, Upper Palaeolithic infant burials. Nature 444 (7117), 285.

Endtmann 2004: E. B. Endtmann, Die spätglaziale und holozäne Vegetations- und Siedlungsgeschichte des östlichen Mecklenburg-Vorpommerns: eine paläoökologische Studie. Dissertation University of Greifswald (2004).

Eriksen 2002: B. V. Eriksen, Reconsidering the geochronological framework of Lateglacial hunter-gatherer colonization of southern Scandinavia. In: B. V. Eriksen / B. Bratlund (eds.), Recent studies in the Final Palaeolithic of the European plain. Proceedings of a U.I.S.P.P. Symposium, Stockholm 1999. Jutland Archaeological Society Publications 39 (Århus 2002) 25-41.

Eriksen / Bratlund 2002: B. V. Eriksen / B. Bratlund (eds.), Recent studies in the Final Palaeolithic of the European plain. Proceedings of a U.I.S.P.P. Symposium, Stockholm, 14.-17. October 1999. Jutland Archaeological Society Publications 39 (Århus 2002).

Fagnart 1997: J.-P. Fagnart, La fin des temps glaciaires dans le Nord de la France. Approches archéologiques et environnementales des occupations humaines au cours du Tardiglaciaire, Mémoires de la Société préhistorique française (Paris 1997).

Fagnart / Coudret 2000: J.-P. Fagnart / P. Coudret, Le Tardiglaciaire dans le Nord de la France. In: B. Valentin / P. Bodu / M. Christensen (eds.), L'Europe centrale et septentrionale au Tardiglaciaire: confrontation des modèles régionaux de peuplement. Actes de la table-ronde internationale de Nemours 1997. Mémoires du Musée de préhistoire d'Île-de-France 7 (Nemours 2000) 111-128.

Fiedorczuk et al. 2007: J. Fiedorczuk / B. Bratlund / E. Kolstrup / R. Schild, Late Magdalenian feminine flint plaquettes from Poland. Antiquity 81, 2007, 97-105.

Fiedorczuk / Schild 2002: J. Fiedorczuk / R. Schild, Wilczyce – a new Late Magdalenian site in Poland. In: B. V. Eriksen / B. Bratlund (eds.), Recent studies in the Final Palaeolithic of the European plain. Proceedings of a U.I.S.P.P. Symposium, Stockholm 1999. Jutland Archaeological Society Publications 39 (Århus 2002) 91-100.

Friedrich et al. 2001: M. Friedrich / M. Kipping / P. van der Kroft / A. Renno / S. Schmidt / O. Ullrich / J. Vollbrecht, Ein Wald am Ende der letzten Eiszeit. Untersuchungen zur Besiedlungs-, Landschafts- und Vegetationsentwicklung an einem verlandeten See im Tagebau Reichwalde, Niederschlesischer Oberlausitzkreis. Arbeits- und Forschungsberichte zur sächsischen Bodendenkmalpflege 43, 21-94.

Fuglestvedt 2007: I. Fuglestvedt, The Ahrensburgian Galta 3 site in SW Norway. Dating, Technology and Cultural Affinity. Acta Archaeologica 78/2, 87-110.

Garrod 1926: D. A. E. Garrod, The Upper Palaeolithic Age in Britain. Clarendon Press (Oxford 1926).

Gautier 1995-1996: Y. Gautier, Späteiszeitlicher Kiefernwald: archäologische und vegetationsgeschichtliche Untersuchungen im Tagebau Cottbus-Nord, Landkreis Spree-Neiße. Archäologie in Berlin und Brandenburg 1995-1996, 40-42.

– 1999: Y. Gautier, Feuerstellen, Dünen, Wald: Bausteine einer spätglazialen Landschaft im Tagebau Cottbus-Nord. Quartär 49/50, 1999, 29-33.

Gob 1991: A. Gob, The early postglacial occupation of the southern part of the North Sea Basin. in: N. Barton / A. J. Roberts / D. A. Roe (eds.), The Late Glacial in north-west Europe: Human adaptation and environmental change at the end of the Pleistocene. Council for British Archaeology Research Report 77 (Oxford 1991) 227-233.

Grimm / Weber 2008: S. Grimm / M.-J. Weber, The chronological framework of the Hamburgian in the light of old and new ^{14}C dates. Quartär 55, 17-40.

Hansen / Brinch Petersen / Aaris-Sørensen 2004: K. M. Hansen / E. Brinch Petersen / K. Aaris-Sørensen, Filling the gap: Early Preboreal Maglemose elk deposits at Lundby, Sjælland, Denmark. In: Th. Terberger / B. V. Eriksen (eds.), Hunters in a changing world. Environment and Archaeology of the Pleistocene - Holocene Transition (ca. 11 000-9 000 B.C.) in Northern Central Europe. Workshop of the U.I.S.P.P.-Commission XXXII at Greifswald, 2002. Internationale Archäologie, Arbeitsgemeinschaft, Symposium, Tagung, Kongress 5 (Rahden / Westfalen 2004) 75-84.

Hansen / Pedersen 2006: K M. Hansen / K. B. Pedersen, With or without Bones – late Palaeolithic Hunters in South Zealand. In: K. M. Hansen / K. B. Pedersen (eds.), Across the western Baltic. Proceedings from an archaeological conference in Vordingborg. Sydsjaellands Museums Publikationer I (Odense 2006) 93-110.

Helbig / De Klerk 2002: H. Helbig / P. De Klerk, Geoökologische Prozesse des Pleni- und Spätglazials in der Hohlform »Reinberg«, Nordvorpommern. Greifswalder Geographische Arbeiten 26, 31-34.

Henke / Schmitz / Street 2006: W. Henke / R. W. Schmitz / M. Street, Die späteiszeitlichen Funde von Bonn-Oberkassel. In: G. Uelsberg / S. Lötters (eds.), Roots/Wurzeln der Menschheit. Philip von Zabern (Mainz 2006) 243-255.

Heuschen et al. 2005: W. Heuschen / F. Gelhausen / S. B. Grimm, M. Street, Neue altsteinzeitliche Kunst aus dem Siegtal. Archäologie im Rheinland 2005, 31-34.

Höck 2000: Ch. Höck, Das Magdalénien der Kniegrotte: ein Höhlenfundplatz bei Döbritz, Saale-Orla-Kreis. Weimarer Monographien zur Ur- und Frühgeschichte 35 (Stuttgart 2000).

Hoek 2001: W. Z. Hoek, Vegetation response to the ~14.7 and ~11.5 ka cal. BP climate transitions: is vegetation lagging climate? Global and Planetary Change 30, 103–115.

Holm 1996: J. Holm, The Earliest Settlement of Denmark. In:L. Larsson (ed.), The Earliest Settlement of Scandinavia and its relationship with neighbouring areas. Acta Archaeologica Lundensia Series in 8°, 24 (Stockholm 1996) 43-59.

– 2003: J. Holm, Rentierjäger im Norden. Archäologie in Deutschland 2003/3, 54-56.

Housley et al. 1997: R. A. Housley / C. S. Gamble / M. Street / P. B. Pettitt, Radiocarbon evidence for the Lateglacial Human Recolonisation of Northern Europe. Proceedings of the Prehistoric Society 63, 25-54.

Housley / Gamble / Pettitt 2000: R. A. Housley / C. S. Gamble / P. B. Pettitt, Reply to S. P. E. Blockley / R. E. Donahue / A. M. Pollard, Radiocarbon calibration and Late Glacial occupation in northwest Europe. Antiquity 74 (Cambridge 2000) 112-119.

Iversen 1954: J. Iversen, The late-glacial flora of Denmark and its relation to climate and soil. Danmarks Geologiske Undersøgelse (Kopenhagen) II, 80, 87-119.

– 1973: J. Iversen, The Development of Denmark's Nature since the Last Glacial. Danmarks Geologiske Undersøgelse 5 (7c), 1-126.

Jacobi 2004: R. M. Jacobi, The Late Upper Palaeolithic lithic collection from Gough's Cave, Cheddar, Somerset and human use of the cave. Proceedings of the Prehistoric Society 70, 1-92.

Jacobi / Higham / Lord this volume: R. M Jacobi / T. F. G Higham / T. C Lord, Improving the chronology of the human occupation of Britain during the Late Glacial. In: M. Street / R. N. E. Barton / Th. Terberger (eds.), Humans, environment and chronology of the Late Glacial of the North European Plain. Proceedings of Workshop 14 of the 15th U.I.S.P.P. Congress, Lisbon, September 2006 (Mainz 2009) 7-25.

Jöris / Thissen 1997: O. Jöris / J. Thissen, Microlithic tool assemblages associated with Long Blade technology. Übach-Palenberg (Lower Rhine area) – a case study on a late Palaeolithic site at the boundary Younger Dryas / Pre-Boreal. In: J.-P. Fagnart / A. Thévenin (eds.), Le Tardiglaciaire en Europe du Nord-Ouest. Actes du 119e Congrès national des Sociétés historiques et scientifiques, Amiens 1994 (Paris 1997) 611-621.

Johnsen et al. 1992: S. J. Johnsen / H. B. Clausen / W. Dansgaard / K. Fuhrer/ N. Gundestrup/ C. U. Hammer / P. Iversen / J. Jouzel / B. Stauffer / J. B. Steffensen, Irregular glacial interstadials recorded in a new Greenland ice core. Nature 359, 1992, 311-313.

Johnsen et al. 1997: S. J. Johnsen / H. B. Clausen / W. Dansgaard / N. S. Gundestrup / C. U. Hammer / U. Andersen / K. K. Andersen / C. S. Hvidberg / D. Dahl-Jensen / J. P. Steffensen / H. Shoji / A. E. Sveinbjörnsdóttir, J. W. C. White / J. Jouzel / D. Fisher, The ‰[18]O record along the Greenland Ice Core Project deep ice core and the problem of possible Eemian climatic instability. Jour. Geophys. Res. 102, 26397-26410.

Julien 2006: M. Julien, À la recherche des campements d'hiver dans le Magdalénien du Bassin parisien. Bulletin de la Société Préhistorique Française 103/4, 683-694.

Kabaciński / Kobusiewicz 2007: J. Kabaciński / M. Kobusiewicz, Kragola near Koło (Central Poland) – the easternmost settlement of Hamburgian Culture. In: M. Kobusiewicz / J. Kabacinski (eds.), Studies in the Final Palaeolithic settlement of the Great European Plain (Poznań 2007) 21-51.

Kabaciński / Sobkowiak-Tabaka this volume: J. Kabaciński / I. Sobkowiak-Tabaka, Big game versus small game hunting – subsistence strategies of the Hamburgian Culture. In: M. Street / R.

N. E. Barton / Th. Terberger (eds.), Humans, environment and chronology of the Late Glacial of the North European Plain. Proceedings of Workshop 14 of the 15th U.I.S.P.P. Congress, Lisbon, September 2006 (Mainz 2009) 67-75.

Kaiser / Clausen 2005: K. Kaiser / I. Clausen, Palaeopedology and stratigraphy of the late Palaeolithic Alt Duvenstedt site, Schleswig-Holstein (Northwest Germany). Archäologisches Korrespondenzblatt 35, 447-466.

Kankaanpää / Rankama 2009: J. Kankaanpää / T. Rankama, The Sujala site in Utsjoki - the Komsa culture reconsidered? In: S. McCartan / R. Schulting / G. Warren / P. Woodman (eds.), Mesolithic Horizons. Proceedings of the 7th International Conference on the Mesolithic in Europe, Belfast 2005 (Oxford 2009) 38-44.

Kobusiewicz this volume: M. Kobusiewicz, The Lyngby point as a cultural marker. In: M. Street / R. N. E. Barton / Th. Terberger (eds.), Humans, environment and chronology of the Late Glacial of the North European Plain. Proceedings of Workshop 14 of the 15th U.I.S.P.P. Congress, Lisbon, September 2006 (Mainz 2009) 169-178.

Kobusiewicz / Kozłowski 1999: M. Kobusiewicz / J. K. Kozłowski (eds.), Post-Pleniglacial re-colonisation of the Great European Lowland. Papers presented at the Conference organised by the Intenational Union of Prehistoric and Protohistoric Sciences, Commission 8, held at the Jagellonian University, Kraków, in June 1998. Folia Quaternaria 70 (Kraków 1999).

Kobusiewicz / Kabacinski 2007: M. Kobusiewicz / J. Kabacinski (eds.), Studies in the Final Palaeolithic of the Great European Plain (Poznań 2007).

Kolstrup 1994: E. Kolstrup, Examples of Weichselian environments: Local versus regional developments. Eiszeitalter und Gegenwart 44, 16-19.

2002: E. Kolstrup, Some classical methods used for reconstruction of Lateglacial environments in the European plain: potentials and limitations. In: B. V. Eriksen / B. Bratlund (eds.), Recent studies in the Final Palaeolithic of the European plain. Proceedings of a U.I.S.P.P. Symposium, Stockholm 1999. Jutland Archaeological Society Publications 39 (Århus 2002) 11-23.

Kowalski / Płonka this volume: K. Kowalski / T. Płonka, New ornamented artefacts from the Polish Lowland and Final Palaeolithic symbolism. In: M. Street / R. N. E. Barton / Th. Terberger (eds.), Humans, environment and chronology of the Late Glacial of the North European Plain. Proceedings of Workshop 14 of the 15th U.I.S.P.P. Congress, Lisbon, September 2006 (Mainz 2009) 179-187.

Kozłowski et al. 1995: S. K. Kozłowski / E. Sachse-Kozłowska / A. Marshack / T. Madeyska / H. Kierdorf / A. Lasota-Moskalewska / G. Jakubowski / M. Winiarska-Kabacinska / Z. Kapica / A. Wiercinski, Maszycka Cave. A Magdalenian site in southern Poland. Jahrbuch des RGZM 40, 1993 (1995) 115-252.

Küßner 2006: M. Küßner, Untersuchungen zum Magdalénien im Einzugsgebiet der Saale. Dissertation University of Halle (2006).

Larsson this volume: L. Larsson, After the cold: Mammal finds, hunting and cultural affinities during the Preboreal. In: M. Street / R. N. E. Barton / Th. Terberger (eds.), Humans, environment and chronology of the Late Glacial of the North European Plain. Proceedings of Workshop 14 of the 15th U.I.S.P.P. Congress, Lisbon, September 2006 (Mainz 2009) 131-140.

Larsson et al. 2002: L. Larsson / R. Liljegren / O. Magnell / J. Ekström, Archaeo-faunal aspects of bog finds from Hässleberga, southern Scania, Sweden. In: B. V. Eriksen / B. Bratlund (eds.), Recent studies in the Final Palaeolithic of the European plain. Proceedings of a U.I.S.P.P. Symposium, Stockholm 1999. Jutland Archaeological Society Publications 39 (Århus 2002) 61-74.

Litt et al. 2001: T. Litt / A. Brauer / T. Goslar / J. Merkt / K. Balaga / H. Müller / M. Ralska-Jasiewiczowa / M. Stebich / J. F. W. Negendank, Correlation and synchronisation of Lateglacial continental sequences in northern central Europe based on annually-laminated lacustrine sediments. Quaternary Science Reviews 20, 1233-1249.

Litt / Schmincke / Kromer 2003: T. Litt / H.-U. Schmincke / B. Kromer, Environmental response to climatic and volcanic events in central Europe during the Weichselian Lateglacial. Quaternary Science Reviews 22, 7-32.

Litt / Stebich 1999: T. Litt / M. Stebich, Bio- and chronostratigraphy of the lateglacial in the Eifel region, Germany. Quaternary International 61, 5-16.

Lowe / Gray 1979: J. J. Lowe / J. M. Gray, The stratigraphic subdivision of the lateglacial of N.W. Europe: a discussion. In: J. J. Lowe / J. M. Gray / J. E. Robinson (eds.), Studies in the lateglacial of North-west Europe, 157-175.

Lowe 2001: J. J. Lowe, Abrupt climatic changes in Europe during the last glacial-interglacial transition: the potential for testing hypotheses on the synchroneity of climatic events using tephrochronology. Global and Planetary Change 30/1-2, 73-84.

Mangerud et al. 1974: J. Mangerud / S. T. Anderson / B. E. Berglund / J. J. Donner, Quaternary stratigraphy of Norden, a proposal for terminology and classification. Boreas 3 (Oslo 1974) 109-128.

Menke 1968: B. Menke, Das Spätglazial von Glüsing. Ein Beitrag zur Kenntnis der spätglazialen Vegetationsgeschichte in Westholstein. Eiszeitalter und Gegenwart 19 (Hannover 1968) 73-84.

Miller / Noiret this volume: R. Miller / P. Noiret, Recent results for the Belgian Magdalenian. In: M. Street / R. N. E. Barton / Th. Terberger (eds.), Humans, environment and chronology of the Late Glacial of the North European Plain. Proceedings of Workshop 14 of the 15th U.I.S.P.P. Congress, Lisbon, September 2006 (Mainz 2009) 39-53.

Møbjerg / Rostholm 2006: T. Møbjerg / H. Rostholm, Foreløbige resultater af de arkæologiske undersøgelser ved Bølling Sø. In: B. V. Eriksen (ed.), Stenalderstudier. Tidligt mesolitiske jægere og samlere I Sydskandinavien. Jysk Arkæologisk Selskabs Skrifter 55, 147-159.

Olive / Pigeot 2006: M. Olive / N. Pigeot, Réflexions sur le temps d'un séjour à Étiolles (Essonne). Bulletin de la Société Préhistorique Française 103/4, 673-682.

Padtberg 1925: A. Padtberg, Das altsteinzeitliche Lösslager bei Munzingen.

Pasda 1995: C. Pasda, Munzingen. In: G. Bosinski / M. Street / M. Baales (eds.), The Palaeolithic and Mesolithic of the Rhineland. In: W. Schirmer (ed.), Quaternary field trips of Central Europe. Vol. 2, 14. Internationaler INQUA-Kongreß Berlin (München 1995) 852-854.

Pasda 2002: C. Pasda, Archäologie einer Düne im Baruther Urstromtal bei Groß Lieskow, Stadt Cottbus. Veröffentlichungen des Brandenburgischen Landesmuseums für Ur- und Frühgeschichte 33, 1999 (2002) 7-49.

Petersen 2006: P. V. Petersen, White Flint and Hilltops – Late Palaeolithic Finds in Southern Denmark. In: K. M. Hansen / K. B. Pedersen (eds.), Across the western Baltic. Proceedings from an archaeological conference in Vordingborg. Sydsjaellands Museums Publikationer 1 (Odense 2006) 57-71.

Pettitt / Bahn / Ripoll 2007: P. Pettitt / P. Bahn / S. Ripoll, Palaeolithic cave art at Creswell Crags in European context (Oxford 2007).

Pigeaud et al. 2006: R. Pigeaud / J. Rodet / T. Devièse / C. Dufayet / E. Trelohan-Chauve / J.-P. Betton / P. Bonic, Palaeolithic cave art in West France: an exceptional discovery: the Margot Cave (Mayenne). Antiquity 80, 2006.
http://antiquity.ac.uk/projgall/pigeaud/index.html

Pollard / Blockley / Donahue 2000: A. M. Pollard / S. P. E. Blockley / R. E. Donahue, Radiocarbon calibration and Late Glacial occupation in northwest Europe. Antiquity 74, 112-121.

Połtowicz 2006: M. Połtowicz, The Eastern Border of the Magdalenian Culture Range. Analecta Archaeologica Ressoviensia 1, 11-26.

Połtowicz-Bobak this volume: M. Połtowicz-Bobak, Magdalenian settlement in Poland in the light of recent research. In: M. Street / R. N. E. Barton / Th. Terberger (eds.), Humans, environment and chronology of the Late Glacial of the North European Plain. Proceedings of Workshop 14 of the 15th U.I.S.P.P. Congress, Lisbon, September 2006 (Mainz 2009) 55-66.

Pratsch 2006: St. Pratsch, Mesolithische Geweihgeräte im Jungmoränengebiet zwischen Elbe und Neman. Studien zur Archäologie Europas 2 (Bonn 2006).

Rankama 2003: T. Rankama, The Colonisation of Northernmost Finnish Lapland and the Areas of Finnmark. In: Lars Larsson / H. Kindgren / K. Knutsson / D. Loeffler / A. Åkerlund (eds.), Mesolithic on the Move. Papers presented at the Sixth International Conference on the Mesolithic in Europe, Stockholm 2000 (Oxford 2003) 37-46.

Rankama / Kankaanpää 2004: T. Rankama / J. Kankaanpää, First Preboreal inland site in North Scandinavia discovered in Finnish Lapland. Antiquity 78, 2004.
http://antiquity.ac.uk/projgall/rankama/index.html

Rust 1943: A. Rust, Die alt- und mittelsteinzeitlichen Funde von Stellmoor (Neumünster 1943).

Scharf / Bittmann / Boettger 2005: B. W. Scharf / F. Bittmann / T. Boettger, Freshwater ostracods (Crustacea) from the Lateglacial site at Miesenheim, Germany, and temperature reconstruction during the Meiendorf Interstadial. Palaeogeography, Palaeoclimatology, Palaeoecology 225, 203-215.

Schirmer 1999: U. Schirmer, Pollenstratigraphische Gliederung des Spätglazials im Rheinland. Eiszeitalter und Gegenwart 49 (Hannover 1999) 132-143.

Siemoneit / Veil 1999: B. Siemoneit / St. Veil, Gadenstedt FStNr.121, Gde Lahstedt, Ldkr. Peine, Reg. Bez. BS. Nachrichten aus Niedersachsens Urgeschichte, Beiheft 2 (Stuttgart 1999) 10-12.

Sommer et al. 2008: R. S. Sommer / F. E. Zachos / M. Street / O. Jöris / A. Skog / N. Benecke 2008, Late Quaternary distribution dynamics and phylogeography of the red deer (*Cervus elaphus*) in Europe. Quaternary Science Reviews 27, 714–733.

Sørensen / Sternke 2004: M. Sørensen / F. Sternke, Nørregård VI – Late Glacial hunters in transition. In: Th. Terberger / B. V. Eriksen (eds.), Hunters in a changing world. Environment and Archaeology of the Pleistocene - Holocene Transition (ca. 11 000-9 000 B.C.) in Northern Central Europe. Workshop of the U.I.S.P.P.-Commission XXXII at Greifswald, 2002. Internationale Archäologie, Arbeitsgemeinschaft, Symposium, Tagung, Kongress 5 (Rahden / Westfalen 2004) 85-111.

Stevens / Hedges 2004: R. E. Stevens / R. E. M. Hedges, Carbon and nitrogen stable isotope analysis of northwest European horse bone and tooth collagen, 40 000 BP – present: Palaeoclimatic interpretations. Quaternary Science Reviews 23 (Oxford 2004) 977-991.

Stevens et al. 2008: R. E. Stevens / R. Jacobi / M. Street / M. Germonpré / N. J. Conard / S. C. Münzel / R. E. M. Hedges, Nitrogen isotope analyses of reindeer (*Rangifer tarandus*), 45 000 BP to 9 000 BP: Palaeoenvironmental reconstructions. Palaeogeography, Palaeoclimatology, Palaeoecology 262/1-2, 32-45.

Stevens / Street / O'Connell / Hedges 2009: R. E. Stevens / T. O'Connell / R. E. M. Hedges / M. Street, Radiocarbon and stable isotope investigations at the Central Rhineland sites of Gönnersdorf and Andernach-Martinsberg, Germany. Journal of Human Evolution 57 (2009) 131-148.

Street 2007: M. Street, Gönnersdorf: Comment (on radiocarbon dates for elk and reindeer). Archaeometry Radiocarbon Dates, Datelist 32 (Archaeometry 49, Supplement 1/August 2007) 16-17. Oxford.

Street et al. 2002: M. Street / M. Baales / E. Cziesla / S. Hartz / M. Heinen / O. Jöris / I. Koch / C. Pasda / Th. Terberger / J. Vollbrecht 2002: Final Paleolithic and Mesolithic research in reunified Germany. Journal of World Prehistory 15/4 2001 (2002) 365-453.

Street et al. 2003: M. Street / M. Baales / E. Cziesla / S. Hartz / M. Heinen / O. Jöris / I. Koch / C. Pasda / Th. Terberger / J. Vollbrecht 2003: Paléolithique final et Mésolithique en Allemagne réunifiée; bilan décennal. In: R. Desbrosse / A. Thévenin (eds.), Préhistoire de l'Europe. Des origines à l'Age du Bronze. CTHS (Paris 2003) 343-384.

Street / Baales / Weninger. 1994: M. Street / M. Baales / B. Weninger, Absolute Chronologie des späten Paläolithikums und des Frühmesolithikums im nördlichen Rheinland. Archäologisches Korrespondenzblatt 24, 1-28.

Street et al. 2006: M. Street / F. Gelhausen / S. B. Grimm / F. Moseler / L. Niven / M. Sensburg / E Turner / S. Wenzel / O. Jöris 2006: L'occupation du bassin de Neuwied (Rhénanie centrale, Allemagne) par les Magdaléniens et les groupes à Federmesser (aziliens). Bulletin de la Société Préhistorique Française 103/4, 753-780.

Street / Terberger 1999: M. Street / Th. Terberger, The last Pleniglacial and the human settlement of Central Europe. New information from the Rhineland site Wiesbaden-Igstadt. Antiquity 73 (Cambridge 1999) 259-272.

Street. / Terberger 2004: M. Street / Th. Terberger, The radiocarbon chronology of the German Upper Palaeolithic: fifteen years of cooperation with ORAU. In: T. F. G. Higham / C. Bronk Ramsey / D. C. Owen (eds.), Conference proceedings, Radiocarbon and Archaeology. Fourth International Symposium, St. Catherine's College, Oxford 2002. Oxford University School of Archaeology Monograph 62, 281-302.

Street / Terberger 2002: M. Street / Th. Terberger, Comments on the sample series »Absolute Chronology of the German Upper Palaeolithic series«. In: R. E. M. Hedges / T. Higham / C. Bronk Ramsey / G. J. van Klinken (eds.), Radiocarbon dates from the Oxford AMS system: Archaeometry Datelist 31, Archaeometry 44/3, Supplement 1 (Oxford 2002) 28-30.

Street / Terberger / Orschiedt 2006: M. Street / Th. Terberger / J. Orschiedt, A critical review of the German Palaeolithic hominin record. Journal of Human Evolution 51, 551-579.

Taute 1968: W. Taute, Die Stielspitzen-Gruppen im nördlichen Mitteleuropa. Fundamenta A/5 (Köln, Graz 1968).

Terberger 2004: Th. Terberger, The Younger Dryas – Preboreal transition in northern Germany – facts and concepts in discussion. In: Th. Terberger / B. V. Eriksen (eds.), Hunters in a changing world. Environment and Archaeology of the Pleistocene - Holocene Transition (ca. 11 000-9 000 B.C.) in Northern Central Europe. Workshop of the U.I.S.P.P.-Commission XXXII at Greifswald, 2002. Internationale Archäologie, Arbeitsgemeinschaft, Symposium, Tagung, Kongress 5 (Rahden / Westfalen 2004) 203-222.

2006a: Th. Terberger, From the first Humans to the Mesolithic Hunters in the Northern German Lowlands. In: K. M. Hansen / K. B. Pedersen (eds.), Across the western Baltic. Proceedings from an archaeological conference in Vordingborg. Sydsjaellands Museums Publikationer 1 (Odense 2006) 26-52.

2006b: Th. Terberger, The Mesolithic Hunter-Fisher-Gatherers on the Northern German Plain. In: K. M. Hansen / K. B. Pedersen (eds.), Across the western Baltic. Proceedings from an archaeological conference in Vordingborg. Sydsjaellands Museums Publikationer 1 (Odense 2006) 111-185.

Terberger et al. 2004: Th. Terberger / P. De Klerk / H. Helbig / K. Kaiser / P. Kühn, Late Weichselian landscape development and human settlement in Mecklenburg-Vorpommern (NE Germany). Eiszeitalter und Gegenwart 54, 138-175.

Terberger / Eriksen 2004: Th. Terberger / B. V. Eriksen (eds.), Hunters in a changing world. Environment and Archaeology of the Pleistocene-Holocene Transition (ca. 11 000-9 000 B.C.) in Northern Central Europe. Workshop of the U.I.S.P.P. Commission XXXII September 2002, Greifswald, Internationale Archäologie Band 5 (Rahden/Westfalen 2004)

Terberger / Lübke 2004: Th. Terberger/ H. Lübke, Hamburger Kultur in Mecklenburg-Vorpommern? Jahrbuch Bodendenkmalpflege Mecklenburg-Vorpommern 52, Jahrbuch 2004, 15-34.

Terberger / Lübke 2007: Th. Terberger / H. Lübke, Between East and West - Hamburgian in Northeast Germany? In: M. Kobusiewicz / J. Kabacinski (eds.), Studies in the Final Palaeolithic settlement of the Great European Plain (Poznań 2007) 53-65.

Terberger / Street 2002: Th. Terberger / M. Street, Hiatus or continuity? New results for the question of pleniglacial settlement in Central Europe. Antiquity 76, 691-698.

Terberger / Tromnau / Street / Weniger 2009: Th. Terberger / G. Tromnau / M. Street / G.-C. Weniger, Die jungpaläolithische Fundstelle Aschenstein bei Freden an der Leine, Kr. Hildesheim (Niedersachsen). Quartär 56 (2009) 87-103.

Theuerkauf 2002: M. Theuerkauf, Die Laacher See-Tephra in Nordostdeutschland: Paläoökologische Untersuchungen mit hoher zeitlicher und räumlicher Auflösung. Greifswalder Geographische Arbeiten 26, 171-174.

Tromnau 2006: G. Tromnau, Comments Concerning the Gaps between Schleswig-Holstein and the Middle Oder in the Expansion Area of Hamburgian Culture. Archaeologia Baltica 7, 7-10.

Usinger 1985: H. Usinger, Pollenstratigraphische, vegetations- und klimageschichtliche Gliederung des Bölling-Alleröd-Komplexes in Schleswig-Holstein und ihre Bedeutung für die Spätglazial-Stratigraphie in benachbarten Gebieten. Flora 177 (Jena 1985) 1-43.

1998: H. Usinger, Pollenanalytische Datierung spätpaläolithischer Fundschichten bei Ahrenshöft, Kreis Nordfriesland. Archäologische Nachrichten aus Schleswig-Holstein 1997, 8 (Schleswig 1998) 50-73.

van der Hammen 1957: T. van der Hammen, The stratigraphy of the Late-Glacial. Geol. Mijnbouw 19, 250-254.

van Geel / Coope / van der Hammen 1989: B. van Geel / G. R. Coope / T. van der Hammen, Palaeoecology and stratigraphy of the Lateglacial type section at Usselo (the Netherlands). Review of Palaeobotany and Palynology 31, 367-448.

Veil / Breest 1995: St. Veil / K. Breest, Figurenfragmente aus Bernstein vom Federmesser-Fundplatz Weitsche bei Lüchow, Lkr. Lüchow-Dannenberg (Niedersachsen). Archäologisches Korrespondenzblatt 25, 29-47.

2000: St. Veil / K. Breest, Der archäologische Befund der Kunstgegenstände aus Bernstein auf dem Federmesser-Fundplatz Weitsche. Die Grabungen 1994-1998. Die Kunde N. F. 51, 179-202.

2002: St. Veil / K. Breest, The archaeological context of the art objects from the Federmesser site of Weitsche, Ldkr. Lüchow-Dannenberg, Lower Saxony (Germany) – a preliminary report. In: B. V. Eriksen / B. Bratlund (eds.), Recent studies in the Final Palaeolithic of the European plain. Proceedings of a U.I.S.P.P. Symposium, Stockholm 1999. Jutland Archaeological Society Publications 39 (Århus 2002) 129-138.

Veil / Veil 2005: B. Veil / S. Veil, Vor 15 000 Jahren – Das Lager der Eiszeitjäger auf dem Gradeberg bei Gadenstedt, Ldkr. Peine. In: M. Fansa / F. Both / H. Haßmann (eds.), »Archäologie/Land/Niedersachsen. 25 Jahre Denkmalschutzgesetz – 400 000 Jahre Geschichte«, Archäologische Mitteilungen aus Nordwestdeutschland Beiheft 42 (Oldenburg 2005) 299-303.

Vollbrecht 2005: J. Vollbrecht, Spätpaläolithische Besiedlungsspuren aus Reichwalde. Veröffentlichungen des Landesamtes für Archäologie mit Landesmuseum für Vorgeschichte 46 (Dresden 2005).

Weber 2006: M. Weber, Typologische und technologische Aspekte des Fundplatzes Le Tureau des Gardes 7 (Seine-et-Marne, Frankreich): ein Beitrag zur Erforschung des Magdalénien im Pariser Becken. Archäologisches Korrespondenzblatt 36, 159-178.

Weinstock 2000a: J. Weinstock, Osteometry as a source of refined demographic information: sex-ratios of reindeer, hunting strategies, and herd control in Late Glacial site of Stellmoor, northern Germany. Journal of Archaeological Science 27 (London 2000) 1187-1195.

2000b: J. Weinstock, Late Pleistocene reindeer populations in Middle and Western Europe. An osteometrical study of *Rangifer tarandus*. BioArchaeologica 3 (Tübingen 2000).

2002: J. Weinstock, Reindeer hunting in the Upper Palaeolithic: sex ratios a reflection of different procurement strategies. Journal of Archaeological Science 29 (London 2002) 365-377.

Wymer 1976: J. J. Wymer, A long blade industry from Sproughton, Suffolk. East Anglian Archaeology 3, 1-15.